THE
INDUSTRIAL ARCHAEOLOGY
OF GLASGOW

THE

INDUSTRIAL ARCHAEOLOGY

OF GLASGOW

John R Hume

1974

BLACKIE

GLASGOW & LONDON

Published by
Blackie and Son Limited
Bishopbriggs, Glasgow G64 2NZ
5 Fitzhardinge Street, London W1H 0DL

ISBN 0 216 89833 1

Set by Typesetting Services Ltd, Hope Street,
Glasgow, in 12/13 point Garamond
Printed and bound in Great Britain by Robert
MacLehose & Co Ltd, 15 Foulis Street, Annies-
land, Glasgow (see A24) on an NP56 Litho
Perfecta

For
Professor S. G. E. Lythe

Preface

This book could not have been written without the help and encouragement of a large number of people. My prime debt is to the University of Strathclyde, and in particular to Professor S. G. E. Lythe, without whose kindly support I could not have tackled the project. The Carnegie Trust also generously financed some of the photographic work and has given a grant for additional illustrations. My colleague John Butt has always been ready to help and advise, and assisted with some of the early fieldwork. He also read the manuscript and made many useful suggestions. Three other colleagues, Baron Duckham, James Treble and Thomas Devine also commented on parts of the manuscript and helped in other ways. Of those outside the University, Frank Worsdall has unquestionably contributed most; indeed in many ways this is as much his book as mine. He made available his notes on the Dean of Guild Court records and on local newspapers, helped with architectural descriptions and attributions and assisted in some of the later fieldwork. Ian Robertson has been a mine of information on many topics and has checked the manuscript with directories and with his own records; David Walker has helped with architectural points; Alex. Young assisted in location maps; James L. Wood collaborated in the study of engineering firms; Michael Moss cooperated in later fieldwork; and John Glover, J. F. McEwan, G. H. Robin, John Devine (W. Beardmore & Co.), M. Clarke (A. & W. Smith & Co.), Spillers Ltd, Gray, Dunn & Co. Ltd, Watson, Salmond & Gray, Alexander Cross Seed Co. Ltd, Mavor & Coulson Ltd, and Adam Knox & Co. were all of great assistance. The staffs of libraries and record repositories were also most helpful, notably those of the Mitchell Library, Glasgow; the National Library of Scotland; Birmingham Public Reference Library; the Glasgow City Archives; and the Scottish Record Office. In particular Richard Dell, Catherine Murdoch and Murdo MacDonald of the Glasgow City Archives have gone out of their way to draw my attention to recent accessions of plans, photographs and documents. Mrs Georgina Buchanan, Economic History Department Secretary, helped in many ways, while the manuscript was expertly typed by Miss Lynda Kelly, Miss Sandra Currie, Miss Maureen Jones and Miss Carolyn MacLean. Lastly, but by no means least, my thanks go to my wife Hope for her moral support and to my small sons Matthew and Kenneth for not creating too much havoc with my papers.

University of Strathclyde, Glasgow   John R. Hume

Contents

List of Line Illustrations

xi

List of Plates

*From Glasgow City Archives

Introduction

In attempting to survey the industrial archaeology of a large city one is immediately faced with problems of selection and compression. When work started on Glasgow in 1964 the city had begun a programme of redevelopment more intensive than any since the late nineteenth century. The traditional industries were shrinking, and the establishment of industrial estates and overspill agreements were encouraging firms to move from older industrial areas. It soon became apparent that most industrial buildings were no longer occupied by the firms for whom they had been built, and that the rate of demolition was likely to rise. It therefore seemed that the most urgent task was to photograph as many buildings and civil engineering structures as possible, even at the risk of superficial coverage. Sites located on field excursions were identified and dated by reference to maps and Post Office Directories, which also gave clues to other sites. With growing expertise, rough criteria were established for dating; these helped to make sense of the Dean of Guild Court reports and records for the period before 1885 for which few plans survive.

The selection of an end date was difficult, and 1914 was eventually chosen in the mistaken belief that building techniques changed after the First World War, but though it transpired that there was continuity in building styles, 1914 does in many ways mark the end of assured prosperity in the west of Scotland. The choice of area was simpler, the city boundaries in 1964 being convenient. Thus to qualify for entry in the inventory a site had to be inside the 1964 boundary, built before 1914 and to have substantial remains. A few post-1914 sites of particular interest were also included.

General conclusions from the material collected are included in the text, though more briefly than one might have wished. One conclusion, however, is perhaps worth stating here. Without decrying the work of the excavator, it seems to me that the most vital task of the industrial archaeologist, particularly in urban areas, is to record extant buildings, machinery and structures before the scrap-man, the incendiary and the bulldozer come. The extent of the documentary record of post-industrial revolution industry can easily be overestimated, and in any case duplicated records of some sites are better than no record at all.

PART ONE

1 Food and Drink

The large-scale preparation of food is a relatively modern development. Apart from the grinding of cereals and pulses to meal and flour all forms of food were prepared on a small scale until the late eighteenth century. Even when, as with baking and butchery, centralisation did occur, units were generally small, and there was little mechanisation. From the 1860s, however, some types of food began to be processed in large central establishments, which supplied not only an expanding city, but also its environs, and even further afield. 'Export' was an adjective frequently applied to jams, confectionery and biscuits, as well as to beer. The importation of grain and meat on an increasing scale also led to the creation of central units for storage and processing, while the growth of chains of retail stores resulted in yet further centralisation.

The organisation of food supply which still characterises the city was established at the beginning of the nineteenth century. Corporation-owned commodity markets supplied retailers with meat, fish, fruit and vegetables, while large warehousemen, millers and refiners distributed less perishable foodstuffs to retailers direct or through wholesalers. More exotic imported foods were handled by agents and brokers, often as a sideline, though tea importing became a specialised trade, and tea warehouses were built in York Street (1843, H57), Robertson Street (1899, G82) and Clyde Place (1906, G144). The York Street warehouse is particularly impressive, with heavy mouldings and small windows.[1]

Grain Milling

Tea was imported, frequently from Scottish-owned and managed gardens, in prepared form, and merely required grading and packaging. Many other foodstuffs, however, were processed centrally before distribution. The grinding of grain and peas to

3

flour was the earliest of such processes to be mechanised. The first mill in Glasgow was probably situated on the Molendinar, a small stream now almost completely culverted, which flowed through the old town. By the middle of the nineteenth century there were two mills left on that stream, the Town Mill, a three-storey building, destroyed by fire in 1857, and the Subdean Mill, in Ladywell Street. There was also at some time, probably in the early eighteenth century, a windmill of the 'vaulted tower' type on the Windmill-croft, the ruins of which can be seen in late eighteenth-century drawings.[2]

As early as the twelfth century, the Molendinar had ceased to be an adequate source of power for the city's mills, and attention was turned to the Kelvin, particularly in its last steep fall to the Clyde at Partick. Clayslaps (M82), Regent (Bunhouse), Scotstoun, Bishop and Slit Mills all used the water of the Kelvin. The Incorporation of Bakers in Glasgow owned Bunhouse and Clayslaps, which were both large complexes and ordered a Watt engine of the sun and planet type for the 'Partick Mills' in 1800, which drove six pairs of stones situated round a large spur wheel. The Slit Mill derived that name from its use by the Smithfield Iron Company for slitting imported bar iron into rods for nail and small tool making. Further upstream there were mills at Dalsholm, Balgray, Garrioch, North Woodside and South Woodside, while on the south side of the city the White Cart Water powered Cathcart (M59), Langside (M65), Pollokshaws (J11) and Cardonald Mills. In the early stages of the industrial revolution, the scarcity of water-power sites in the Glasgow area led to the adaptation of some of these mills to new and more profitable uses. Dalsholm, Balgray and Cathcart became paper mills (A6, A27, M59); the last two also made snuff. North Woodside was reconstructed as a flint mill in 1846, and continued to grind flints until about 1963 (B38). Pollokshaws Mill became a water-turbine factory about 1907, after a period of disuse (J11), and Cardonald actually remained a meal mill until closure in the 1930s.[3]

The use of water power declined with the advent of the steam engine, which gave greater flexibility in the location of mills in response to changing sources of grain. One of the earliest steam-powered mills was that of Gardner & Brock (founded 1825), whose successors, Harvie & McGavin now prepare rice in their

Anderston Grain Mill, converted from a cotton store (H80). Another early steam mill was Port Dundas Grain Mills (c 1843, C60) on the banks of the Forth & Clyde Canal. The first Tradeston Mill was built about 1846, but was destroyed in a memorable dust explosion in 1872. The oldest part of Washington Grain Mills, which still operates (H84), dates from about 1849. These, and most of the later mills, were located close to the river, or the canal, to be near the point of importation of grain; thus Anderston, Tradeston and Port Dundas became, with the older group at Partick, the main centres of milling. The 1850s saw the construction of City of Glasgow Mills at Port Dundas (1851, C45) and the first Kingston Mill, while Cheapside (1860, H91) (Fig 1), Caledonian (1862, C56) and Crown (1862, H83) followed in the 1860s. During the 1870s, additional mills were built on the south side of the river, at Centre Street (c 1872, G159) and Tradeston Street (c 1875, H135) and both Tradeston (1873, G145) and Kingston (1875, H127) were rebuilt. The 1880s saw the introduction of roller milling, and apart from the simple re-equipment of existing mills, Mavisbank (1885, H157) was rebuilt from a warehouse and the complete reconstruction of Bunhouse and Scotstoun (1887, L41) Mills at Partick was started. The site of Bunhouse was bought after a fire in 1886 by John Ure of Crown Mills, and the splendid new Regent Mills (1887, L46) were built on the site. The last new foundation in the city was the Victoria Mill in Tradeston, started in 1879 (H183), but in 1910 an extensive reconstruction of the old Springfield Free Warehouses produced the Riverside Flour Mills (H125) and in 1931 part of the former Port Dundas Sugar Refinery became the Wheatsheaf Mills (C43).[4] From the 1870s city millers faced increasing competition from American flour imports.

These mills were basically flour mills, though other grain products were made in most of them. Another group of mills was primarily concerned with milling animal feeding stuffs and other relatively coarse products, the oldest being Bishop Mills (L47), reconstructed after a fire about 1853. Others were the Calton (c 1878, F50), Gorbals (1890, G171) and Parkhead (c 1897, E19) grain mills.[5]

Construction of the large steam mills was very similar to that of contemporary warehouses. Early examples, like Port Dundas, Washington and City of Glasgow, were rubble-built, with no

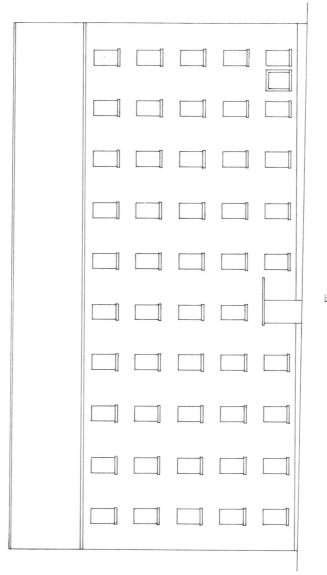

Fig 1

Elevation of Cheapside Flour Mills (H91) built for A. & W. Glen in 1860

architectural pretensions. Washington, Caledonian and Crown Mills all had impressive frontages, the new facade of Washington Mills being particularly fine. Kingston Mills, originally a plain rubble building, was rebuilt in polychrome brick in Venetian style. The Regent Mills are chiefly impressive for their bulk, though their proportions are good. Unusually for the period, the buildings are stone-faced, and the interior is of fireproof construction. The introduction of brick produced some most interesting effects. W. F. McGibbon created a medieval castle for Scotstoun Mills, and a Flemish composition for the Victoria Mills, while in the Gorbals Grain Mill effective use was made of moulded red and white brick. At Riverside the reinforced concrete grain silos are early examples of the use of that material. The height of mills varied between two and seven storeys, with five storeys the preferred size.

Grain Storage

Grain importing created a need for storage accommodation, which was met by the construction of some large warehouses near the docks. Many of these were for general storage (see Chapter 5) but some were specialist grain stores. In James Watt Street four grain warehouses were built between 1848 and 1864 (H58, H60, H63, H64), and not far away, in William Street, a large store was constructed in 1860 (H36). On the south side warehouses were built in West Street (1887, H137) and Tradeston Street (1889, H136). Grain was also brought to the city by rail and the Caledonian and North British Railways both built large grain stores in the 1870s at Buchanan Street and Queen Street Stations respectively (G5, G33). The larger millers also had stores attached to their mills, as at Centre Street Mills, where a narrow, seven-storey granary faces the mills across the street. On a smaller scale, grain was stored for consumption by horses, and there were warehouses in Cornfield Street (1872, F40), Boden Street (1873, F135), Kennedy Street (1878, C85) and Pollokshaws Road (1908, G195) for that purpose. The ultimate in bulk grain storage is the Meadowside Granary (L19), the Clyde Port Authority's central grain silo, construction of which started in 1911. Up to that time, grain had been imported

7

mainly in bags, and bulk carriage and storage necessitated vertical silos, as at Meadowside and Riverside, rather than a large floor area. Most of these buildings were quite plain, but those in James Watt Street, particularly 44–54 (H60), have fine classical frontages. Occasional examples were of fireproof construction, but the majority had wood floors on cast-iron columns.[6]

Sugar Refining

Sugar refining was another food-processing industry that was mechanised at an early date. The first sugar house in Glasgow was founded in 1667 by a group of four merchants, who employed a Dutchman as master boiler. It was followed during the next forty years by three others. These early concerns had all disappeared by the mid nineteenth century, though the five-storey building of the Eastern Sugar House (founded 1664) lasted until about 1850. In the second half of the nineteenth century there were three refineries, all of which had ceased production by 1880. The firm of Hoyle, Martin & Co., which also had premises in Greenock, operated a refinery in Washington Street from 1852 (H78), the Alston Street Sugar Refinery was swept away during the building of Central Station in the 1870s, while the largest of the three, the Port Dundas Sugar Refinery (C44), established in 1865, only operated until c 1877. The decline of this industry in Glasgow was probably the result of competition from Liverpool and Greenock, where raw sugar could be imported cheaply and easily, and from Continental sugar producers. The two recently surviving refinery buildings conform to the standard pattern of multi-storey buildings, found in other existing early sugar houses. The Washington Street refinery was seven storeys high, and only three bays long, and the main block of the Port Dundas establishment was also seven storeys high, though much longer.[7]

Confectionery Manufacture

Glasgow's links with the sugar trade were not, however, severed by the closure of the last refinery. A large confectionery and jam industry grew up from the 1860s, expansion being most rapid after 1880 when cheap Continental sugar became available. The earliest sizable confectionery works was that of Robert Wotherspoon in Admiral Street (c 1866, H147), and its foundation was followed by that of John Buchanan & Brothers in Stewart Street (1869, C117). Both these concerns seem to have begun in a fairly small way, but by 1914 they were very large indeed. Other factories, founded in the 1880s, in Dunmore Lane (c 1881, G181), Kingston Street (c 1884, H132) and Charlotte Street (rebuilt 1888, F125), were relatively small. Hay Brothers, whose works were started in Kingston in 1875, moved to a large new factory in Stanley Street about 1890 (H207). An unusual unit was the Sweetmeat Automatic Delivery Company's fine single-storey works in Stamford Street, built between 1899 and 1911 (F92), which was opened specifically to make chocolate bars for automatic vending machines. Chocolate was also a speciality of Carsons Ltd, whose Barrowfield Works (F164) was built in stages between 1902 and 1910. A large jam and confectionery works was built in Herbert Street (B49) in 1907, replacing an earlier building destroyed by fire. A small factory in Thornwood Avenue (1907, L20) for J. S. Birrell was the start of an enterprise which expanded rapidly after 1918. Many of the firms mentioned had a large export trade, for example in the late 1880s the Hay Brothers were shipping a significant part of their output to the West Indies while Stewart and Young, who occupied a former weaving factory in Broad Street (F99) described themselves as 'export confectioners' and had a steamship as their trademark. The ultimate collapse of confectionery manufacturing was the result of competition from specialist English firms.[8]

The buildings occupied by confectioners were generally multi-storey. John Buchanan & Brothers had two-, four-, five- and six-storey buildings, including two early (1907) reinforced concrete structures. The older buildings were stone-faced. Wotherspoon's works in Admiral Street and Hay Brothers' Stanley Street buildings were both constructed of red and white brick, the Stanley Street factory having a neat corner turret. Montgomery's Kingston Street works had a three-storey sandstone frontage, but the Dunmore Lane and Thornwood Avenue factories were of plain brick.

Baking

Bakers use the products both of millers and of sugar refiners. Small bakeries abounded in early nineteenth-century Glasgow – more than two hundred bakers and flour dealers were listed in the 1825 edition of Pigot & Company's directory. Little bakehouses continued to be built in the city up to and after 1914, but there was a pronounced tendency to concentrate bread and biscuit making in large central bakeries from the 1850s. This was at least partly a consequence of the development of bakery machinery. Initially these two branches of the trade were carried out in separate factories, but from about 1880 there was a trend towards integration. The oldest surviving large bakery building is probably Parkholm Biscuit Factory (c 1857, H124), closely followed by Gray, Dunn & Company's biscuit factory in Stanley Street (1861, H172); the original building has been demolished here. Another biscuit bakery, in Dorset Street (H12), founded in 1876, was destroyed by fire a few years later and rebuilt in 1881. Macfarlane, Lang & Co, which became the largest Glasgow biscuit firm, founded their Victoria Bread and Biscuit Factory (F41) about 1880, in a former power-loom factory; at first bread only was made, but in 1885 a biscuit factory was added on the same site. Eventually their premises covered most of a large block before they moved the biscuit factory out to Tollcross between the wars. Clutha Bakery (1881, H211) specialised in rusks. A pioneer of large-scale bread baking was the United Co-operative Baking Society (UCBS), whose first bakery, in Seaward Street, was opened about 1870 (H145). This was the most successful of several co-operative baking ventures, an early one being the Calton Baking Society; later examples included the Friendly Bread Association, founders of what became the City Bakeries, Clarendon Street (c 1887, B58). The first UCBS bakery, however, paled into insignificance beside the gigantic bakeries of J. & B. Stevenson in Cranstonhill (1877, H29) and Plantation (1881, H212), which started in a small way in 1865. By 1888 the firm was producing about 100,000 loaves a day in Glasgow, and had opened a London bakery in Battersea. In 1888 it was claimed that the change-over from the family baker to the large mechanised firm had been pioneered by this firm. Their bread was by that time being sent all over Scotland. Their example was followed by Bilsland Brothers at their Hydepark Bakery (1881, H97), W. & D. Beattie in Dennistoun (1886, D14) and by the UCBS, who started to build a vast factory (G158) in McNeil Street in 1886. Though not quite as large as the concerns already mentioned, Kelvinside (c 1893, B33), Dundashill (1901, C50) and Hubbards (1905, B65) bakeries were of significant size, as were establishments in Stanley Street (c 1883, H169), St George's Road (1898, C38), Victoria Road (1903, I19), Copland Road (1903, 1904, K33, K36), Craigton Road (1911, K67) and Soho Street (1907, F39). Smaller bakeries were often sited in the centre of tenement blocks, frequently behind retail shops, though some large ones (Dorset Street Biscuit Factory, St George's Road bakery) were similarly situated. Examples of smaller 'back yard' premises may be seen in Abercromby Street (1906, F75), Eglinton Street (c 1896, I2) and Gallowgate (1897, F52).[9]

Most of these bakeries were brick-built, though Parkholm, Hydepark and Kelvinside have stone frontages. Plain red brick was commonest, sometimes very plain, as in Gallowgate, Abercromby Street and Kingston. In Macfarlane, Lang's later buildings, at Soho Street, in the Clutha bakery and in Galbraith's Craigton Road premises some attempts were made to relieve the severity of a brick box. The main block at Victoria Bakery was particularly successful, with low relief arches separating the bays, and a pleasing top to the stair tower. The great glory of bakery building in Glasgow was, however, the use of red and white brick, and of moulded brick, to achieve a very rich effect. The first bakery in the grand manner was Cranstonhill and the main bakehouse at Hydepark, though not so ornate, is similar in style. The most spectacular example (the UCBS bakery in McNeil Street) is fortunately still extant. The earlier parts are in Flemish Style, but the main frontage to Adelphi Street is French Renaissance in character, and is enriched with sandstone corner towers. In part of Gray, Dunn's biscuit factory in Stanley Street white glazed brick is effectively used to decorate a dark-red brick facade, though here the original design (Fig 2) has been obscured by the addition of a storey. Red and white brick is used more conventionally in Beattie's bakery, in Dorset Street and in the oldest surviving block of the Gray, Dunn factory. In Plantation Bakery sandstone is used in combination with brick, and there are some pleasing sculptured panels, including one depicting the technique of baking by hand. The interior construction of bakeries has not been investigated in detail but the Cranstonhill bakery was part fireproof, and part wood floored, as was the first bakehouse at Hydepark. Additions made to several bakeries including Cranstonhill, Hydepark and Parkholm after 1900 were steel or concrete framed. The largest bakeries were tall.

Fig 2
Elevation of part of Biscuit Factory, 115 Stanley Street (H172), built in 1893
for Gray Dunn & Co. to designs by Stark & Rowntree

Cranstonhill, Plantation, Hydepark and Victoria had five storeys, and the ÙCBS had four, though Beattie's, on a less restricted site, had a three-storey main block. Even the smaller bakeries were generally three or four storeys high, owing to the small sites available. Built in 1926, the City Bakeries in Clarendon Street reached a height of six storeys.[10]

Meat Storage and Processing

The handling of meat was centralised much earlier than its processing. Meat and cattle markets and slaughterhouses were well established by the beginning of the nineteenth century but cold stores for imported meat did not come on the scene until the 1880s, nor did sausage factories, the earliest meat-processing factories. The first cold store in the city seems to have been that of John Bell & Sons, in Cheapside Street (1888, H93), which was enlarged in stages till 1911. Conversion of existing buildings in George Street (*c* 1900, G70) and Commerce Street (1919, G145) followed, with the construction of a new cold-store and ice factory in Old Wynd in 1901 (G100), and of a very large store in Melbourne Street just before the First World War (F6). An ice factory and cold store for fish was built for J. & T. Sawers in Rutherford Lane in 1899 (G4). Apart from the last-named, these stores were presumably started to cater for the importation of chilled and frozen meat from the Americas and Australasia. Sausage making on a large scale was made possible by the development of mechanical mincing and filling machines. McGhee & Burt patented a 'combined gas engine and mincing machine' in the 1880s and R. D. Waddell also devised sausage machines, which he used in his North Woodside Road factory, founded in the 1880s and greatly extended between 1895 and 1900 (B51). William Annacker built a large sausage works in William Street (H32) in 1898-9, and the Scottish Co-operative Wholesale Society opened an extensive ham-curing and sausage works in Milnpark Street (1905, H164). Throughout the period, however, meat processing remained a small-scale industry. The premises built for these purposes were quite interesting. The Old Wynd, Rutherford Lane and Melbourne Street stores were, logically, windowless, though only in the last-named was this frankly expressed in the architecture. Bell's (later Eastman's) red and white brick building was more conventional. The scws factory in plain red brick was not particularly distinguished, but Waddell and Annacker tried to produce the more impressive building. In terms of bulk, Waddell undoubtedly won, but Annacker's works possessed an unexpectedly fine sandstone frontage.[11]

Minor Food Processing Industries

Before the coming of the railways there had been numerous cowhouses in the city, including a very large one on the site later occupied by the Vulcan Maltings on Hundred Acre Hill (C67). There were in 1820, 65 cowkeepers in the city, with 586 cows. Subsequently milk, cheese and butter were brought in from a distance by rail or road, usually in prepared form. Two retail co-operative societies have their own creameries, however. Cowlairs has one in Kemp Street (c 1901, C6) and Shettleston's is in Pettigrew Street (c 1910, M42). Other milk-bottling plants were added after c 1925, when bottled milk replaced milk distributed from churns. Minor food producing units included a coffee and spice grinding mill (c 1871, G115) typical of warehouse architecture of the period, a single-storey pickle factory (1892, K66), and a four-storey margarine factory (c 1900, F157).[12]

Food Warehouses

The creation of large chains of retail grocery and provision stores in the later nineteenth century led to the building of central warehouses as distribution centres. Sir Thomas Lipton, the doyen of Victorian grocery magnates, had his first warehouse in the former Lancefield Cotton Work (H107), and in 1905 his firm added a new store next door (H106). The earliest large purpose-built grocery warehouse is that of Bishop & Henderson (Cooper & Co.) in Herbert Street (1890, B47). This firm constructed an even larger building in Bishop Street just before the First World War (*c* 1913, H37). Alexander Massey & Sons had their central store in Thistle Street, the original buildings being replaced in 1912 (G168), and Andrew Cochrane & Son Ltd built a warehouse in Stevenson Street two years later (F61). On a smaller scale, a store in East Wellington Street was constructed for John Fleming, 'ham curer and provision merchant' (1896, E13). Obviously not intended for long term storage, there were many fruit warehouses near the fruit market in Candleriggs, mostly conversions from eighteenth century or later warehouses and dwelling houses, though a handful were purpose built. A large building in Brunswick Street (1883, G108), built for Simons, Jacobs Ltd, survived a fire which destroyed the similar block facing Candleriggs in 1912. Thomas Russell had two warehouses in Blackfriars Street (1899, G110; 1904, G111), the later one incorporating an auction room. Most of these buildings were of brick, though those of Lipton, Simons, Jacobs and Russell (his earlier store) had sandstone facades. The Massey, Cochrane and later Bishop & Henderson warehouses had terra-cotta facing bricks, in the case of the last named applied to a reinforced concrete frame.[13]

Brewing and Malting

Glasgow men have always been thirsty, and the profits from tappit hens of beer and drams of whisky attracted the attention of entrepreneurs at an early date. The Wellpark Brewery of J. & R. Tennent is reputed to have been founded in 1556, and is still in operation, after many rebuildings. In 1736 Robert Luke's 'Brewarie' was adjacent to one of the Molendinar tanneries 'with large Killn Lofts, Cellars, and other Store-houses'. By the end of the eighteenth century there were three large breweries, Anderston, Greenhead and Wellpark, and several smaller ones mainly in Gorbals and Calton. The Anderston Brewery of Murdoch, Warroch & Co. seems to have been a model concern, laid out in the form of a hollow square, while Greenhead Brewery of Robert Struthers & Co. had a Watt engine as early as 1800. In 1825 Pigot & Co. listed twenty-two brewers, of whom six were specifically described as brewing ale and porter. The only one of these breweries, apart from Tennents', still in existence is the Greenhead Brewery (*c* 1800, F108), now a bottling plant. Some later nineteenth-century brewery buildings still survive, most of them dating from the 1880s, a period of rapid urban growth. A notable feature of the latter is that they were almost all designed by Edinburgh brewery architects. The Home Brewery, Invernairn Street, founded in 1865 (E14) was built to designs by P. L. Henderson in 1895, and this architect was also responsible for the Slatefield Brewery, Slatefield Street (1881, F15) and the Anchor Brewery, Davidson Street (1889, F180). John Cunningham designed extensions to the Greenhead Brewery in 1887 and 1892, while R. H. Paterson did the 1896 rebuilding of the Clydesdale Brewery, Victoria Road (1883, I18) for The Tonbur Brewery Ltd (see pp. 18, 23). City of Glasgow Brewery in Petershill Road (1866, M27) was also rebuilt in the 1880s. These late nineteenth-century breweries were relatively small, and served purely local needs. Indeed Edinburgh, Alloa and English beers seem to have been drunk in quite large quantities by the end of the 1880s. Bass was bottled by the Annfield Bottling Stores (1873, F10) and Whitbread and Vaux opened bottling works and stores in Garscube Road in 1907 (C30) and 1911 (C27) respectively.[14]

Until the end of the nineteenth century most of the large breweries seem to have had their own maltings, and some had surplus malting capacity. The Great Canal Brewery of Hugh Baird & Co. developed a trade in malt, and eventually Hugh Baird abandoned brewing altogether to concentrate on malting. The firm of Hugh Baird & Sons built a large new maltings close to the brewery, in Garscube Road (1888, C29), and in 1893 they started building an even bigger complex in Vintner Street, Port Dundas (C67). These, with two other blocks belonging to the same firm, were the only large specialised maltings in Glasgow.[15]

Almost all these buildings were brick built, though there was until recently a sandstone block of maltings, with two kilns, at Wellpark. A store and malting block at City of Glasgow Brewery is also stone-built, as was the Tonbur Brewery (Fig 4). The latter had frontages to two main roads, that on Victoria Road in the French Renaissance manner. The only one of the latterly-existing Glasgow breweries to exceed three storeys in height was Wellpark, though the main brewhouse there has now been replaced. Malt

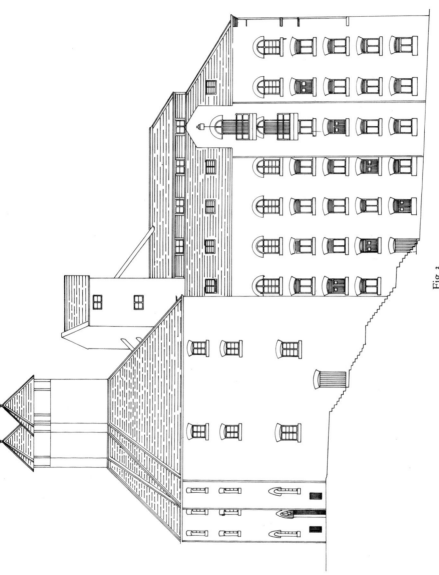

Fig 3

North elevation of Great Canal Maltings, 580 Garscube Road (C29) constructed
to designs by Russell & Spence for Hugh Baird & Son in 1888

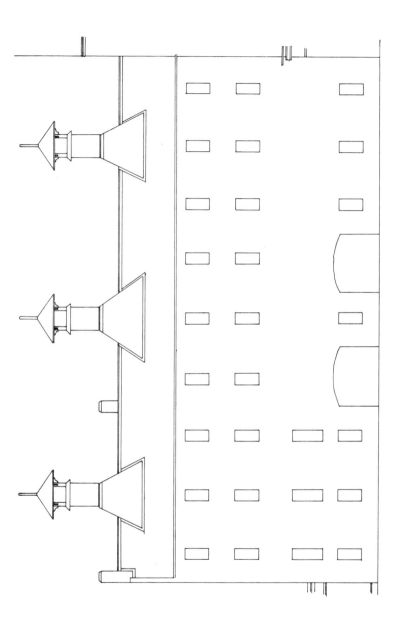

Fig 4

Elevation to Pollokshaws Road of Tonbur Brewery, 44–50 Victoria Road (118) as rebuilt for the Tonbur Brewery Co. Ltd in 1896, R. H. Paterson, architect

barns were larger, those at Slatefield (now demolished) being five storeys high, while The Great Canal Maltings were five, later six storeys (Fig 4) and the Vulcan Maltings in Vintner Street had a main block seven storeys high, with an attic. A notable feature of the Whitbread bottling works is its very English-Georgian style, the work, appropriately, of a London architect.

Distilling

Distilling reached Glasgow much later than brewing. The first commercial distillery in the city is reputed to have been that founded by Baillie William Menzies in Kirk Street, Gorbals in 1784 but by 1825 there were ten. The still-surviving Port Dundas Distillery of J. Gourlay & Co. (c 1820, C65) became one of the two largest in Scotland, and there is only one other operative distillery left in the city. It is, and has been for many years, a 'patent still' distillery, producing grain whisky, though at least until the 1880s malt whisky was also made. The nearby Dundashill Distillery (c 1811, C52) of Daniel McFarlane became the largest malt distillery in Scotland with twelve stills in the 1880s, but was bought by the Distillers' Company Limited (DCL) about 1902 and closed down. It is now used as a cooperage and bonded store. Another relatively early distillery was Adelphi, in Inverkip Street, founded about 1825 (F151). Initially quite small, this concern eventually expanded to take in the whole of one side of the street, and bonded stores of very large size were built on the other side (1882, G152). It made both grain and malt whisky, falling a victim to DCL rationalisation about 1902 and after a period as a bond later demolished. Camlachie Distillery (F29), producing malt whisky only, was set up about 1853 by Bulloch & Co., and was later greatly extended. In 1920 it, too, fell into the DCL net and is now a store. A fragment of Haghill Distillery survived till very recently (D13). A brewery at Haghill existed c 1803, and this appears to have been converted to a distillery about 1837. The other distillery presently in production is Strathclyde, founded 1928 and hence outside our period.[16]

Like most of the brewers, the distillers made their own malt in the nineteenth century and the malt barns and kilns dominated most distilleries. To economise on floor space, malt was made at Adelphi on trays. The other characteristic feature of distilleries was the great bulk of the whisky stores, their relatively enormous size being dictated by the necessity of maturing whisky before it could be sold. The earliest distilleries were stone-built, as might be expected, and almost all of the surviving buildings at Dundashill are stone. Adelphi and Camlachie were probably brick built from the start, and most of Port Dundas has been rebuilt in brick. One block there, now cut down in height, features cast-iron beams of unusually large size, and a flat-roofed, seven-storey warehouse there was one of the largest in the city. The remaining building at Haghill consisted of a single-storey rubble dwelling house on top of large brick-vaulted cellars.[17]

Bonded Warehouses

The bonded warehouse, where whisky stocks could be stored 'duty free' during maturing became very important in Glasgow with the growth of blending. This practice of mixing neutral grain whisky with strongly-flavoured malt whisky is said to have been introduced by Ushers of Edinburgh, but spread rapidly. Glasgow, with its good communications and trading links both with the Highlands and Islands and with the colonies and America was a natural focus for this new industry. Before blending became important there were whisky warehouses in the city centre, for example, in Oswald Street (*c* 1844, G84) and New Wynd (*c* 1859, G103), but several bonded stores were built in the late 1870s and many more between 1897 and 1903. Apart from purpose-built warehouses, cotton mills, railway arches, general warehouses and even a church (in Oswald Street) were converted for the storage and blending of whisky. Such adaptations required little structural alteration, as the equipment used was simple, consisting of large blending vats and stirrers, and rudimentary bottling plant. One of the earliest purpose-built bonds is in York Street (1877, H53), though the interior was reconstructed in 1901. In 1882 a start was made on building the large warehouses in Inverkip Street associated with Adelphi Distillery (G152) and a handsome store block for the Glasgow and South Western Railway in Bell Street (G58). The great boom in the building of bonded warehouses started in 1897 with the construction of three very large stores, in Borron Street (C68), Ballater Street (G160) and Washington Street (H82). In the following year two smaller warehouses, in Waterloo Street (H47) and Cadogan Street (H48) were added, and between 1901 and 1905 bonds were constructed in James Watt Lane (H56), Scotland Street (H201) and Nicholson Street (G182). Only new foundations have been mentioned, but additions were made to existing warehouses until 1906. Apart from these large bonded stores there were smaller wine and spirit stores belonging to wholesalers or retailers, for example a wine store in Goosedubs (1877, G99) and another in Keith Street (1910, C37).

The chief characteristic of most of the bonded stores is their large size. The majority are four, five or six storeys high, some with additional attics or basements, and some, such as the Ballater Street, Washington Street and Bell Street blocks cover a considerable area. There is little relationship between date of construction and facade material, since the prestige of the blending firms often demanded stone frontages, sometimes very ornate as in Wright and Greig's Waterloo Street building. In high-class commercial or industrial areas more attention was paid to appearance, for example in Washington Street, Cadogan Street and Scotland Street. Internally the earlier bonds resembled other types of warehouse, with cast-iron columns supporting wooden beams and floors. An interesting intermediate type of internal structure was used in Bell Street, where closely-spaced cast-iron beams were linked by mass-concrete arches. Later, steel and reinforced concrete were used for bond construction, for example in Ballater Street, Borron Street and Nicholson Street, though for the outside walls brick became more or less standard. Terra-cotta bricks were used in facing the side and rear walls of the warehouses in Washington Street and Scotland Street.[18]

Aerated Water Manufacture

For the total abstainer, and for the myriad children of a rapidly growing Glasgow, aerated waters provided a suitable alternative to whisky and beer. The manufacture of aerated waters could profitably be carried out on a small scale, and most of the Glasgow firms were initially small, though some expanded rapidly. Some brewers and bottlers, such as the Barrowfield Brewery, long demolished, and Mair and Dougall of the Annfield Bottling Stores, made aerated waters as a sideline. Other firms, however, concentrated solely on this trade. One of the earliest was John Glass, who made soda water, lemonade, ginger beer, 'nectarine' and other beverages at his 'Glasgow Aerated Water Manufactory' in Clydeferry Street, Anderston, in the early 1850s. By 1873 there were thirteen aerated water manufacturers. The oldest surviving factory is that of Barclay Brothers, whose Oxford Street premises (1885, G174) incorporated a tenement of dwelling houses. They were followed by R. F. Barr, who started his works in the Gallowgate in 1889 (E18). Additions were made to the premises right up to 1914, and the firm is still in existence. Five factories were built in the 1890s, in Mordaunt Street (1892, F137), Garscube Road (1896, C28), Farnell Street (1897, C33), Durham Street (1897, H210) and Maxwell Road (1898, H225). Small establishments were founded in Helen Street (*c* 1900, K55) and Bankier Street (1907, F58) and construction of the biggest single building (H178) devoted to aerated water manufacture was started by the Scottish Co-operative Wholesale Society in Seaward Street in 1914 to replace a smaller works founded in 1897.[19]

Most of these factories were brick built, and one or two storeys high, though Barclay Brothers' tenement was four storeys high, as was Orr Comrie's Garscube Road works. The scws building has four storeys and a basement. The Garscube Road works was designed by Sir J. J. Burnet and was a listed building; the only other architecturally interesting works is that of John Mackay & Co., in Durham Street. This has a Tudor frontage to MacLellan Street, while the Durham Street facade has impressive Renaissance doorways. The Maxwell Road factory of G. & P. Barrie, a Dundee firm, was very unusually though not surprisingly designed by a Dundee architect, J. Sibbald.

Other Beverages

As an alternative to straightforward aerated waters, such as ginger beer, 'ginger hop', lemonade and 'sparkling Kola', one could in the 1880s and 1890s drink non-alcoholic beers, products of the Tonbur Brewery, Victoria Road (1896, I18) and other firms. That such beers were not all that was claimed was suggested in the *Scottish Wine, Spirit and Beer Trades Review* by a writer who stated that the popularity of these drinks with teetotallers was explained by the low, but significant amount of alcohol they contained. Other non-alcoholic beverages made in Glasgow included fruit extracts, made by the Excelsior Sauce and Pickle Works, formerly a cotton mill in Rutherglen Road (G165) and Camp Coffee. It is perhaps indicative of the growing popularity of this coffee essence in late Victorian times that the factory in Charlotte Street (G124), originally a converted villa, was extended three times and then completely rebuilt within the brief span of 1891 to 1898.[20]

[1]Cleland, James, *The Rise and Progress of the City of Glasgow* (Glasgow 1820), 193–4

[2]*Glasgow Herald*, 27 March 1857; Oakley, C. A., *The Second City* (London 2nd edn 1967), 20; ibid, 10–11; Donnachie, Ian L., and Stewart, Norma K., 'Scottish Windmills: an Outline and Inventory', *Proceedings of the Society of Antiquaries of Scotland*, 98, 1964–6, 276–99

[3]*The Incorporation of Bakers of Glasgow* (Glasgow 1931), 2–16, 19–21, includes illustrations of Bunhouse and Clayslaps; Birmingham Reference Library, Boulton & Watt MSS: [BRL, B & W MSS], Portfolio 209; Simpson, William, *Glasgow in the 'Forties'* (Glasgow 1899), plate 40; ibid, plate 42

[4]*The Engineer*, 34, 1872, 145 quoting a report by Professor McQuorn Rankine, stated that the explosion (on 9 July) was the result of a stoppage of feed to one pair of stones causing overheating and ignition of dust; Witherington, R., 'History of Milling', *The Cooperative Wholesale Societies*

Limited: *Annual 1887* (Manchester and Glasgow 1887), 312 (I am indebted to Mr James Kinloch for this reference); the first roller plant at Scotstoun was installed in 1889, was destroyed by fire in 1909, and rebuilt in 1911 (information supplied by Spillers Ltd); *The Incorporation of Bakers*, 7, 8, 20, 21

[5]Butt, J., Donnachie, I. L., and Hume, J. R., *Industrial History in Pictures: Scotland* (Newton Abbot 1968), 14

[6]Glasgow City Archives [GCA] Valuation Department negative no 107 shows frontage of Washington Mills complete; Butt, J., *The Industrial Archaeology of Scotland* (Newton Abbot 1967), 51

[7]McUre, J., *A View of the City of Glasgow* (Glasgow 1736), 282–3; Gordon, J. F. S. (ed), *Glasghu Facies* (Glasgow 1866), 543–4, comments that the Eastern Sugar House was still standing then, but a note in Simpson (plate XI) states that the building was condemned in 1848 and removed a few years later; eighteenth–

nineteenth century sugar houses exist in Aberdeen (NJ 947062) and Greenock (NS 275765)

[8] Buchanan Bros factory is described and illustrated in *Stratten's Glasgow and its Environs* (London 1891), 147, the illustration being reproduced in Butt *et al.*, 31; Barrowfield Works is illustrated in Butt *et al.*, 17, wrongly described by Hume as a leather works; *Industries of Glasgow* (London 1888), 114; Stratten, 139–40

[9] *Industries of Glasgow*, 89; *Pigot & Co.*'s *Directory*, 1825; *Industries of Glasgow*, 138; *Fifty Years in the Baking Trade* (Glasgow 1923), Bilsland Bros firm history; the Cranstonhill and UCBS bakeries are illustrated in Butt *et al.*, 30, 31; Reid, William, *History of the United Cooperative Baking Society Ltd* (Glasgow 1920), passim

[10] *Industries of Glasgow*, 102

[11] Ibid, 95, 109

[12] Cleland, *Rise and Progress*, 193

[13] Matthias, P., *Retailing Revolution* (London 1967) contains material on the Lipton, Massey, Templeton and Cochrane grocery chains

[14] McUre, 285; John Struthers bought a brewery in Gallowgate in 1767 which, enlarged by his brother Robert, became one of the largest in Scotland; it was eventually moved to Greenhead, Senex (Robert Reid), *Old Glasgow* (London 1864), 184–5; the Anderston Brewery was the first to brew porter in Glasgow, ibid, 185; BRL, B & W MSS, Engine Book, 2; Portfolio 204; *The Scottish Wine, Spirit and Beer Trades Review* (12 May 1888), 163

[15] Barnard, A., *Noted Breweries of Great Britain and Ireland* (London 1889), vol 2, 460–84, gives a detailed description of the Great Canal and other maltings of the

Baird Co., including a malt roasting house in Vintner Street, precursor of C67

[16] Cleland, *Rise and Progress*, 96; Barnard, A., *The Whisky Distilleries of the United Kingdom* (London 1887, reprinted Newton Abbot 1969), 18–23, and illustration in Butt *et al.*, 23; the eighteenth century dates quoted by Barnard for Port Dundas and Dundashill do not stand up to inspection, as Fleming's map of 1808, which features 'public works' does not show any distilleries at Port Dundas; Dundashill is illustrated in Barnard, *Distilleries*, 24–31; ibid 31; *Glasgow Herald*, 8 May 1848; I am indebted to Dr I. A. Glen for the post-Barnard history of distilling in Glasgow

[17] Barnard, *Distilleries*, 31

[18] Thom & Cameron acquired Houldsworth's Anderston Cotton Mill for use (see chapter 2) as a blending store, *Industries of Glasgow*, 93; ibid, 145; *The Scottish Wine, Spirit and Beer Trades Review* (12 January 1888), 71; *The Building News* (8 April 1898), I am indebted to Mr David Walker for this reference

[19] *Post Office Directory*, 1853–4, Appendix, 203; *Post Office Directory*, 1872–3; *Victualling Trades Review, Hotel & Restaurateurs' Journal* (12 July 1889), 196, gives a description of Barclay Bros factory by that time owned by the International Mineral Water Co.; Flanagan, James, *Wholesale Cooperation in Scotland 1868–1918* (Glasgow 1920), 364–5

[20] *Scottish Wine, Spirit and Beer Trades Review* (3 May 1887), 'some temperance drinks are of a greater strength than London porter and . . . their popularity has increased in proportion to the number of proof spirits they contained'

2 Textile Industries

The manufacture of textiles in Glasgow has probably been practised as long as there has been a community. Hand-spun yarn would be woven on hand looms into cloth, at first for local consumption, later for export. By 1658 there was a waulk mill for woollen cloth, and though the Union of 1707 resulted in the decline of the woollen industry, in 1725 a white linen manufactory was started at Graham's Hall. Linen printing began in 1738 and by about 1780 there were approximately 3000 hand looms in the Barony parish of Glasgow producing linen goods which were printed for handkerchiefs, gowns and bed curtains. The skills acquired in making these fine fabrics made the Glasgow area especially suitable for the introduction of cotton weaving, initially as a complement to linen manufacture but eventually supplanting it. The city became the administrative centre for cotton weaving over a wide area – in 1791 there were about 15,000 looms belonging to Glasgow manufacturers, each annually producing goods valued at £100, and employing an estimated nine persons at different stages of manufacture. The connections of Glasgow merchants with the West Indies – a major source of cotton – and the availability of capital derived from foreign and colonial trade reinforced the rôle of Glasgow as a major centre of cotton manufacture in the late eighteenth and early nineteenth centuries.[1]

Cotton Spinning

The supply of yarn to 15,000 looms was made possible by the introduction of mechanical spinning. The earliest cotton mills in Scotland were at a considerable distance from Glasgow, at Penicuik, Rothesay, Barrhead and Johnstone, but yarn, spun on the Arkwright frames installed in these early mills, came to Glasgow for distribution to weavers. Fine yarn was also imported from Lancashire, and much coarse yarn made in the west of Scotland was exported to England, America, Russia and the continent. The pressing need for adequate supplies of water for power meant that most of the early mills though often Glasgow-financed were set up outside the city, since its rivers have relatively little fall, and the available millsteads were already occupied by grain or paper mills. The only water-powered cotton mill in Glasgow was built on the Kelvin at South Woodside (B62) by William Gillespie in 1784, and even it suffered severely from water shortage. In summer the dam, which contained two hours supply of water, was allowed to fill, and the mill then worked until it was empty. To obtain six hours of work employees had to attend for sixteen or seventeen hours. Not till steam power was introduced could Glasgow become a major centre of cotton spinning. The first steam-powered mill was that of William Scott & Co. at Springfield, where an engine was installed in January 1792. This was not a Watt engine; it was built by Robert Muir, a local man. From a plan of 1797 it appears that this mill, 120 feet long by 20 feet broad, was soon supplemented by a larger one, 130 feet by 45 feet (Fig 5). Another early steam mill of comparable size was that of John Pattison in Mile End, where the main building was 130 feet by 48 feet, five storeys and attic high, of stone, with a slate roof and a thirty-two-horsepower steam engine by Boulton & Watt, probably the largest in the west of Scotland when completed in 1800. By 1812 this mill housed 152 mules with a total of 24,792 spindles, and 84 carding engines. This mill was demolished to make way for Bridgeton Cross (CR) station (1896, F106).[2]

The Springfield and Mile End Mills, with those of William Gillespie in Woodside and Anderston were much the largest cotton mills in Glasgow by 1800. Their supremacy was, however, soon challenged by others, mainly in the Bridgeton-Calton and Anderston areas. The only recently surviving mill built in the first decade of the nineteenth century was also the most famous. This was Henry Houldsworth & Company's Anderston Cotton Work in Cheapside Street which was almost certainly the first 'incombustible' mill in Scotland, and the first large brick building in Glasgow. Its design was attributed by Skempton & Johnson to William Creighton, an employee of Boulton & Watt but this is not supported by the

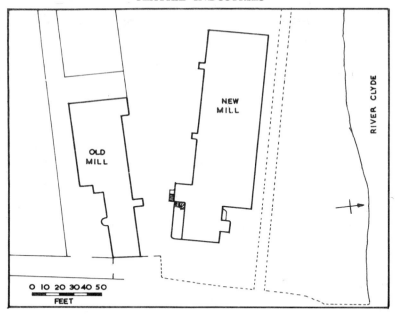

Fig 5
Plan of Springfield Cotton Mill, the property of David Todd. The Old Mill
was probably the first steam-powered cotton mill in Glasgow

admittedly scanty evidence in the Boulton & Watt papers. The drawing of the forty-five horsepower engine supplied for the mill has the structure of the mill in pencil with the comment 'copied from Mr Houldsworth's Sketches – Augt. 1804' while the correspondence between Creighton and Boulton & Watt explicitly refers to the engine and engine house. Indeed Creighton wrote in May 1804 that 'Great care is intended to be taken in making every thing firm in the [engine] house which with the mill & machinery is all to be incombustible . . . they intend to begin building shortly'. As he had been writing regularly about the engine since 1802 it seems most unlikely that he had a hand in the design of the mill. Houldsworth's mill was one of the sights of Glasgow at the time of its construction. A Mr Houston, a Belfast banker touring Scotland, wrote in 1805:

> I saw a new Cotton Mill at Anderston near Glasgow, one half of which was built, this half was 7 stories high 30 feet wide & 14 windows in length – the floors were supported by metal pipes – which at the same

27

time served the purpose of conveying Steam for Heating the House – the Joists are also of metal likewise the window frames & sashes, & not a piece of Timber in the House except the roof – as the floors were to be laid with tiles. I was told the expence [*sic*] of metal exceeded Timber 25 p ct which was saved in three years by the difference of Insurance – the pipes &c only cost 16/- per cwt.

Houston's comment on the roof was only true inasmuch as the sarking was wooden: the roof trusses, in four pieces, were cast iron and appear to have been designed to rest on short columns continued from the lower floors. At a later date the trusses were raised to provide more attic space, and central columns with cantilever beams to the original support points were substituted. The price differential between iron and timber was enough to deter most cotton entrepreneurs, and not until the 1840s were any further 'fireproof' mills built in Glasgow (C78, F149, G53, G165). The steam heating was necessary for the planned spinning of fine yarns: in 1816 Henry Houldsworth stated that the average temperature in the mill was 74–76°F (for counts of 100–200), and that about a quarter of the coal consumed was used for heating.[3]

Cotton spinning mills continued to be built in fair numbers until the 1850s; as far as one can judge they were mainly mule mills. Hand mules continued in use at least until the 1850s, though by that time both self-acting mules and throstles were becoming common. In 1852 at Sawmillfield Factory (C34) there were 5732 hand mule, 3648 self-acting mule, and 3168 throstle spindles. The persistence of hand mules is perhaps an indication of stagnation in the industry, though mills advertised for sale are hardly likely to be in the van of progress. By the 1850s connection had been established by rail with Lancashire, and it was partly the ease with which yarn could be imported that deterred spinners from investing in new plant. In addition countries to which yarn had been exported were by that time developing their own textile industries.[4]

The oldest surviving cotton mill in Glasgow is now the Broomward Cotton Work (c 1815, F79) originally a five-storey brick building, now cut down to two storeys with unusually slender columns supporting timber beams and floors. David Elder, the famous marine engineer, designed the mill work for this mill. The main block of the Lancefield Spinning Company's Mill (c 1826, H107) is intact, though the windows have now been bricked in. A later block (*c* 1840) still in use as a spinning mill in the 1850s, was demolished a few years ago. All but one of the other surviving pre-1850 spinning mills are of brick, with two of the 1820s existing as fragments only, Bartholomew's second Arcadia Street mill (F70) which had a Watt engine and another, better preserved, Bartholomew mill in Greenhead Street (*c* 1840, F112). The remaining handful date from the 1840–50 period with Couper, Walker & Company's large mill in Broad Street the largest (*c* 1850, F98) and others in Reid Street (*c* 1846, F161), Kelvinhaugh Street (*c* 1848, K9) and Fordneuk Street (*c* 1849, F100). The last named has been extensively rebuilt. The only stone-built mill of the 1840s, in Royston Road (*c* 1845, C78), was of 'fireproof' design, the others being of normal wood and iron construction.[5]

Though expansion of cotton spinning ended after 1850, and many firms ceased production thereafter, including Houldsworths, two large spinning mills were built in the 1870s and 1880s. The earlier was the Clyde Spinning Company's mill (1871, F167) in Cotton Street, Dalmarnock, which significantly was equipped with machinery from Manchester. This mill, which differed little from earlier examples, except in its larger windows and generally larger size, was not fireproof, as was convincingly demonstrated when it burned down in August 1970. The Glasgow Cotton Spinners Company Limited was very different, both in conception and in plant. Modelled on the 'Oldham Limiteds' which were proving such a success in the 1880s, its mills (1884, F165), designed by Joseph Stott of Oldham, were both much larger and more technically advanced than any hitherto seen in Glasgow, embodying a relatively new type of fireproof construction, with hollow tiles in place of brick arches.[6]

Integrated Mills

Besides those firms which engaged in cotton spinning only, there were several which combined spinning with weaving. The power loom was introduced to Glasgow by James L. Robertson of Dunblane who installed a Cartwright loom in an Argyle Street workshop in 1793, large scale adoption following in 1803, when John Monteith had two hundred looms in Pollokshaws. Foster & Corbet reintroduced the power loom into Glasgow in 1806. These early pioneering efforts were not immediately followed up, but in the early 1820s a boom in power-loom weaving started. Many firms built weaving mills only, but in some cases integrated mills were planned, such as 'Wood's Mill' in James Street (c 1834, F118), the oldest recently surviving example, the handsome South Sawmillfield Mill (c 1838, C34) and the Albyn Mills in Waddell Street (c 1845, G157). There were also cases where weaving was 'tacked on' to an existing spinning mill, as at Lancefield and at the long-demolished Oakbank and St Rollox mills. The integrated mills were very similar in appearance to contemporary spinning mills, Wood's Mill being of brick, South Sawmillfield and Albyn of stone (Fig 6). None of the three was 'fireproof', all having wooden floors and beams on cast-iron columns.[7]

Weaving Factories

Nothing is known of the premises occupied by Monteith or Foster & Corbet, the oldest identifiable weaving factory in the city being Alexander Brown & Company's Rutherglen Road mill (c 1822, G165). The four-storey building facing Rutherglen Road may well be original, while two large multi-storey mills were added at the rear. The older still survives, though it has been extended fairly recently; the more recent (now cut down to one storey) was probably added in the 1840s, and was 'fireproof'. Perhaps the finest of the early weaving mills was Bishop Garden (c 1824, H38), which had an all-timber interior, with two rows of wooden pillars supporting longitudinal beams. A restricted site was effectively used in Graham Square, where G. Grant Junior's six-storey and attic brick building (c 1825, F8) has wooden beams and floors supported on slender cast-iron columns. Gilkieson's Cook Street mill (c 1844, G189) is also on a small site, and is notable for its almost square plan and for its large windows (Fig 7). The Barrow-field Weaving Company's four-storey factory (c 1829, F29) was an

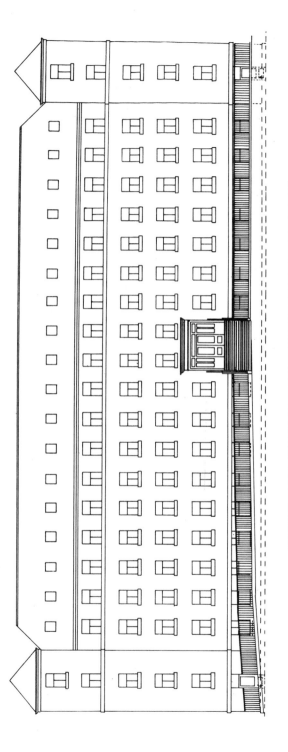

Fig 6

Elevation of South Sawmillfield Mill, 6–12 Burns Street (C34) built for Alexander Brown & Co., cotton spinners and weavers, and converted to a lodging house for George Young in 1891

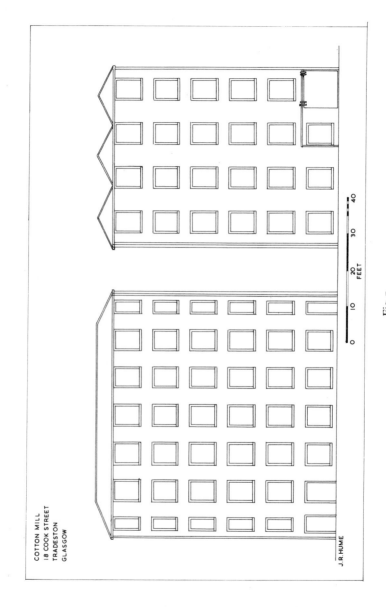

COTTON MILL
18 COOK STREET
TRADESTON
GLASGOW

J.R.HUME

0 10 20 30 40
      FEET

Fig 7

Elevations to Cook Street (L) and Commerce Street (R) of Cook Street Cotton Mill, 18 Cook Street, constructed for Robert Gilkieson, junior, power-loom cloth manufacturer, about 1844

eastern, brick equivalent of Bishop Garden, but had cast-iron columns. As with the integrated mills, design of these pioneer power-loom weaving factories was closely comparable with that of spinning mills: the classic weaving shed had not then appeared.[8]

William Fairbairn stated in his *Mills and Millwork* that the north-light weaving shed was introduced about 1830, but does not indicate to whom the innovation was due.[9] Whoever first used it is immaterial: where land was cheap it was the ideal way to build a factory for light work, and it has only recently been superseded by other methods of roofing a large floor area. Its particular value for weaving was in the even lighting provided, and in the rows of columns supporting the roof, which conveniently doubled as drive-shaft supports. The earliest weaving sheds in Glasgow were probably in Pollokshaws, either at Auldfield (1851, J9) or at Coustonholm (1858, J18). Coustonholm certainly had weaving sheds, Auldfield may have had. Weaving sheds began to appear in Bridgeton and Calton about 1860. Newhall Street (1859, F152), Fielden (1860, F95) and Brookside (1862, F101) mills were all single storeys and others followed in the mid 1860s, such as Atlantic (1864, F127) and Marquis Street (1866, F126). From then till after 1900 classical weaving sheds continued to be built, until large areas of the east end were covered with them. The last were also among the largest – River Street Factory (1855, F168), Barrowfield Weaving Factory (1889, F162), and finally Clutha Weaving Factory (1900, F163). Weaving factories were not confined to the eastern districts, and were also found in Grovepark Street (1857, B54), Dennistoun (1860, D6), Pollokshaws (*c* 1891, J12), and Govan (*c* 1886, K60; *c* 1877, K45); though nowhere in the same concentration as in the Bridgeton–Calton–Dalmarnock region.

Though most of the weaving factories built after 1860 were single storey, multi-storey buildings were also constructed where the land available was restricted. Parts of Craigpark Factory (D6) built in the 1860s were two storeys high, with striking use of white brick in decoration, while the main block of the Parkhead Factory (1865, F28), the Broomward weaving factory (*c* 1867, F78) and part of Newhall Street Weaving Factory (1865, F152) had three storeys, the two last named with an attic storey. There was then a lull in building until about 1880 when four-storey mills were built at Grovepark (1878, B54) and Burnside Works (1885, F104) and a three-storey and attic addition was made to a weaving mill in Rogart Street (1880, F85). The last, multi-storey weaving mill was in the appropriately named Muslin Street (1900, F121). All these buildings were brick-built, some with white or moulded brick ornament.[10]

Thread Making

Paisley's reputation as a centre of sewing thread manufacture has completely and rightly overshadowed that of Glasgow, but there were several sizable firms in the city specialising in thread. Initially thread makers bought in yarn from spinners to double, dye and spool it, and the Glasgow firms were of this type. Two, however, John Clark Junior & Co. of Mile End (c 1818, F83) and R. F. & J. Alexander of Duke Street (1849, G53) integrated vertically by becoming spinners also. John Clark Junior & Co.'s mills were very large indeed, covering two blocks in Rogart Street, and although most of them have been demolished, two five-storey and basement blocks survive, the older of which was probably built in 1854, the newer in 1878, with rolled iron or steel joints in place of the normal wooden beams found in the older part (Fig 8). Alexander's 'fireproof' mill in Duke Street, designed by Charles Wilson, one of the most distinguished Glasgow architects of the day, is one of the most outstanding industrial buildings surviving in Glasgow (Fig 9). Only slightly later was the short-lived Clyde Thread Works in Main Street, Bridgeton (1854, F153), whose five-storey stone-built mill, long since demolished, was converted to a weaving factory after only six years. Equally brief was the existence of the Beehive Thread Works (c 1886, F47), a four-storey and attic brick building on a very restricted site. The last thread works in Glasgow was the Viking Thread Mills in Pollokshaws (c 1914, J13) which worked until 1969, though the Campbellfield Twisting Factory (1882, F36) is still operating. Both of these are of brick construction.[11]

All the buildings mentioned so far have, with one exception, ceased to be used for their original purpose. Cotton manufacture

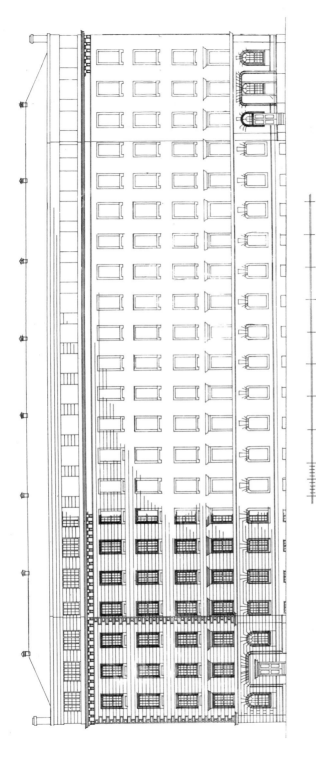

Fig 8

Elevation of Cotton Mill, 100 Duke Street (G53) designed by Charles Wilson
in 1849 for R. F. & J. Alexander, cotton thread manufacturers

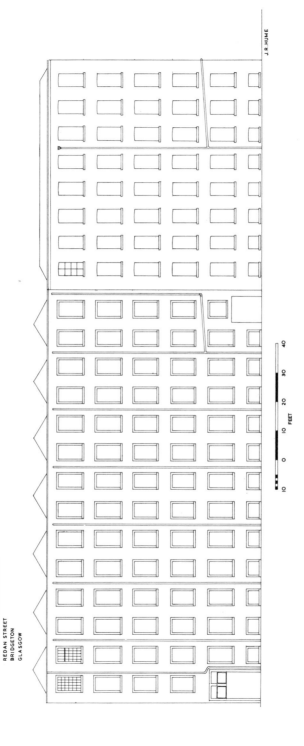

Fig 9

Elevation of part of John Clark Junior & Co.'s Mile End Thread Works, Rogart Street (F83), probably built in 1854 (left) and 1878 (right). The older part is sandstone rubble, the later of red and white brick

ended in many of them more than a hundred years ago, and since then they have provided accommodation for a host of new industries. Even before the cotton era ended, mortality of cotton firms was high, and a mill might pass through many hands before conversion to other purposes. Multi-storey mills made ideal stores: Lancefield was used by Thomas Lipton as a grocery store; Bishop Garden became a wool store; Anderston was until 1964 a bonded warehouse. Some also found alternative manufacturing use: Barrowfield Weaving Factory was a confectionery works for a time, so was Mile End Mills; Mile End Thread Works is part of an engineering works; the Glasgow Cotton Spinners Company's works is now a cardboard box factory; both Alexander's and Sawmillfield became lodging houses. The single-storey buildings were also used as stores, for clothing manufacture, as at Barrowfield, and wool spinning, as at Brookside. The importance of the part played by the cotton industry in its death throes in providing relatively cheap, conveniently arranged space for warehousing or for expanding industries has not been fully appreciated.

Woollens

Apart from the spinning of cotton, and its weaving into muslins, lappets, velvets, checks, zephyrs, ginghams, and a host of other fabrics, there were several other branches of the textile industry in Glasgow. The woollen industry (which flourished in the Borders and in the Hillfoot towns from the mid-nineteenth century) had little impact, one of the few sizable factories in the city being C. S. Cochran's merino spinning mill (1833, H35) in St Vincent Street in which French methods of merino spinning were used. The internal structure of his mill was unusual with a central row of cast-iron columns flanked by rows of wooden pillars (Fig 10). W. Holmes & Brothers, Greenhead Factory (1873, F107) were commission wool combers and spinners and also made woollen and cotton cloth. Mixed cotton–woollen fabrics were woven by Renison and McNab & Co. at Boden Street Factory, which was taken over by William Hollins & Co., and still operates. The manufacture

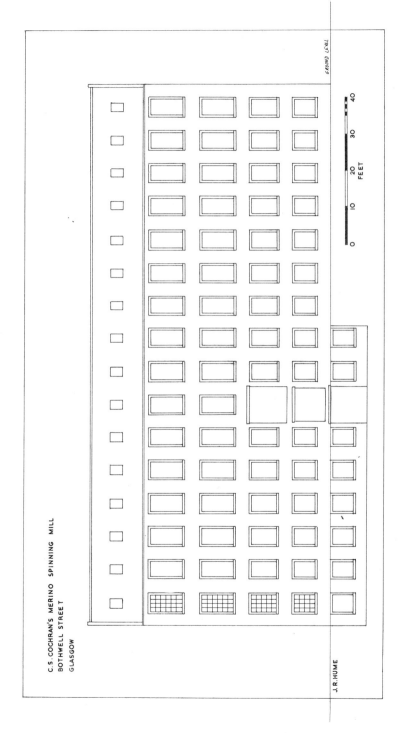

C.S. COCHRAN'S MERINO SPINNING MILL
BOTHWELL STREET
GLASGOW

GROUND LEVEL

0   10   20   30   40
          FEET

J.R.HUME

Fig 10

Elevation of Merino Spinning Mill, 335 St Vincent Street (H35) built for
C. S. Cochran & Co., worsted and woollen spinners about 1835

of woollen hosiery is probably a recent development though cotton hose were made in the city from an early date. An isolated three-storey and attic hosiery factory was built for James Ormond in Crownpoint Road in 1874 (F42).[12]

Carpet Weaving

Much the most important wool-using industry in Glasgow was, and is, carpet-weaving, introduced in 1757 but revolutionised by the invention of the chenille carpet by James Templeton and John Quigley in 1839. Templeton started the manufacture of these carpets in premises rented from John Clark Junior & Company, and after a fire in 1856 moved to what is now Templeton Street, occupying a cotton mill. The firm expanded on this site (F109) adding weaving sheds, and a three-storey block (1868–9). With a view to introducing spool axminster carpets, a new factory was built facing Glasgow Green, the famous 'Doge's Palace' which collapsed during erection in 1889, killing twenty-nine women in adjacent weaving sheds. Eventually completed in 1892, it was described in 1898 as 'a rather startling new wing of a carpet factory, designed by Mr W. Leiper in the Italian Gothic style, and built of gaudy-coloured bricks . . . we have no hesitation in saying that we think the experiment is a decided success'. Though expansion on the Templeton Street site continued, with the construction of a four-storey building facing London Road (1896–7) and other blocks after 1914, existing buildings were bought and converted for carpet manufacture. In 1901 the Broomward Cotton Work and Weaving Factory in Kerr Street (F78, F79) were taken over for chenille axminster carpets, and in 1907 Brookside Weaving Factory was bought for spool axminster; other factories in Bernard Street (F130) and Tullis Street (F149) were purchased after 1914. Chenille carpet-making, having gravitated to Tullis Street, finally ceased in 1970.[13]

The other important Glasgow carpet firms were founded by Templeton employees, with the exception of J. & J. S. Templeton, started in 1855 by James Templeton and his son John S. to make

Brussels carpets by the Jacquard method. The firm's Crownpoint Road factory (F87) underwent development comparable to that of the parent firm, with a three-storey and attic prestige building added in 1886 and a reinforced concrete block built in 1912. Here the last steam engines in the east end of Glasgow worked until closure in 1967. J. & J. S. Templeton was absorbed into the parent firm in 1906. James Templeton's first foreman was John Lyle, who left in 1853 to form the firm of John Lyle & Co. He moved to Fordneuk Street in 1868 (F84) and the buildings on this site were gradually extended until 1911. When the capacity of this factory was exceeded, the firm moved across Rogart Street, where a dyeworks was established in existing buildings (F86) and then across Broad Street to take in the four-storey mill and weaving shed of two power-loom weaving factories (F103, F104). Another important firm in its day was Anderson & Lawson, founded by a former head designer at Templeton's, John Lawson. Both Lyle's and Templeton's are today major producers of carpets and though they have built new factories elsewhere still have a strong hold on the East End.[14]

Linen and Jute

Other textile manufactures were of minimal importance: silk, jute and flax manufacturing had their representatives, as did machine lace-making, but all the firms involved were either small in scale or short-lived. One of the most ambitious firms was W. & J. Fleming, who expanded rapidly until about 1866, only to crash, after conversion to the Glasgow Jute Company Limited, in 1877. At its height, the company had two large works, Baltic & Clyde (1858, F124; 1866, F123, F125, F144), which were mainly single storey, but which incorporated two three-storey blocks (Fig 11). Not far away, J. Y. Adams built his single-storey Dundee Works (1863, F140) for jute manufacture, while the Craigpark Factory (D6) was taken over in 1868 for flax and jute spinning. Part of Sawmillfield cotton mill (C34) was also used for jute manufacture, by the Clyde Jute Company (*c* 1870–*c* 1900). The only linen

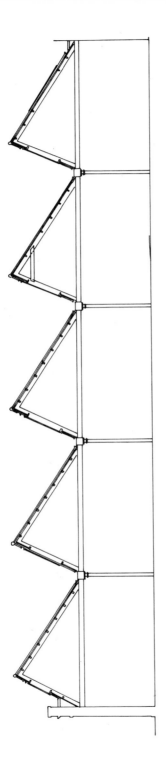

Fig 11

Section of part of the Baltic Works, Hozier Street and Baltic Street (F144) of
W. & J. Fleming, jute manufacturers, designed by John Gordon about 1860.
This type of construction was typical of east-end weaving sheds (cf plate 22)

manufacturer of any consequence in nineteenth-century Glasgow was Alex. Fletcher, who occupied a former cotton mill at St Rollox (C78). It is not surprising that Glasgow failed to become a major jute and linen centre: Dundee and the east were already well established by the 1850s, and in any case Glasgow's textile skills were those required in fine, rather than coarse cloth making.[15]

Silk and Lace

Silk weaving was fairly important in the west of Scotland in the late eighteenth century, especially in the Paisley area. Glasgow also had a share in this industry, with six silk factories in 1840, all spinning waste silk. The most famous was the Govan factory of Pollok, Morris & Son, destroyed by fire in 1873, and there were others in Port Dundas, Govanhaugh and in Tullis Street, Bridgeton, where part of the mill may survive in a complex group of buildings (F149). The last to be established was the Parkhead Silk Factory in Gallowgate (c 1899, E16), which may have been processing artificial, rather than natural silk. Machine lace-making was introduced into Scotland from Nottingham by Alexander Morton, whose first factory in Newmilns, Ayrshire, was soon surrounded by many others. In Glasgow the industry was represented by two firms, both of which occupied buildings from earlier phases of textile manufacture: T. I. Birkin & Co. occupied the Clyde Works (F125) from 1882 to 1939, while Goodall & White started in Baltic Jute Works (F124) between 1890 and 1894, then moved to Burnside Works (F104) finally closing in 1911.[16]

Textile Finishing

Textile finishing was a natural adjunct to spinning and weaving, and in a few cases was in the hands of the same firms or individuals. Todd, Higginbotham & Company, proprietors of the Springfield Cotton Work also had a print and dyeworks in Ballater Street, while David Dale, whose spinning mills were all outside Glasgow, was a partner in the long-vanished Barrowfield Dyeworks. The first large bleachfield in the city was at Gray's Green, set up in 1729 with the aid of the Board of Trustees, probably catering for the embryonic linen industry of the city. By the end of the eighteenth century there were several bleachfields within the present city boundary, naturally on the outskirts of the built-up area, since bleaching at that time involved the exposure of cloth to the sun for long periods. After Charles Tennant started making bleaching powder at St Rollox in 1799 (see chapter 3) this was no longer necessary, so that bleachworks could be set up nearer the town centre, and existing bleachfields could sell off most of their land. It has proved rather difficult to identify and date early Glasgow bleachfields, but there were certainly examples at Wellmeadowfield (Pollokshaws), Bellgreen, Bellshaugh and Kirklee (Kelvinside), Springfield (Dalmarnock), Kelvinhaugh and Hogganfield (Millerston). By the mid-nineteenth century there were about half a dozen bleachworks in and around the city. Those with recently surviving remains are Newlandsfield (1792, J16), Wellmeadow (J23), one in Maryhill Road (c 1855, B59) and Milnbank (c 1828, D9). None now function.[17]

Both the dyeing of piece goods and yarn, and the printing of linens and cottons were practised in Glasgow. The earlier of these trades was linen printing, which started in 1738. Cloth had to be bleached before and during printing, initially in the open, hence the term 'printfield' applied to many of the earliest establishments. One of the first was Dalsholm, founded by William Stirling, a Glasgow merchant, who moved to Cordale in the Vale of Leven about 1770 to found what became the most important centre of textile printing in Scotland. Dalsholm was demolished in 1872 to make way for Dawsholm Gas Works (A16). There were also printfields in Dalmarnock, Pollokshaws, Anderston, Govanhaugh, Finnieston and Govan, but no remains survive. Dyeing was introduced into the city in 1740 when the Harlem Dyeworks was set up. The most celebrated Glasgow dyeworks was the Barrowfield works, founded in 1785 by David Dale and others, with P. J. Papillon as a technical expert in Turkey Red dyeing, taken over by Henry Monteith & Co. in 1805 and subsequently used for printing Bandana handkerchiefs. Dyeworks became very numerous in the city. There were nearly fifty in 1846, mostly small, but with the decline in textile manufactures nearly all have disappeared, leaving W. McConnell & Co., Davidson Street, as the only active old-established dyeworks in Glasgow (1888, F179). The buildings of others survive in West Street (c 1880, H187), Gairbraid Avenue (1901, A28), Strathclyde Street (1870, F169), Springfield Road (c 1826, F188) and Ballater Street (c 1878, G160). General textile finishing services were probably provided at many of the dyeworks and bleachworks and at Riverbank Works (c 1893, J14) and Barrowfield Finishing Works (1907, F159) but more specific treatment was given in the once numerous calender works, of which a handsome example survives in Frederick Lane (1875, G38) and in a cloth-shrinker's workshop in Ruby Street (c 1893, F142).[18]

The textile finishing processes, involving as they do extensive use of water, are not really suited to multi-storey accommodation, and the Glasgow examples are mainly one or two storeys in height. Where taller buildings are found, as in the surviving four-storey block at the Adelphi Dyeworks (G160), the upper floors were probably used for storage and packing. The common patterns of factory building are to be found in the surviving buildings, with stone, as at Newlandsfield and Wellmeadow, giving way to plain red brick, as in the City of Glasgow Dyeworks, Gairbraid Avenue (A28) and to red and white brick as in the Dalmarnock (F179) and Clyde Dyeworks (F169).

Laundering

Related to textile finishing, but using substantially different techniques, is laundering. For centuries the province of women working in their homes, the washing of clothes and household linen on a large scale seems to have developed in Glasgow about the mid-1870s, though the great expansion of laundries falls into the period 1895–1910. The earliest surviving example is the City of Glasgow Steam Dyeing and Laundry Work, Napiershall Street (c 1873, B48), but this, and another early laundry in Eglinton Street (c 1877, G192) were small. The first sizable laundry in Glasgow was the Great Western Steam Laundry, Crow Road (1883, L1) and it remained an isolated example until the mid-1890s when the Wellmeadow Laundry (1894, J23), Glasgow Laundry & Carpet Beating Works (c 1895, I13) and Castlebank Laundry (c 1896, A23) were set up. Numerous others followed, of which the largest were the Alexandra Park (c 1901, A21), Kelvindale (1900, A29) and Cathcart (c 1905, M62) laundries. Most followed the example set by the Great Western Steam Laundry and employed single-storey buildings, although some had two-storey offices, such as the Castlebank Laundry, and one or two such as the Royal Laundry (1899, L8) were all on two storeys. Constructional materials were similar to those employed in other textile finishing plants, the most notable building architecturally being the Great Western, which was of stone with an ashlar front, designed by an Aberdeen architect, J. R. Mackenzie. The advent of cheap domestic washing machines and of self-service 'launderettes' has drastically reduced the demand for laundry services, and most of the surviving laundry buildings have been converted to other uses.

Ropemaking

One other branch of fibre processing should be mentioned – ropemaking. Ropeworks were a natural complement to a port, and there were at one time several in Glasgow. The earliest – still commemorated in Ropework Lane – was described in 1736 as consisting of 'great store houses, spinning houses, Garden and boiling houses and old green for spinning large cables tarred & white ropes'. The oldest recently surviving was part of the Anderston Ropework (c 1849, H81), a two-storey building in Stobcross Street, and not far away, in Elliot Street (1869, H116) stands an impressive four-storey rope store. The Govan Ropeworks (1890, H49) was the largest in the city, with a ropewalk extending under Edmiston Drive. Owned latterly by the Gourock Ropework Company, it was closed recently and demolished, leaving a small rope and twine works in Caroline Street, Parkhead (1890, E25) as the only active survivor of this industry in the city. However, a disused rope walk in Shettleston (*c* 1877, M40) still exists. The long narrow buildings of a rope walk do not lend themselves to re-use; this probably explains their low survival rate.

[1]Gordon, 84, extract from Town Council Minute; McUre, 323, and Gibson, J., *The History of Glasgow* (Glasgow 1777), 243, Warden, A. J., *The Linen Trade, Ancient and Modern* (London 1864), 505; Sinclair, Sir J. (ed), *Statistical Account of Scotland* (Edinburgh 1795) [OSA] vol 5, 502; Devine, T. M., 'Glasgow Merchants in Colonial Trade *c*1770–1815' unpublished PhD thesis, Department of Economic History, University of Strathclyde, 1972

[2]OSA vol 12, 116; *Report of Select Committee on the State of the Children Employed in the Manufactories of the United Kingdom* (1816) vol 3, 473; Cleland, J., *Rise and Progress*, 96; Scottish Record Office, Register House Plans, RHP 492(2) 'Plan of the Villa of Springfield the property of David Todd, Esq., surveyed in August 1797 by William Kyle, Glasgow' and RHP 79 'Plan of Springfield Works, the property of Charles Todd, Esq., 1835', show the old and new mills, while the latter features in Simpson, plate 32; *Glasgow Herald*, 2 November 1812, advertisement for the sale of Pattison's Mill; BRL, B & W MSS, William Creighton to Boulton & Watt, Glasgow 29 November 1800: Mr Pattison pleased with his engine 'intends to ornament & keep it in good style'

[3]Guildhall Library MSS, 11937/36, Sun CD series, passim, I am indebted to Dr John Butt for this information; Butt, 52, shows interior of Houldsworth mill, exterior is illustrated in Butt *et al.*, 43; Skempton, A. W., and Johnson, H. R., 'The First Iron Frames', *Architectural Review*, 131 (1962), 186; BRL, B & W MSS, Portfolio 353, William Creighton to Boulton & Watt, Glasgow, 10 May 1804; 'Drive through Scotland 1805' MS volume

in the possession of J. L. Blakiston-Houston, Beltrim Castle, Gortin, Co Tyrone; *Report on Children in Manufactories* (1816), vol 3, 473

[4]*Glasgow Herald* advertisements 3 August 1847, 1 November 1849, 1 April 1850, 12 July 1858; ibid, 23 February 1852

[5]Aerofilms Ltd negative 45887, August 1934, shows in the bottom right hand corner the mill complete; *Engineering*, 1 (1866), 103, obituary of David Elder; Butt *et al.*, 42, shows the earlier part of Lancefield; a plan of the Bartholomew mills in Arcadia Street is reproduced in Tann, Jennifer, *The Development of the Factory* (London 1970), 16 (this is dated *c*1796, but the captions on the plan refer to 'present engine, boilers & house in this compartment' and to 'engine house', indicating the latter is for the second engine, which was ordered in 1823, BRL, B & W MSS Engine Book, 76, Portfolio 484), Aerofilms negatives 45887 and A109436, 5 April 1963 show that the newer mill was five storeys high, with a seven storey warehouse block at one end

[6]*The Engineer*, 33 (1872), 445; *Scottish Daily Express*, 15 August 1970

[7]*New Statistical Account of Scotland* (Edinburgh 1845) [NSA], vol 6, 152–3; South Sawmillfield, in the guise of a common lodging house, is illustrated in Cunnison, J., and Gilfillan, J. B. S. (eds), *Third Statistical Account of Scotland: Glasgow* (Glasgow 1958) [3rd SA], plate 23, Oakbank is described in Bremner, David, *The Industries of Scotland, Their Rise, Progress and Present Condition* (Edinburgh 1869), 291–3

[8]Butt, 76, gives a front elevation of Bishop Garden

[9]Fairbairn, William, *Mills and Millwork* (London 2nd edn 1864), part 2, 115–16

[10]*Industries of Glasgow*, 261, shows a stylised view of the main block and weaving sheds at Grovepark

[11]The Clyde Thread Works is illustrated in Cowan, James, *From Glasgow's Treasure Chest* (Glasgow 1951), 48

[12]Cochrane's mill is illustrated in Butt *et al.*, 45; NSA vol 6, 167–9; *Industries of Glasgow*, 180; Wells, F. A., *Hollins & Viyella* (Newton Abbot 1968), 104, plate facing 160, shows a weaving shed in Boden Street Factory

[13]Gibson, 247; Butt, 102, shows the 'Doge's Palace' on the left, the 1896–7 block in the centre, and the cotton mill on the right, Oakley, *The Second City*, 171, shows a recent view; *The Builder*, 9 July 1898, 29; Young, Fred H., *A Century of Carpet Making 1839–1939* (Glasgow 1943), passim; a chenille setting loom has been preserved in Kelvingrove Museum; there is an illustrated note on chenille axminster weaving at Tullis Street in *Industrial Archaeology*, 8 (1971), 306–7, 332–4

[14]Butt *et al.*, 47, shows a carpet loom in the Crownpoint Road Factory; Young, passim

[15]Post Office Directories; the lineshaft supports in Clyde works were by Thomson Bros of Dundee, who probably also supplied the machinery

[16]*Some of the Leading Industries of Glasgow and the Clyde Valley* (Glasgow 1896), 211; *Second report of the Select Committee on the act for the regulation of Mills and Factories*, 13 April 1840, 82; *Glasgow Herald*, 22 March 1873; Post Office Directories

[17]Clow, A., and N. L., *The Chemical Revolution* (London 1952), 217–18; Warden, *The Linen Trade*, 719; note, however, that the fine linen from Graham's Hall was bleached at Dalwhern (Dalquhurn), Alexandria; McUre, 323

[18]Gibson, 244; the first edition of the Ordnance Survey 1:2500 plan of Glasgow shows a large area of 'Bleaching Ground' adjacent to the Barrowfield Print and Dye Works (site later occupied by Glasgow Cotton Spinning Co.'s Mills, F165); Thomson, Alexander, *Maryhill 1750–1894* (Glasgow 1895), 14–15; Clow, A., and N. L., 207, 217–18, 228; *Post Office Directory*, 1846–7

3 *Chemical and Related Industries*

The early history of the Scottish chemical industry has been most ably discussed by A. and N. L. Clow in their stimulating book *The Chemical Revolution* and it is clear from this and other accounts that the Glasgow district was a natural focus for chemical manufactures at a time when links with textile finishing were strong. Apart from the famous St Rollox Chemical Works (C83) of Charles Tennant & Co., about half-a-dozen works were producing sulphuric acid by the 1820s, and soda manufacture was added by most firms as soon as the Leblanc process had been proved profitable. Most of the chemical works were at that time in the Port Dundas area, where the prevailing wind carried fumes away from the city centre and residential districts. Though contemporary directories often omit detailed information about firms' products, it is clear that in the early years of the nineteenth century soda, sulphuric acid, other mineral acids and mordants were important products, and that Glasgow manufacturers were to the fore in new developments. Charles Macintosh, of waterproof fame, pioneered manufacture of lead and calcium acetates as mordants in the 1780s, and in 1808 White & Bain had a 'sugar of lead' (lead acetate) works in Bishop Street, Anderston, and an 'iron liquor' (iron acetate) factory in Gallowgate. The Tennants were the first to burn the charge outside the lead chambers in sulphuric acid making, and were pioneers in the use of steam in lead chambers, in the substitution of pyrites for sulphur, and in the use of the Leblanc process for soda manufacture. One of their managers, J. MacTear, devised a method of recovering some of the sulphur from the noxious 'alkali waste' left over from the Leblanc process, which was used at St Rollox in the 1870s.[1]

St Rollox was much the largest chemical works in the city, and, in the 1830s and 1840s allegedly the largest in the world. Its principal product was bleaching powder, made under a patent of 1799, but, as already indicated, other substances were also made:

soda, from by-product sodium sulphate; soap, from soda; and a range of sulphites and sulphates. Another famous works, long demolished, was the Hurlet Alum Works, for a time the largest of its kind in Britain. Smaller firms included R. & J. Garroway of Netherfield Chemical Works (1851, E1), still happily in existence, and Alexander Hope Junior & Co., who moved from Port Dundas to Provanmill in 1901 (M31); both made in 1876 soda, inorganic acids, mordants and chemical manures. The old-established merchant firm of Alexander Cross & Sons set up a chemical works in 1872 in the old Eagle Foundry (C63), which was by 1888 making superphosphate, sodium nitrate, ammonium sulphate and potash salts as fertilisers. Another Port Dundas firm, Joseph Townsend & Co., specialised in arsenic compounds, other mordants, and saltpetre at their Townsend Street works (1856, C59). Acetate mordants, originally produced from malt vinegar, were from c 1820 made from a cheaper substitute, pyroligneous acid, a crude acetic acid derived from wood by dry distillation. Probably the largest Glasgow makers of pyroligneous acid were Turnbull & Co. of Camlachie (c 1813, F30), who had small wood distilleries in several places in the west of Scotland, including Balmaha and Kilkerran, whence crude acid was sent for purification and conversion to acetate mordants.[2]

Dyestuffs

Though synthetic dye-making never became important in Glasgow, the extraction and modification of natural dyestuffs was at one time quite a significant industry. The most famous concern was George Macintosh's Cudbear Works. Cudbear, a dyestuff made from lichen, was first manufactured by its inventor Cuthbert Gordon in Leith. George Macintosh, in 1777, removed the works to Glasgow, and to maintain secrecy built a ten-foot wall round the factory. After a long period of prosperity, exhaustion of the raw material and changing fashion in colours resulted in closure in 1852, immediately followed by a sale of the plant and building materials. There were several dyewood mills in Glasgow where natural dye extracts were prepared, notably at Balgray, on the Kelvin (now Kelvindale Paper Mill, A27) and at the Carntyne works (c 1883, E10) of what is now the British Dyewood Company.[3]

Soapmaking

The first 'soaperie' in the city, built as early as 1667 in connection with a whaling enterprise, was at the south-east corner of Candleriggs and Ingram Street and lasted till 1785. McUre described it as 'Four Lodgings, Cellars, Houses of Store and other Conveniences for Trade, being a pretty square Court'. By 1825 there were eight soap-makers, and by 1872 nineteen. One of the largest was Tennant & Co., whose soap interests were hived off to Ogston & Tennant in 1898. Of the other soap-makers, Charles Whitelaw, whose Sydney Street Works (c 1853, F2) still survives, was probably the most important, producing in 1876 about 2000 tons of hard soap. Two other former soapworks still exist, in Scotland Street (c 1877, H202) and Milton Street (1891, L112).[4]

Chemical factories have tended to be demolished rapidly after closure for a number of reasons. The buildings were often mere sheds, and rapidly changing techniques and short plant life meant that they were frequently designed for short-term use; in addition they were subject to the corrosive action of products and by-products. The dominating features of most nineteenth-century chemical works were, in fact, the chimneys, which were tall to disperse noxious fumes. 'Tennant's Stalk', with a height of $455\frac{1}{2}$ feet was the largest chimney of its day, but was soon surpassed by the nearby 'Townsend's Stalk' (468 ft). The lead chambers and Gay Lussac and Glover towers of the lead chamber sulphuric acid makers were also prominent. Other structures were usually one storey, brick or rubble, occasionally with pantiled roofs for ventilation, as at St Rollox and Camlachie. The most interesting survival from the heavy chemical industry is part of Townsend's works, which has an exposed framework of very heavy cast-iron columns and steel beams, though at St Rollox the attractive 'new' office block of c 1830 lasted until closure. At Carntyne, Sydney

Street and Scotland Street the buildings are of red and white brick, while the Milton Street factory is plain red brick; apart from Sydney Street, which is single storey, all are two storey. The most permanent memorial of the Glasgow chemical industry will, however, probably be the enormous mounds of alkali waste, now grassed and built over, which St Rollox Works spewed forth.[5]

Chemical-based Industries

Though not strictly 'chemical industries' other industries relying on chemical change or using the methods of the chemical industry were numerous. Brewing and distilling, textile finishing, sewage disposal and gas manufacture are discussed in Chapters One, Two and Seven, while match manufacture, rubber processing, glass making, ceramics manufacture, oil refining, paint making and tanning were all well represented in Glasgow. Match factories were notoriously inflammable, two, in Govan and Townhead, being destroyed by fire, though the much-altered remains of two others, in Maryhill (*c* 1879, B11) and Dennistoun (*c* 1849, F17) could recently be seen. Matches are still made by Bryant & May in Maryhill (B8). The first rubber works in Glasgow was probably Charles Macintosh's pilot plant for his waterproofing process, later transferred to Manchester. George MacLellan's still active works in Maryhill (*c* 1876, B15) is the oldest, and was followed by Kent Works, Ruchill (*c* 1885, B16), Thistle Rubber Mills, Tradeston (*c* 1886, G188), and St Mungo Works, Govan (1901, K44). Typical products of the MacLellan and Kent Works were machine belting, hose, valves, wringer rollers, rubber balls and fishing stockings, while the St Mungo Works made golf balls. Gutta percha and balata, natural products related to rubber, were used by R. & J. Dick in their Greenhead works (1859, F112) for making shoes and transmission belting. Synthetic plastics were not made on a large scale before 1914, but in that year the Netherton Works of Ioco Ltd (A1) was opened to make plastic laminates.[6]

Glassmaking

A large glass cone is a prominent feature in many eighteenth- and early nineteenth-century views of Glasgow. This was the property of the Jamaica Street Bottle Works (1730) and was replaced in 1792 by a larger one which lasted until *c* 1834. The main use for bottles was in the wine, beer and spirit trade, and owing to the city's connections with this trade, bottlemaking has remained the mainstay of Glasgow's glass industry. Other early bottleworks were at Lancefield, Port Dundas and Govanhaugh, while the tradition has more recently been carried on by the Caledonian (1892, B24) and North British Bottleworks (*c* 1904, E8). The last-named is now the only operating glassworks in the city. Crown (window) glass was being made at the Jamaica Street works in 1752 but in 1853 the Glasgow Glass Works at Port Dundas was described as 'the only crown sheet and plate glass manufacturers in Scotland'. The manufacture of plate glass was transferred to Murano Street about 1874 (B23) under a new firm. Fine glass for domestic use and display was made by a number of firms; the most important was the Verreville Company (1776–7). Lancefield works also made 'crystle' glass. The only fine glass works to survive into recent times was the St Rollox Flint Glass Works of Cochran & Couper (*c* 1838, C84).[7]

Physical remains of these industries are more substantial than those of the heavy chemical trade. The Dennistoun match factory had a two-storey rubble building, probably original, until demolition, but the Maryhill works has been extensively rebuilt. Most rubber works are handsome, MacLellan's having a neat, pedimented building and a tall, three-storey and attic block, facing the canal, both brick, while the nearby Kent Works is a three-storey structure with semicircular windows on the top floor. The front block of the Thistle Works is of solid red brick, with an early reinforced concrete addition at the rear. St Mungo and Ioco works are plain, but R. & J. Dick's Greenhead Factory has a handsome ashlar frontage to Glasgow Green – changing to red and white brick at the rear. The most interesting glassworks buildings recently existing were at St Rollox, where two cone stumps lasted until 1966. Both the Murano Street factories and the North British works are functional in design, though the low-relief arches on the facade of the last-named are attractive.[8]

Brickmaking

As good deposits of coarse clay exist throughout Glasgow, and cheap coal was available, it is not surprising that the ceramics industry flourished. The basic use of clay is brickmaking, and an association between bricks and pottery is suggested by Fleming's account of the Delftfield Pottery (1748) which had brick walls a yard thick, faced with sandstone. More specifically he says that the Kingfield Pottery made bricks until a tax of three shillings per thousand was imposed in 1780. Certainly until *c* 1810 brick buildings were rare in Glasgow, though there were probably some in the east end, where clay deposits overlay easily worked coal seams. McArthur's map (1778) shows land in Calton belonging to John Anderson 'Brick Layer', and tile works of Anderson and of M. Bogle. The first really large brick building seems to have been Houldsworth's Mill of 1804, and the surviving east-end cotton mills (all post 1815) are brick (see chapter 2). Machine brickmaking was introduced *c* 1850, and between 1860 and 1890 brick, mainly from local works, was used almost universally for factories and widely for internal partitions, side and rear walls in stone-faced commercial and domestic buildings. The last Glasgow brickworks was Polmadie, with clay pits at Mall's Myre, which closed as late as 1963, though just outside the boundary at Shettleston (NS647643) there is a works with an orthodox Hoffman kiln. Fragments still exist of the Crown Fireclay Works (1860, F24), which made glazed and fire bricks and sanitary ware.[9]

Potteries

Between 1750 and 1850 an important pottery industry developed in Glasgow, supplying both local and export markets, only to collapse almost as quickly as it rose. Local clays were coarse, clay beds were covered by the advancing built-up area, most potteries were too small to resist English competition, and attempts at mechanisation seem to have been inept. The most complete account of early Glasgow potteries is that of Fleming, and it is clear from this and other sources that most of them were in the east, the earliest at Blackfaulds (1595), though Delftfield in Anderston (1748) must be regarded as the first modern pottery. Nothing remains of this, nor of many of the others discussed by Fleming, but parts of the Eagle (1869, F129), Possil (c 1881, M19) and Port Dundas (1831, C102) potteries survive, long turned to other uses. Fragments also exist of the North Woodside Flint Mill, rebuilt in 1846, which calcined and ground flint for the great Verreville Pottery. The only remaining city pottery, Govancroft (1914, M44) is very much alive, producing high-quality earthenware. Examples of Glasgow pottery may be seen in the Old Glasgow, Kelvingrove, and Huntly House (Edinburgh) museums.[10]

Clay Pipe Making

Though conventional potteries were important, they were not so distinctively 'Glasgow' as the once-numerous clay pipe factories. Pipe making was at its height in the second half of the nineteenth century, when enormous numbers were made, largely for export. Pipe fragments are commonly excavated in North American pioneer settlements, where they can be used in dating. Most factories, such as those in Pinkston Road (1874, C17) were small, but there were some large enterprises, notably William White & Son's Bain Street works (1876, G121) with an output in 1891 of 14,400 pipes per day and William Christie's works in Craignestock Street (1877, F66), making 9000 pipes per day. The last in operation was in Charles Street, and closed in 1967 (c 1889, C81), where the hand methods used were recorded by I. C. and Ll. de S. Walker.[11]

As indicated, no brickworks now exist in the city, but the buildings were probably very functional, the most substantial being the kilns. The North Woodside Flint Mill had a single-storey ashlar grinding block with an internal low-breast wheel, a brick drying shed and a circular-section brick kiln, now reinforced in concrete. Of the potteries, both Eagle and Possil had large three-storey red and white brick buildings, while Port Dundas and Govancroft had single-storey red brick buildings. White's was the finest of the pipe factories with two four-storey blocks in red and white brick, with a two-storey link building. The Craignestock Street and Charles Street factories were both three storeys and the Pinkston Road factory was two storeys high. The type of kiln used in pipe making is illustrated in the Walkers' article (see footnote 11).[12]

Paint and Colour Making

Oil refining and paint and colour manufacture were closely connected in late nineteenth-century Glasgow, particularly since fine lubricating oils were still largely animal and vegetable, rather than mineral, in origin. Links with the chemical industry were strongest in pigment making; the most important pigment was probably white lead, the speciality of Alexander, Fergusson & Co. at their Glasgow Lead and Colour Works (c 1874, B10) and of the Clyde Lead Works, occupiers of a former iron tube works in Kinning Park (H213). There were other colour works in Dobbies Loan (1873, G7; 1889, C103), Milnpark Street (c 1895, H166) and Port-man Street (c 1895, H170). Most of them probably made paints as well as pigments. The oldest specialist paint factory building surviving is the Tradeston Paint Mills (1866, H186), now a ware-house; in the same block Blacklock & McArthur's works, rebuilt 1888–1900 (H185) is still used as a paint warehouse. Probably the largest paint works in the city is the Glasgow Oil & Chemical Works of Hannay, Gourlie & Hinshelwood in Glenpark Street (1883, F21), built up over some thirty years. Other recently surviving paint factories were in French Street (c 1876, F160), Brown Street (1891, H66), Vermont Street (c 1893, H204) and Bardowie Street (1902, M24). The late date of most of these works is notable, probably reflecting a trend to increasing specialisation within this group of industries.[13]

Oil Refining

Apart from supplying oil to paint manufacturers, oil refiners and merchants dealt in pure and blended lubricating oils, and sometimes in greases. They also supplied lighting oils at an early date, but by the 1860s mineral oil (paraffin) had supplanted animal and vegetable oils for lighting. Mineral oils were being used as lubricants, but, at least in the early 1890s do not seem to have been very generally adopted. One of the largest firms in the lubricating oil trade was Jamieson & Co., with premises in Clydeferry Street (c 1844, H85), while another old-established concern was that of William Walls, whose North Frederick Street works, founded c 1855, was rebuilt after a fire in 1866. Other important oil works were in Dobbies Loan and Kyle Street (1870, C93, C94), Dunblane Street (1904, C111), and Crownpoint Road (c 1890, F34). An unusual little factory was one in Mansion Street, Possil (c 1889, M21) which made turkey-red oil, a sulphonated vegetable oil, for dyers. Elder Park Works, Uist Street (1903, K65) specialised in printing ink and distilled rosin.[14]

Candlemaking

Candlemaking was an important trade in the eighteenth century and earlier, and is commemorated in the street name 'Candleriggs', but the invention of gas lighting and of improved oil lamps tended to reduce demand. The industry revived with the substitution of paraffin wax (initially derived from shale oil) for tallow, but incandescent gas and filament electric lighting eventually almost killed it. Recently only one candlemaking firm, Shearer & Harvey, has existed in the city (c 1897, K34).

Of the paint and colour makers' premises the most impressive are undoubtedly Blacklock, McArthur & Co.'s Venetian Gothic warehouse (Fig 12) and adjacent four-storey ashlar block, though Hannay, Gourlie & Hinshelwood's premises have a neat brick facade with a tower. The Tradeston Paint Mills are tastefully

Fig 12

Elevation to Cook Street of Paint Warehouse, 118 Tradeston Street (H185),
designed in 1896 for Blacklock, McArthur & Co., paint manufacturers, by
W. F. McGibbon

constructed of sandstone, with a crow-step-gabled office. Both the Milnpark Street works and Alexander, Fergusson & Co.'s premises are pleasing examples of the use of red and white brick. The other paint factories are mostly undistinguished architecturally, with the exception of one of the Dobbies Loan factories (1873, G7) which is a handsome composition with a central tower. William Walls and Jamieson & Co. had the most architecturally correct of the oil refineries, with handsome dressed stone facades; the former has an unusual brick-arched interior. Most of the remaining oil works had plain brick buildings though the Dunblane Street works had a substantial main block with a large round-headed doorway. Shearer & Harvey's works is a single-storey brick shed.

Tanning

Though tanning is based on pastoral farming, its processes are specifically chemical in nature. It was practised in Glasgow from an early date, and for much of the eighteenth century was a major industry. The Glasgow Tanwork Company was established soon after the Union, and during the eighteenth century many of the greatest city merchants had a share in it. Its premises were on the Molendinar near Glasgow Cross, and were described by McUre as a 'prodigious large building, consisting of bark and lime pits, store houses . . . ; the buildings are so considerable that it is admired by all strangers who see it.' By 1764 two other tanneries had been founded nearby, and a fourth on the lands of Hydepark, Anderston. George Macintosh (of Cudbear fame) was a clerk in the Tanwork, and left to set up as a shoemaker. By 1773 he and the Tanwork Co. were employing 300 shoemakers each making shoes for export. Tanning lost its dominant position as Glasgow widened its industrial base, but throughout the nineteenth century tanning and leatherworking were important industries. The oldest recently surviving tannery was the Pleasance Leather Works, London Road (c 1861, F59) and the largest, the St Ann's Leather Works of John Tullis & Son (1869, F119). Both specialised in machinery belting, while the Pleasance works also made laces and hosepipes. Martin & Millar in 1888 were producing leather for belts, harness and saddlery, soles and machinery at Glenpark Tan Works (c 1864, F18). One of the smaller firms, Barrowfield Leather Works (c 1878, F155) is still operating, as is the Dalmarnock Tannery of Andrew Muirhead & Son, formerly the Dalmarnock Flax & Jute Works (F140). In the 1880s the traditional methods of tanning with bark extracts and alum encountered competition from a new technique, using bichromates. Some tanneries, such as Tullis's, adopted this method, and one new factory, the Eglinton Chrome Tannery in Firhill (c 1892, B35) was built for the purpose.[15]

Leather Finishing

Tanning is, of course, the basic process in leathermaking, but for many purposes the leather must be curried (treated with fats and waxes) and perhaps given a finished surface. Tanneries sometimes curried their own leather, but there were also specialist curriers; the most important was probably Hamilton Caldwell, whose Scotia Leather Works (F134) founded 1873 and extensively rebuilt, is the largest surviving leather factory building. The original St Catherine's Leather Works of Thomas McBride, currier, still exists in Moir Lane (c 1880, G127), as does its successor in Ingram Street (1910, G65). There was also an extensive trade in finished leather, both Scottish and imported, in which primary and secondary processors were involved, as well as specialist city-centre merchants. Montrose Street has the oldest warehouse (1864, G69), with Schrader & Mitchell's Fox Street premises a close second (1868, G94). The same firm built a new warehouse in Howard Street in 1903 (G91). Others are to be found in Old Wynd (1899, G102) and St Andrews Square (1876, G132), the latter prominently named 'Tannery Buildings'.[16]

Leather Products

Boots, shoes and bags were generally made by specialist firms. The employment of domestic shoemakers by George Macintosh has already been mentioned, and until *c* 1850 boots and shoes still seem to have been made by individuals in their own workshops. In the 1853–4 Post Office Directory Mair's Boot and Shoe Warehouse in Jamaica Street advertised ready-made boots and shoes made in batches by hand craftsmen. The buildings of two shoe factories set up in the 1860s survive, in Elcho Street (*c* 1867, F53) and Oxford Street (*c* 1865, G150). The former belonged to A. & W. Paterson, who advertised it as the Clydesdale Steam Factory, producing shoes for eleven retail stores, as well as for export and wholesaling. Machine shoemaking was never strongly established: the St Crispin Works (Cornwall Street, H208) of 1895 had, for example, only a short life as a shoe factory. The trend to the importation of shoes from England and elsewhere is illustrated by a large boot and shoe warehouse in Saracen Street (1910, C3). Gutta percha moulded shoes (colloquially 'gutties') were made by R. & J. Dick at their Greenhead Works. Leather bags are the speciality of the Greenbank Leather Works in Dumbarton Road (1895, L24). Two other related sites are the privately owned Hide, Wool and Tallow Market, Greendyke Street (1890, G131) and a gut works in Vinegarhill Street (1907, F26).[17]

Of the industries mentioned in this chapter, tanning produced the most distinctive buildings – the drying houses of the older tanneries with their wooden louvres. Both the Pleasance and St Ann's works had this feature on the top floors of multi-storey blocks, while the drying shed of the Eglinton Chrome Tannery was a single-storey corrugated iron clad building. The Barrowfield Leather Works in recent years had no drying shed, nor have the remains of Glenpark. Currying works had no special features, though the Glasgow examples were all four or more storeys high; the Scotia works with its tower and water-tower is particularly striking. Leather warehouses do not differ markedly from other commodity stores though Schrader, Mitchell & Weir's Howard Street building is a fine specimen of 'modern movement' architecture. Of the shoe factories, Elcho Street resembles a warehouse, though the Oxford Street block is an interesting composition with round-headed windows on the upper floors. The Saracen Street warehouse is a fairly early example of the use of reinforced concrete. John Keppie's Hide, Wool and Tallow Market, with its red sandstone frontage, could well be mistaken for a public building, though its most interesting feature is its unusual design of roof truss.

[1]Tennant, E. W. D., *One Hundred and Forty Years of the Tennant Companies* (London 1937), passim; Hume, J. R., 'The St Rollox Chemical Works, 1799–1964', *Industrial Archaeology*, 3 (1966), 185–92; Checkland, S. G., *The Mines of Tharsis* (London 1967), passim; *Pigot & Co.'s Directory* (1825) lists five soda manufacturers, and assuming that all these made their own sulphuric acid, seven sulphuric acid makers; NSA, vol 6, 165–6; P. Fleming's Map of the City of Glasgow and Suburbs (1808), reproduced in Gunn, J., and Newbigin, M. I., *The City of Glasgow: its Origin, Growth and Development* (Edinburgh 1921) facing 72; Haber, L. F., *The Chemical Industry during the Nineteenth Century* (Oxford 1958), 4; Clow, A., and N. L., 146, 149; MacTear, J., 'On the Growth of the Alkali and Bleaching Powder Manufacture in the Glasgow District', *Chemical News*, 35 (1877), 26; Haber, 99, also *Some of the Leading Industries of Glasgow and the Clyde Valley*, 222

[2]Haber, 15; it is stated by the Clows (193) that the ground for St Rollox was purchased from J. & R. Tennent, but in fact it was bought from J. Pattison (GCA Register of Sasines, Glasgow, 1799 B10/2/72 disposition dated 29 April 1799); as early as 1801 Tennant, Knox & Co. bought a 12 horse-power engine from Boulton & Watt for grinding manganese (manganese dioxide) and chalk, BRL, B & W MSS, Engine Book 2, 3, Portfolio 228; Clow, A., and N. L., 239; Muspratt, S., *Chemistry, Theoretical, Practical and Analytical* (Glasgow 1860), vol 2, 158–69, GCA, T-HB 257, Plan of Hurlet Alum Works, 1824; *Some of the Leading Industries of Glasgow and the Clyde Valley*, 224, 244; *Industries of Glasgow*, 86; NSA, vol 6, 166; *Industries of Glasgow*, 130, date of

Camlachie works given as 1806, but Directory date is 1813

[3]Stewart, George, *Curiosities of Citizenship in Old Glasgow* (Glasgow 1881), 69–71, *Glasgow Herald*, 23 February 1852, Thomson, 39

[4]Cleland, *Rise and Progress*, 87, Senex (Robert Reid), *Old Glasgow* (Glasgow 1864) 439, map facing 432, McUre, 281–2; *Pigot & Co.'s Directory*, 1825, *Post Office Directory*, 1872–3; Tennant, E. W. D., *A Short History of the Tennant Companies* (London 1922), 22; *Some of the Leading Industries of Glasgow and the Clyde Valley*, 240

[5]Bancroft, R. M., and Bancroft, F. J., *Tall Chimney Construction* (Manchester 1885)

[6]*Glasgow Herald*, 6 March 1848, fire at lucifer match factory in Kirk Street, Townhead; *Some of the Leading Industries of Glasgow and the Clyde Valley*, 246–7, includes description of the process of match making; ibid, 234; *Industries of Glasgow*, 150; information from George MacLellan & Co.; *Stratten*, 101–2; Chalmers, Thomas, *100 Years of Guttapercha* (Glasgow 1946), passim

[7]NSA, vol 6, 157; Clow, A., and N. L., 287; Senex, *Old Glasgow*, 82–3, includes a description of hand bottlemaking at Jamaica Street; Clow, A., and N. L., 283; first window glass made in Scotland, *Glasgow Herald*, 14 March 1853; *Stratten*, 62

[8]Thistle Rubber Mills and St Rollox Flint Glass works are illustrated in Butt et al., 66, date 1858 given for St Rollox (by J. R. H.) is wrong

[9]Fleming, J. Arnold, *Scottish Pottery* (Glasgow 1923), 77; map reproduced in Gunn, J., and Newbiggin, M. J., map 3; *Industries of Glasgow*, 144

[10]Fleming, 73–146, 219–30, 233–9, this source is to be treated with caution;

Glasgow Herald, 16 June 1848, New North Woodside Flint Mill to let

[11]Walker, I. C., and Ll. de S., 'Mcdougall's Clay Pipe Factory, Glasgow', *Industrial Archaeology*, 6 (1969), 146, footnotes 3, 4; *Stratten*, 180; Walker, I. C., and Ll. de S., 132–6, 139–41, 145–6; there is a reconstruction of a clay pipe maker's workshop in the Huntly House Museum, Edinburgh

[12]GCA Valuation Department negatives show flint mill complete. Recent excavations by the Glasgow Corporation Parks Department have revealed the ground plan of the grinding block, and the drying floor and flues, together with quantities of the chert used in grinding

[13]Murphy, William S., *Captains of Industry* (Glasgow 1901), 237–8, *Stratten*, 122; Young, A. McL., and Doak, A. M., *Glasgow at a Glance* (Glasgow 1965), plate 115

[14]*Stratten*, 123, 148, 172; *The Engineer*, 22 (1866), 54 (fire at Walls)

[15]Stewart, 66–7; McUre, 283; 'A Plan of Part of the City of Glasgow & Course of the Molendinar Burn, 1764', reproduced in Gunn and Newbigin, Fig 2; Senex, *Old Glasgow*, 38, 122 (footnote); OSA, vol 5, 504; Murphy, 271–6; *Industries of Glasgow*, 140

[16]Young and Doak, plate 163, second Schrader & Mitchell warehouse

[17]*Post Office Directory* 1872–3, appendix 180; Chalmers, 25–6; the present Hide, Wool and Tallow Market is a replacement of one destroyed by fire; the latter is illustrated in *Industries of Glasgow*, 147

4   *Engineering and Shipbuilding*

Though Glasgow's reputation as a centre of heavy engineering and shipbuilding goes back to the early nineteenth century, the most rapid period of growth in these industries came after 1850. It is therefore not surprising to find physical remains in such number and variety as to pose problems of logical organisation. The method adopted here is to discuss first the different branches of secondary metal manufacture, and then engineering in its various forms.

Forging

Presumably blacksmiths practised in Glasgow almost from its foundation – certainly the Incorporation of Hammermen can trace its origins to the sixteenth century. The earliest sizable metalworking concern seems to have been the Smithfield Iron Company (1732), with a 'great manufactory' near the Broomielaw and a slit mill at Partick, which specialised in plantation tools for British colonies. Forging grew markedly in scale with the advent of the steam engine and other iron machinery, though one-man businesses persisted – there were 107 smiths in the city in 1825. The Lancefield Forge became well-known for the quality and size of its work; the large forgings for Brunel's *Great Eastern* were made there, and it had the second Nasmyth hammer in Scotland. Steam hammers rapidly replaced tilt and helve hammers, and Condie and Rigby, both West of Scotland engineers, made important design modifications. Glen & Ross, Arcadia Street (*c* 1856, F111) and John Yule & Co., Hutchesontown, specialised in steam hammer construction. An alternative forging tool was the hydraulic press, introduced in the 1880s and used both by specialist firms, like William Beardmore & Co., Parkhead Forge (E11) and Charles McNeil & Co., Kinning

Park Iron Works (1875, H163), and by such concerns as the North British Locomotive Co. Parkhead Forge was started about 1837 by Reoch Brothers & Co. to rework scrap iron, and was built up by Robert Napier and William Rigby for large marine forgings. William Beardmore turned to the manufacture of guns and armour plate about 1886, and the works expanded rapidly until after 1914. The heaviest press at Parkhead (12,000 ton) was made by Duncan Stewart & Co., London Road Ironworks (1865, F105), specialists in heavy forging presses. Lighter 'smithy' work was done in most engineering works, but also by such surviving blacksmith/farriers as those in Old Castle Road (18th century, M58) and Margaret Street (c 1851, G40) and by larger specialists like John Deas in Sydney Street (c 1889, F3).[1]

Ironfounding

Another basic method of shaping metal – casting – was used in the city at least as early as the eighteenth century. In 1801 there were three ironfounders – James McLachlane and John Roberton in Gorbals and John Napier in Jamaica Street – pioneers of what became one of Glasgow's greatest industries, not only in its own right, but as the basis of heavy engineering. Many of the early engineering works were, in fact, referred to as foundries, a famous example being Camlachie Foundry, built for John Napier in 1812 when his Jamaica Street works became inadequate. John's son David and nephew Robert were both at Camlachie before setting up their own Lancefield and Vulcan foundries near the Clyde. Other early examples were the Edingtons' Phoenix and Eagle (c 1820, C63) foundries at Port Dundas, and H. & R. Baird's Old Canal Basin Foundry. This firm had strong links with Shotts and Muirkirk Ironworks, but the family later turned to brewing and malting (see p. 16).[2]

Ironfounding received a great impetus from the invention of the hot-blast process for iron smelting, first because it cheapened all grades of iron, and secondly because the proportion of number one pig iron – especially suited to fine castings – increased. Though the only iron smelting works actually in the city, apart from the short-lived Garscube Works, was Govan (1839, I3), Clyde Ironworks is just outside the boundary, and Glasgow was the most important shipping point for iron from the Lanarkshire works. Number one pig was ideal for ornamental architectural work, and the leading firm in this field was Walter Macfarlane & Co., whose first works (1850) was in Saracen Lane. The firm moved to Washington Street in 1862, and then to a very large 'green field' site at Possil in 1869 (M17). In 1876 it could confidently be stated that 'the manufacture of [architectural and sanitary] castings has become quite a feature of the iron industries of Glasgow . . . indeed it may be said to have originated in Glasgow, the first person to "strike out" successfully . . . being Mr. Walter Macfarlane'. The other major firm in this trade was George Smith & Co., whose Sun Foundry in Kennedy Street (1870, G12) still stands; here Thomas Shanks's first iron sanitary appliances were made.[3]

The other great specialist branch of ironfounding in the 1870s was pipe making, when it could be claimed that Glasgow 'might be regarded as the headquarters of that branch of the iron trades'. The principal firms were then Thomas Edington & Sons, Phoenix Foundry, D. Y. Stewart & Co., Charles Street (c 1852, C79), R. Laidlaw & Sons, Milton Street (c 1853, C101) and Barrowfield, and Robert Maclaren & Co., Port Eglinton. All used machinery extensively and had a large export trade. One of the smaller firms, Shaw & McInnes, of the Firhill Ironworks (c 1866, B20) still flourishes. Other important branches of ironfounding were: stove making, Etna (c 1854, I1) and Sawmillfield; domestic range making, Keppoch (c 1875, C14), Milton (c 1856, B56) and Paragon (c 1865, H171); and railway chair making, Anderston (1823, H92). The firm which introduced the manufacture of American stoves, Smith & Wellstood of Bonnybridge, had an ornate workshop and warehouse in Renton Street (1873, C107), while Carron Company had a warehouse at Port Dundas (c 1830, C54), and later built a fine city-centre block in Buchanan Street.[4]

The most numerous group of foundries, however, made general engineering castings, such as cylinders, gasholder columns, machine tool components, sugar pans and other sugar machinery parts. George Bennie & Co., Kinning Park (c 1860, H173), Blythswood Foundry, North Street and Hayfield Foundry, Rutherglen Road, were among the leading firms in the 1870s. More recently Pinkston Iron Works, Pinkston Road (1871, C70); Whitevale Foundry, Rowchester Street (c 1882, F32); Crown Point Foundry, Fielden Street (1864, F91); Partick Foundry, Castlebank Street (c 1864, L29) and Cyclops Foundry, Fore Street (1898, M92) have been engaged in this field, though all but Whitevale have now closed. Strictly outside our period, but included as one of the largest foundries in Britain, is the now-demolished Clyde Foundry, Helen Street (c 1922, K51) of Harland & Wolff.[5]

The chief requirement of foundries is a large floor area. Where small castings were made, as at Saracen, Sun, Keppoch, and part of Firhill, the headroom required was not great and the moulding

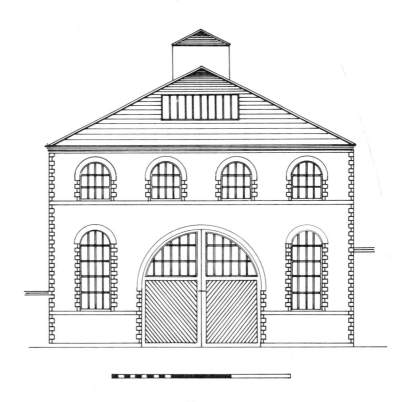

Fig 13
Front elevation of McEwan, Law & Lindsay's Cyclops Foundry, 42 Fore Street (M92), built 1898, R. Brown, architect

shops often resembled weaving sheds in construction. Apart from its large roof ventilators, there was little to distinguish an engineering or pipe foundry from a normal machine shop. Most firms turned out some of their products 'fitted', and fitting shops varied in size and complexity according to product. D. Y. Stewart, at St Rollox, R. Laidlaw & Sons, Milton Street, Etna and Milton all had multi-storey fitting shops. Foundries were normally brick-built, but some early ones, such as the Eagle and Milton works, were of stone, as also was the frontage of the Saracen Foundry. The finest of the brick-built foundries was probably the Cyclops (Fig 13). The largest foundry in bulk was certainly the Clyde Foundry, whose steel frame was covered with reinforced glass. As regards melting equipment, there is nothing to suggest that this differed in Glasgow from practice elsewhere. There are modern cupolas at Firhill and Whitevale, but at Keppoch an old cupola was used till closure.[6]

Steel Founding

This is a more specialised trade, and it is, therefore, not surprising that there were few steel foundries in Glasgow. Crucible steel castings were made by the Avon Steel Works, Glenpark Street (c 1869, F20), a relatively small concern. Somewhat larger were the Caledonian Steel Foundry in Helen Street (1893, K56) and Rennie's foundry in Cuthelton Street (c 1906, M45), both of which had high single-storey buildings. Beardmores, too, had a very large steel-framed steel foundry at Parkhead, now closed, but still standing.[7]

Brass Founding

Also less massive in output than ironfounding was the non-ferrous castings industry, though its products were indispensable both to engineering and to shipbuilding. In 1876 it was claimed that since 1850 'two or three score' brass foundries and coppersmiths' shops had been built, mainly in the Anderston and Finnieston districts, serving locomotive builders, marine engineers and sugar machinery makers. Some of the larger engineering firms had their own brass foundries. The oldest existing brass foundry buildings are in Minerva Street (1869, H15) and Nelson Street (1865, H134), while part of John Glover's Bridgeton Brass Foundry dates from *c* 1830 (F148). The nearby Calton Brass Foundry of Allan & Bogle (*c* 1876, F76) specialised in brewery machinery, and the Victoria Brass Foundry in Gorbals Lane (1876, G172) and associated finishing works in Buchan Street (1889, G175) made brass lamps and bells. The heavy end of the trade was represented by Steven & Struthers, originally of the Anderston Brass Foundry, Elliot Street (1870, H21) who moved to Eastvale Place in 1903 (K7). They specialised in bells and propellers, the latter being the staple product of the Bulldale Street foundry (*c* 1901, M2) of Bull's Metal & Marine. It is impossible to generalise about the form of brass foundries, as they varied from large single-storey structures, as at Bulldale Street, to four-storey buildings, as in Gorbals Lane. The products made by most brass foundries could readily be machined on light tools in buildings of more than one storey. Melting in the smaller works was done in crucibles in 'pit fires'; larger quantities of metal could be melted in air furnaces.[8]

Coppersmithing

Coppersmiths' shops were less numerous than brass foundries. Of the five recently extant, three dated from the 1870s, in Robertson Lane (*c* 1870, H51), Lancefield Street (*c* 1879, H108) and Tradeston Street (1876, H184); the remaining two in Woodville Street (1897, K40; 1903, K38) dated from the turn of the century. The Lancefield Street works is a low single-storey brick building while the Tradeston Street example, in red and white brick, is one and two storeys high. The Woodville Street factories both now belong to Blairs Ltd, and consist of steel-framed shops covered in corrugated-iron and brick, with a neat three-storey brick office block.[9]

Tubemaking

The manufacture of welded iron tubes was introduced into Glasgow in the 1830s from South Staffordshire by Andrew Liddell of the Globe Foundry, Washington Street. Growing demand from the gas industry eventually necessitated a move to the new Globe Tube Works, McAlpine Street (*c* 1859, H77). Gas tubes were made by butt welding, while in steam and water tubes the seam was lap welded, the latter process being introduced by Marshall & Wylie, Glasgow Tube Works, Swanston Street (1859, F170). Lap welded tubes were later made at the Govan Tube Works, Broomloan Road (*c* 1873, K61) and the Vulcan Tube Works in Cornwall Street (*c* 1872, H213). David Richmond started a tube works in the Florence Street premises vacated by P. & W. MacLellan in 1874 (G154), and his successor there, James Wilson, built a three-storey warehouse in Oxford Street (1882, G176). Another Govan tube works was built in Helen Street in 1871 (K61) and rebuilt in 1880–8, but the last works, and the largest was the Tollcross Tube Works of the Clydeside Tube Co. Ltd (1913, M43) which actually spanned the city boundary. By that time steel had largely replaced wrought iron in tubemaking. The so-called Tradeston Tube Works in Wallace Street (1899, G185) seems to have been only a warehouse. All the tube works built as such were single storey, increasing in height and roof span with time. The offices at Globe and Vulcan are architecturally interesting, while the Tradeston Tube Works has a fine wrought-iron grille in the fanlight above the main entrance.[10]

Metal Coating

The coating of ferrous objects with zinc or enamel to prevent corrosion was at one time a fairly important city industry. The earliest recently extant factory was the Anderston Galvanising Works, Elliot Street (*c* 1865, H23), and the only works still operating is the Clyde Galvanising Works (1875, H122) of Smith & McLean, now much rebuilt. The Lancefield Galvanising Works, Lancefield

Street (1886, H110) was a small single-storey workshop, like the Anderston works, but the Whiteinch Galvanising Works (1898, L13) was a substantial red brick block. Probably the largest such works was Frederick Braby & Co.'s Eclipse Iron and Galvanising Works, Petershill Road (c 1880, M28), with steel-framed workshops. Braby's also engaged in structural engineering. The only specialist enamelling works, in Harland Street (c 1898, M95), is a pleasant example of red brick factory architecture.[11]

Rivet, Bolt and Nut Making

So far, the production of semi-finished components by forging or casting, or of finished products involving little machinery, has been considered. Of other items used in the engineering industries, nuts, bolts and rivets are perhaps the most important. In the nineteenth century rivet making was a major industry, since rivets were used in shipbuilding, boilermaking and structural engineering in enormous numbers. At first they were hand made, but machinery was introduced in 1840 by James Miller & Co. of Stobcross Street, and by 1876 there were 'at least a dozen works in and around Glasgow' producing nuts and bolts as well as rivets. There are remains of three works: Bilsland's four-storey Victoria Bolt & Rivet Works, Elliot Street (1874, H27), now much cut down; Clyde Rivet Works, Laidlaw Street (1872, H193), a single-storey building; and Crosher's works in Admiral Street (c 1888, H146). All were brick-built. P. & W. MacLellan also made bolts, nuts and railway spikes in their MacLellan Street factory (1872, M79). Bolt making resembled rivet making in the preparation of the forged blanks; these were then screwed by machine.[12]

Wireworking

Another basic metal-working trade was wireworking, which was represented in Glasgow by the manufacture of wire ropes, for collieries, ships' rigging and cranes; of woven wire for paper machines and filters; and of heavy-gauge woven wire for machinery and window guards. The oldest recently extant building associated with wire-rope making was in Anderston Quay (1856, H103), while the earliest representative of general wireworking is W. Riddell & Co.'s factory in Wesleyan Street (1859, F48), whence they moved in 1888 to Springfield Road (M47) to a works now occupied by Begg, Cousland & Co. Ltd, wireworkers. The Caledonia Wire Works in Thistle Street (c 1884, G153) and George Christie's first factory in Weir Street (1891, H144) were roughly contemporary with Riddell's second works. Christie moved to a much larger building in Broomloan Road in 1907 (K48). Other works built in the 1890s were the Baltic Wire & Metal Works (c 1894, F176) in Dale Street, which specialised in paper machine wires and was closed down by the United Wire Works, and a general wireworking factory in Watson Street (1891, G117). Wire ropes were made at the Govan Ropeworks (K49), and at a works built in Dobbies Loan (1914, G6). All these buildings were of red, or red and white brick apart from the two first-named. The most striking were the Anderston Quay block, in Italian Renaissance style and Christie's Weir Street block, with distinctive crow-stepped gables.[13]

ENGINEERING

In considering basic metal-working trades first, we have bypassed the early development of engineering. Though reference has been made to the rapid growth of engineering and metalworking after 1850, some branches were well-established before then. Textile machinery making had probably passed its peak, but sugar, railway and marine engineering and iron shipbuilding were soundly based.

Millwrighting

The earliest engineering products made in Glasgow were probably textile machines and mill gearing for grain mills. Both of these were mainly of wood until the late eighteenth century, so early mill-wrights and machine makers were as much carpenters as metal workers. At the beginning of the nineteenth century, there were at least three millwrights in the city, including James Cook, who had come from Fife in 1788 as a time-served millwright, and set up as a flax spinner. Later he took up cotton spinning, but also fitted out many grain mills, and pioneered the making of sugar machinery, and stationary and marine steam engines. Early nineteenth-century millwrights of distinction included David Elder (see p. 77), and Charles Randolph of Centre Street, whose millwrighting business became the nucleus of the marine engineering empire of Randolph & Elder after 1852. By that time millwrighting had become a branch of general engineering, as iron had replaced wood as the material for gears and shafts. Dating from this period is the Cranstonhill Foundry (*c* 1854, H22), built for James Aitken & Co., who combined millwrighting and engineering with ironfounding. This is one of the finest surviving early engineering buildings in the city. More recently Adam Knox & Co. (F43) did much mill-wright work for east end textile mills, while larger engineering firms had their own millwright departments.[14]

Textile Machinery Manufacture

Spinning wheels and hand-looms were probably made by car-penters at an early date, while knitting frames were made by frame smiths, of whom there were four in 1801. By that time there were four specialist textile machine makers, of whom the most important were William Dunn of John Street and Girdwood, Pinkerton & Co., later Claud Girdwood & Co. The latter turned to heavy engin-eering, made at least one sizable beam pump, and eventually became bankrupt during the construction of a large marine engine. More lastingly successful was the Houldsworths' textile machinery business, started to serve their own mills in Anderston and Wood-side, but formed into a separate company in 1823. At first this firm, the Anderston Foundry, made both spinning and weaving machinery, but competition from Lancashire concerns led to concentration after the 1860s on power-looms. The standard Anderston Foundry loom was widely used, and many survive. The firm also made wire-working looms. Isaac Whitesmith & Co., Florence Street (c 1860, G155) also made power-looms. The only surviving textile machinery makers in the city are J. & T. Boyd, Old Shettleston Road (c 1875, E9), who specialise in ring spinning and preparation machinery. The manufacture of weaving accessories was an extensive ancillary trade; in 1825 there were six shuttle-makers, twenty-two reed makers and six 'weaver's implement' makers, numbers which suggest small-scale businesses. Later, factories were built, of which the most striking is James Neilson's reed and heddle works in John Street (1866, G41) with a lotus chimney in red and white brick; reeds and heddles were also made in Savoy Street (1898, F145). Weaving utensils were the speciality of Sylvan Works, Broad Street (c 1854, F86), while William Gunn's shuttle factory in Dunn Street (1871, F128) is now part of Arrol's engineering works.[15]

The important west of Scotland textile finishing industry created a demand for bleaching, dyeing and printing machinery, largely met by local firms, such as Duncan Stewart & Co., London Road Ironworks (F105), John Dalglish, Avenue Ironworks, Pollokshaws (c 1874, J8) and Pollok, Macnab & Highgate, Carntyne. One of the more notable Glasgow successes was in sewing machine manu-facture. R. E. Simpson & Co. were making machines of the Singer pattern as early as 1860, and the Singer Manufacturing Co. itself opened a branch factory in Bridgeton (1871, F116) which had an output of 54,096 machines in 1872. Its success led the rival Howe Sewing Machine Co. to build an even larger works in the same area (1872, F96). By the mid-1880s Singers had outgrown the Bridgeton factory and moved to Clydebank, while the Howe company had turned to the manufacture of bicycles and tricycles. Native Glasgow firms making sewing machines included Kimball & Morton, of Bishop Street, examples of whose machines still exist.[16]

The relatively light construction of most textile machinery meant that most factories could be more than one storey high. The surviving part of the Anderston Foundry has three storeys, as had Whitesmith's and Sylvan Works. The two large sewing machine factories were both four storeys, as is Neilson's works. Most were brick built, but Singer, Neilson and Whitesmith all had stone frontages to their factories. J. & T. Boyd's works is a classic example of red and white brick factory building, with rivetted beams supporting wooden floors.

Machine Tool Manufacture

Machine tool manufacture was at first a branch of general engineering, and as such was widely practised by Glasgow firms. There were also some specialists, and though they never achieved worldwide fame as general-purpose tool builders, within their own spheres most of them had a good reputation. G. & A. Harvey at their Albion works (1880, K43) made heavy lathes, slotting, planing and boring machines, which were also manufactured by Sharp, Stewart & Co. after their move from Manchester to Atlas Works (C8) in 1888. At their Windlass Engine Works (c 1863, H101) Neilson Brothers made boring machines and radial steam hammers for a time, and at the nearby Cranstonhill Tool Works (1872, H24), Dron & Lawson specialised in screwing machines. Perhaps the most important group of firms made heavy tools for plate-working in boilermaking, shipbuilding and structural engineering, such as bending and straightening rolls, edge planers and punching and shearing machines. G. & A. Harvey were engaged in this trade, as were James Bennie & Co., Clyde Engine Works (c 1899, M78), Smith Brothers & Co., Kinning Park (c 1866, H167) and Hugh Smith & Co., Possil Engine Works (1876, C2). Hugh Smith (Possil) Ltd are now one of the leaders in the world shipbuilding tool market. The two last-named firms were founded by members of the family which founded A. & W. Smith (see p. 76). The heavy tool-makers naturally used workshops like those of other 'heavy' engineers, but much of Dron & Lawson's work was done on three floors of a red and white brick building. Smith Brothers' works, rebuilt c 1873, is a fine example of red and white brick construction.[17]

Stationary Steam Enginemaking

Though stationary steam engine manufacture never became a full-time speciality, early engineers such as James Cook, Robert Napier and Claud Girdwood all made such engines before 1830. 'Second-generation' firms, such as Mitchell & Neilson and Alexander Chaplin & Co., followed, the latter specialising in small semi-portable engines with vertical boilers at their Cranstonhill Works (*c* 1858, H25). The most important stationary steam engine builders were probably the sugar machinery makers such as P. & W. McOnie, who started in 1840 making engines for local users but quickly turned to exporting, and W. & A. McOnie, who built 820 steam engines between 1851 and 1876, of which only 25 were for Europe (H190, H195). A. & W. Smith made reciprocating engines for sugar mills until the 1950s. The growth of the electricity supply industry led several Glasgow firms to produce both large slow-speed and small high-speed generating engines. Duncan Stewart & Co. made sizable engines for Pinkston Power Station (C71) while Alley & MacLellan (I22, I24), the Anderston Foundry Co. (H92), David Carlaw & Sons (H17), Drysdale & Co. (F102, M1) and James Howden & Co. (H198) built high-speed engines, some of which are still in use. Howdens also made fan engines, and Duncan Stewart & Co. and their successors, Davy United, built rolling mill engines. In all these cases, steam engines were ancillary to the main specialities of the firms concerned.[18]

Sugar Machinery Manufacture

The general engineering firms of the early nineteenth century also pioneered the manufacture of sugar machinery, the earliest in the field being James Cook, who made beam-engine powered sugar mills from about 1815. The greatest group of specialist firms was started by Peter McOnie, who had been a foreman with Stark & Fulton, an Anderston firm which failed in 1840. With his brother he founded the firm of P. & W. McOnie with works in Scotland

Street (H190) where sugar machinery was made and repaired. After several changes in the partnership, it became Mirrlees and Tait in 1860, with a new works on the other side of the street (H196), subsequently greatly extended. Among the inventions developed by the firm were the Weston centrifugal extractor for sugar refining, the Yaryan evaporator, and the diesel engine. In 1883 a separate company, Watson, Laidlaw & Co., was set up to make centrifugals, with works in Laidlaw Street (H197).[19]

In 1851 when Tait joined the McOnies, the works manager, Andrew McOnie, left, and went into partnership with his brother William as W. & A. McOnie. Their works was also built in Scotland Street (H195); the firm eventually joined Robert Harvey & Co. (founded 1870) to form McOnie, Harvey & Co. One of the partners of W. & A. McOnie, with the firm's chief draughtsman, founded Aitken & McNeil, of the Colonial Ironworks, Govan (c 1882, K57). Another Scotland Street firm was Blair, Campbell & McLean, who occupied Howden's first works (H191) before moving to new works in Woodville Street (1903, K38). The firm still exists as Blairs Ltd, but no longer makes sugar machinery. The only Glasgow company still engaged in this industry is A. & W. Smith, Tradeston Street (c 1855, H188). Other makers included Duncan Stewart & Co. and Walker, Henderson & Co., Bishop Street Engine Works (1865, H41).[20]

The works themselves resembled other large engine shops, the earliest, Cook's, being a two-storey stone structure. Factories built in the 1840s and 1850s, including those of P. & W. and W. & A. McOnie, and A. & W. Smith, were also stone built. In the 1860s, brick came in, red and white brick characterising the Bishop Street Engine Works, and red brick being used in additions to Mirrlees & Tait's and A. & W. Smith's works, and in the first blocks of Watson, Laidlaw & Co.'s and Aitken, McNeil & Co.'s factories. Steel-framed buildings were constructed for Duncan Stewart & Co., Blair Campbell & McLean, Aitken & McNeil and Watson, Laidlaw & Co., those of the two first-named with corrugated-iron cladding, the others having brick cladding or infilling. Most were single-storey, with three- or four-storey office blocks.

Marine Engineering

As with sugar machinery making, marine engineering had close links with the building of stationary steam engines, and indeed with early general engineering. The engine of the *Comet*, Europe's first commercial steamship, was basically a land engine made by John Robertson from castings by David Napier, who also constructed the boiler. Napier and James Cook went on to engine several of the earliest Clyde steamships, Napier-designed and engined boats being pioneers of extra-estuarial steam navigation. David Napier sold his Camlachie works to his cousin Robert, and moved to Lancefield in 1821, going on to London in 1836. Robert also moved to Lancefield, where his firm built engines until 1901. Robert Napier & Son's marine engineering works became in the middle decades of the nineteenth century one of the best in Britain, with David Elder as chief draughtsman. Many of the second-generation Clyde engine shops were set up by Napier (David and Robert) trained men, including James & George Thomson, Tod & MacGregor, and perhaps the most important, John Elder, son of David, who went into partnership with Charles Randolph in 1852. Their compound marine engine (1853), especially when combined with high pressure steam and the surface condenser (from 1860) had a markedly lower fuel consumption than the low pressure simple engines of the time. Elder died in 1869, after setting up a shipbuilding yard in Govan (1863). Randolph's old works in Centre Street was greatly extended in 1858–60 (H130), and replaced by an immense new engine works at the Govan yard in 1874 (K1), though before the old works was vacated the first large triple-expansion marine engine, designed by A. C. Kirk, was built there.[21]

Apart from Thomas Wingate & Co., whose works was built at Springfield (1823), other early engine builders sited their shops in Anderston, Lancefield and Finnieston, including Tod & MacGregor, Carrick Street, later Warroch Street (1834), and A. & J. Inglis, Warroch Street (1847). These have been demolished, the only surviving fragments being parts of Barclay, Curle's engine shop on Finnieston Quay (1863, H118) and of J. & G. Thomson's Finnieston Street works (1846, H117). Another group of firms was founded in the late 1860s and 1870s, including Muir & Caldwell

(1865, H115) and David Rowan & Co. (1867, H113), both in Elliot Street, James Howden & Co., Scotland Street (H190, then 1870, H191), Hutson & Corbett (1874, K11) and Anderson & Lyall Whitefield Road (1867, K27). Howdens eventually moved to large new works farther along Scotland Street (1897, H198) but by that time specialised in marine auxiliaries, especially forced draught equipment. Alexander Stephen & Sons was the only yard in Glasgow, apart from Fairfield's and Yarrow's, with its own engine shop 'on the premises' (completed 1872).[22]

After the 1870s no new engine works of any consequence was built until c 1909, though existing works were extended. The advent of the internal combustion engine brought new entrepreneurs into engine building, such as Walter Bergius, whose Kelvin Motor Works (1909, C99) made small engines for fishing boats, and Harland & Wolff, who built large diesel engine works in Anderston Quay and Lancefield Street (1909, H94; c 1914 H104). Perhaps the most interesting new factory was Barclay Curle's North British Diesel Engine Works, South Street (1913, M93), its design obviously influenced by that of the AEG turbine factory of Peter Behrens.[23]

There was a clear evolutionary pattern in the design of marine engine works, with the increasing size of engines being reflected in the growing height and bay width of erecting shops. New structural materials were adopted as they became available: stone walls were replaced by brick, brick piers by cast-iron columns, wooden beams by wrought iron. The most interesting recently extant example was the Randolph, Elder & Co. works in Centre Street, with a massive erecting shop finished externally in Egyptian style. The internal structure consisted of heavy laminated timber beams, supported on cast-iron columns and brick piers, and supporting both crane rails and suspended floors. This very fine building was demolished in 1970. In the first part of Elder's Fairfield Engine Works composite wood and cast-iron construction was also used. Later built-up steel columns became standard, with steel beams and roof trusses. Most steel-framed shops had brick walls, free standing (as in the Harland & Wolff shops) or with brick infill in a steel framework (as in the North British Diesel Engine Works) but some had corrugated-iron cladding. Large doorways, often arched, were universal.

Boilermaking

Until well into this century, boilermaking was closely associated with marine engineering. David Napier at Camlachie was both boilermaker and marine engineer, and the largest marine engineering firms had their own boiler shops, for example the London & Glasgow Engineering & Iron Shipbuilding Co., Lancefield Street (1864, H112), J. & G. Thomson, Kelvinhaugh Street (1880, H1) and A. & J. Inglis, Pointhouse (1873, L35). These works made shell boilers, but Yarrow's specialised in water-tube boilers at their Scotstoun works (1906, M100). Independent marine boilermakers included William Mitchell, Lancefield Boilerworks (1865, H19) and Lindsay Burnet & Co., Moorepark Works (c 1884, K50). Other firms specialised in land boilers, such as Penmans, who still make shell boilers at their Strathclyde Street works (1889, F181), Crownpoint (c 1860, F88), and West of Scotland (1898, J21). One of the most famous Glasgow boilermaking firms was John Thomson & Co., whose Lilybank Works in Eglinton Street was demolished in the 1920s when the company moved to Dalmarnock. The locomotive building works also made their own boilers. All these works were of brick or iron-clad steel, and all had large doorways, often brick-arched, for removal of completed boilers.[24]

Locomotive Building

This is yet another branch of engineering with roots in early general engineering. The first Glasgow locomotive builders (1831) were Murdoch & Aitken, who made a wide range of products at their long-demolished Hill Street (now Melbourne Street) works. Other pioneers were Stark & Fulton of Anderston, Thomas Edington & Sons and the St Rollox Ironworks, but none of these had lasting success and it was Mitchell & Neilson of Hydepark Street (c 1836, H102) who finally gave up the manufacture of marine and stationary engines to become the first specialist locomotive builders. In 1860-1, the firm, by then Neilson & Co., moved to a rail-linked 'green field' site at Springburn (C9). The works

manager during the move, Henry Dübs, left in 1864 to found th
Glasgow Locomotive Works, Aitkenhead Road (I20), which wa
equipped throughout with Whitworth machine tools. The Neilso
of Mitchell & Neilson, Walter Montgomerie (son of 'hot blas
inventor J. B. Neilson) was ousted from Neilson & Co. by Jame
Reid, and started up the Clyde Locomotive Works (1884, C8
opposite the latter's works. It was not a success, and was taken ove
by Sharp, Stewart & Co. of Manchester in 1888. Renamed th
Atlas Works, it became fairly prosperous, and in 1903 amalgamate
with Dübs & Co. and Neilson & Co. (by that time Neilson, Reid &
Co.) to form the North British Locomotive Co. Ltd, then the large
locomotive building firm in Europe. With the ensuing centralisatio
of administration a new office block in Flemington Street was com
pleted in 1909 (C10), which now serves as a technical college.[2]

Other Glasgow commercial locomotive builders were Alexande
Chaplin & Co., who made vertical-boilered shunting locomotive
from 1867 to 1902, first in Port Street (c 1858, H25) and from 189
in Helen Street (K53), and D. Drummond & Sons, later the Glas
gow Railway Engineering Co. Ltd, which made small locomotive
in Helen Street (c 1891, K54) in the 1890s. The latter firm also mad
railway material of other kinds as did William Beardmore & Co
with their wheel and axle forge in Rigby Street (1903, E4), an
P. & W. MacLellan, who made goods rolling stock for export a
their Clutha works (1872, M79). The railway companies themselve
built locomotives and rolling stock, and made other kinds of railwa
material at their large central workshops (see p. 124).[26]

The construction and layout of these works varied widel
Murdoch & Aitken's factory was three storeys high, with a larg
arched doorway, while Mitchell & Neilson's works also seems t
have been on several floors. Where land was not so expensive
single-storey buildings were laid out, as at Neilson & Co.'
Springburn works, St Rollox Works, and at Cowlairs. The origina
Cowlairs machine shop, erecting shop and running shed were sti
extant until closure of the works in 1968. As the size and weigh
of locomotives increased improved cranes were installed and talle
erecting shops built so that completed machines could be lifte
over each other. Both steel and cast-iron columns were used, wit
brick or corrugated-iron cladding, at Neilson's, St Rollox, Cow
lairs, and most notably at Atlas, where the Mons shop complete

after 1914 was particularly impressive. Unusual features were the castellated dining room at Neilson's Springburn works and the statuary at the entrance to the North British administration building in Flemington Street, which incorporates the front elevation of a North British Railway 'Atlantic'.

Vehicle Building

Probably even older than railway vehicle building in Glasgow is coach, van and lorry building. The proportion of metal work in horse-drawn road vehicles was low, and a high level of traditional craftsmanship was involved, so productive units tended to be small. The best craftsmen were employed in coachbuilding, which tended to be separate from van and lorry construction. Coachworks usually had showrooms attached, and were situated in the fashionable western area of the city centre; van and lorry works were to be found in industrial areas, like Bridgeton. The oldest coachworks recently surviving was in North Street (*c* 1854, H39), while others still exist in St Vincent Street (*c* 1870, H14) and Buccleuch Street (1869, C119). The last-named became the Glasgow Veterinary College, while at St Vincent Street the workshops were in the centre of a tenement block, with showrooms on the ground floor of one of the tenements. The only works making both coaches and carts seems to have been in Govan (1912, K64) but by that time 'coachbuilders' were probably making motor-car bodies. Spring van and lorry builders (cartwrights) were to be found in Van Street, Parkhead (1904, E15), Orr Street, Camlachie (*c* 1880, F45), Bartholomew Street (*c* 1896, F175) and Kennedy Street (*c* 1877, G16). There was no particular pattern in the buildings used in these trades, though as most of the components were fairly light, workshops tended to be two or three storeys high. The fashionable coachworks had stone frontages, but the workshops at the rear were normally brick.[27]

Glasgow was the centre of the short-lived indigenous Scottish motor-car industry, and retains, through Albion Motors (now part of British Leyland), a foothold in commercial motor building. The earliest firms started in second-hand premises. Those used by the Mo-car Syndicate, then by Arrol-Johnston, have long disappeared but the Hozier Street factory used by the Argyll Company has only recently been demolished (F123). Albion and Halley Motors started in Finnieston and Camlachie, moving to Scotstoun in 1903 (M97) and about 1907 (M3) respectively. These two firms specialised in commercial vehicles and Albion eventually absorbed Halley. The short-lived All British Car Company occupied part of the Greenhead Weaving Factory (F114) and the single-storey weaving sheds used there and by Arrol-Johnston and Argyll were copied, on a larger scale, for the new Albion and Halley works. Before the development of the all-metal car body in the 1930s, coach-built bodies were the rule, and a few specialist body-builders' workshops were constructed in the city, for example at Maxwell Road (1907, I4) and Kilbirnie Street (1913, H220). The latter is an early example of reinforced concrete construction, and is still occupied by the original owners, William Park & Co.[28]

Shipbuilding

It may seem artificial to divorce shipbuilding from marine engineering, but while marine engine-building had strong links with other branches of engineering, iron shipbuilding involved basically different techniques and organisation. Its closest technical links were with boilermaking – hence the survival of the term 'boilermaker' for a powerful group of Clyde shipyard workers – and with structural engineering. There was no tradition of wooden shipbuilding on the upper Clyde, as it was scarcely navigable until the end of the eighteenth century, and the only yard to build substantial numbers of wooden ships was John Barclay's Stobcross yard, opened in 1818. Apart from a few isolated vessels built by non-specialist firms, iron shipbuilding began in Glasgow in 1836, when Tod & MacGregor opened a yard at Mavisbank. They moved to Meadowside in 1844–5, and the dry dock they built there in 1857–8 has only recently been filled in (L28). Shipbuilding in Govan began in 1839, when MacArthur & Alexander opened a small yard to the east of Govan Ferry. This was bought by Robert Napier in 1841 and greatly extended. Immediately to the west, Smith & Rodger opened a yard in 1842 which was bought in 1864 by the London & Glasgow Engineering & Iron Shipbuilding Co. Though most of it was swept away after Harland & Wolff took over in 1912, some of the buildings survived until recently (K15). In 1851, Alexander Stephen, who had previously built ships on the east coast, leased a yard at Kelvinhaugh, and moved to a new yard at Linthouse in 1869 (L12). A. & J. Inglis, who started as marine engineers in Anderston (1847), opened a yard at Pointhouse, on the Kelvin, in 1862 (L36).

John Barclay's son Robert assumed Robert Curle as a partner and began iron shipbuilding at Stobcross; the new firm opened a yard at Whiteinch in 1855, and later concentrated work there (M90). J. & G. Thomson, who like Inglis and Tod & MacGregor had started as engine builders, started shipbuilding at Govan in 1851, but moved to Clydebank in 1870; the new yard and the town that grew up round it perpetuate the name of the old yard. Randolph and Elder also branched out from marine engineering, initially occupying Robert Napier's old yard in Govan, but moving in 1863 to Fairfield (K1) which became the most important yard on the upper Clyde in the late nineteenth century. Charles Connell was manager at Kelvinhaugh for Stephens, and left to found his Scotstoun yard in 1861 (M103). Yarrow's, presently at Scotstoun (M100) moved from London in 1906–7 owing to the high rates and labour costs at their Poplar yard.[29]

Contrary to most other industries, in shipbuilding the products and some of the machinery are larger than the buildings. Perhaps surprisingly, the large cranes which now dominate most shipyards were not introduced until the very end of the nineteenth century. Up to that time, temporary derricks were used to position, while boilers, engines and other heavy items were normally installed in the finished hull either by one of the Clyde Trust's large hand (later steam) cranes or by sheer-legs. The last sheer-legs at a Glasgow yard was at Pointhouse. The buildings used for preparation of material tended to be rather nondescript. Those for ironworking were usually one storey high, sometimes open-sided, though woodworking and other light shops might have more than one storey – the most notable recently surviving was the woodworking shed at

Pointhouse (L36), with wood cladding on a wrought- and cast-iron framework. The replacement of wrought-iron by steel (*c* 1880–90), which made possible the use of larger plates, the development of a measure of prefabrication, and an increase in the average size of ships, made most of the larger yards invest in new plating shops and mould lofts, as well as in new cranes, from the 1890s. Most of these new shops were steel-framed, many built by Sir William Arrol & Co., probably the largest being those at the Govan shipyard of Harland & Wolff. There was latterly one covered berth on the upper river, at Yarrow's yard, and one overall gantry, at Fairfield's. While workshop buildings tended to be undistinguished, yard office blocks were relatively large and often imposing, as they housed large design and estimating staffs, and clerks to handle wages and the numerous subcontracts involved in building most ships. The Fairfield offices in Govan Road were particularly impressive, but D. & W. Henderson at Meadowside (L28), Barclay, Curle at Clydeholm, and Stephens at Linthouse also had extensive offices. The modernisation of surviving yards has resulted in the demolition of most of the older buildings.[30]

Structural Engineering

This branch of the engineering industry seems to have developed in the 1850s and 1860s with increasing substitution of cast- and wrought-iron for masonry and timber in the construction of buildings, bridges and piers. Early firms in this field were R. Laidlaw & Son (later Laidlaw, Sons & Caine), Barrowfield Works, A. & W. Smith, Eglinton Engine Works (H188), P. & W. MacLellan (1860, G154; 1872, M79), Smith & Naysmith, and John Yule & Co. Their work included bridges, piers, iron roofs, penstocks and gasholders. The greatest was, however, William Arrol & Co. (*c* 1868, F136), who not only built such world-famous structures as the Forth Railway Bridge, the second Tay Bridge, and Tower Bridge, London, but also pioneered the use of steel frames for factory buildings. Lighter iron and steel buildings were made by A. & J. Main in their Clydesdale Iron Works (*c* 1876, M18), and later prefabricated buildings were the speciality of

Cowiesons, Charles Street (*c* 1907, C82). Other heavy structural shops were Arrol Brothers' Germiston Iron Works (*c* 1883, M29), Lambhill Iron Works (1881, M12) and Clydeside Ironworks (*c* 1898, M96) and medium-sized firms include Temple (*c* 1890, A20) and Possil Iron Works (*c* 1884, M23). The last sizable works built was that of the Glasgow Steel Roofing Co. (1906, M16), specifically designed to counter German competition, though P. & W. MacLellan opened a large extension in 1913 (H205).[31]

The heavy nature of most structural work necessitated large workshops, though an alternative in the early years was to resort to construction in the open air, as at Barrowfield. The earlier firms used brick buildings, the best surviving examples being at Dalmarnock and A. & W. Smith's, where the large bays built for bridge work are now used for sugar machinery manufacture. Later firms used their own techniques from the start, and additions to the older works were often also steel-framed. Corrugated-iron cladding was more or less standard in these newer buildings.

Other Engineering Products

It would be impossible to do full justice to the diversity of Glasgow's output of engineering products. The following list indicates, however, the products of a few firms: agricultural machinery (D16, F9, F19); bakery machinery (C80, H152); lifting blocks (H149); boats (H143, M94); chains (K62); chemical plant (B2); compressors (I22); cranes (C100, E5, H25, I23, K53); edge tools (G119, G123, H20); electrical engineering (F82); gas engines (F46); guns (E11); hydraulic machinery (F57, G27); ironmongery (G122, H2, H26); laundry machinery (G43, L17); liquor trade (F76, G45); machinery merchants (F113, F115, G80); metal casks (C31, G10); numerical printing machinery (H17); nut cracking machines (F43); pumps (F102, I23, M54); pneumatic machinery (K31); refrigerating machinery (B55); tinsmith work (F146); valves (I22, J24, M76); water turbines (J11); weighing machines (L39); winches (H101); woodworking machinery (G110, G155); and wringers (F46). This list includes most of the engineering and associated sites in the inventory not already mentioned.

[1] Lumsden, H., and Aitken, P. H., *History of the Hammermen of Glasgow* (Paisley 1912), 6; Simpson, plate 40, shows the slit mills; McUre, 322, describes the Broomielaw building as 'a great building of Ashler-work for accommodating a great manufactory of all Sorts of Iron work, from a Lock and Key to an Anchor of the greatest size', *Pigot & Co.'s Directory, 1825*, 500–1; *Some of the Leading Industries of Glasgow and the Clyde Valley*, 81–4; Butt, *et al.*, 76, shows a steam hammer by R. G. Ross & Co., successors to Glen & Ross; *Industries of Glasgow*, 90 (Glen & Ross); see also McLean, Angus (ed), *Local Industries of Glasgow and the West of Scotland* (Glasgow 1901), 59; Murphy, 133–8 (William Beardmore)

[2] *Post Office Directory 1801–2*; Bell, D. (ed), *David Napier, Engineer 1790–1869* (Glasgow 1912), passim; William Baird & Co. MSS, Department of Economic History, University of Strathclyde, Letter-book of Muirkirk Iron Co., 1809–12; Barnard, A., *Breweries*, vol 2, 478

[3] Thomson, 43, refers to Garscube; Simpson, plate 24, illustrates Govan, see also Murphy, 145–9; *Some of the Leading Industries of Glasgow and the Clyde Valley*, 68; Armitage Shanks Ltd, Barrhead, early Shanks handbill

[4] *Some of the Leading Industries of Glasgow and the Clyde Valley*, 69; *Industries of Glasgow*, 99 (Shaw & McInnes), 95 (Milton); plans of the Carron buildings in Glasgow are preserved at Falkirk

[5] *The Engineer*, 22 (1866), 117, description of Bennie's Kinning Park Foundry; *Glasgow Herald*, 9 April 1852, description of Hayfield foundries (Upper and Lower); *Industries of Glasgow*, 142 (Whitevale)

[6] The second Saracen Foundry was a most attractive Gothic structure, see trade card in Old Glasgow Museum collection; the third Saracen Foundry is illustrated in *Stratten*, 98, 99, the illustrations being reproduced in Butt *et al.*, 77, 82

[7] *Stratten*, 198 (Avon Steelworks)

[8] *Some of the Leading Industries of Glasgow and the Clyde Valley*, 126–8; *Industries of Glasgow*, 208 (Minerva Street), 276 (Nelson Street), 161 (Bridgeton); an air compressor by Allan & Bogle is on display in Kelvingrove Museum; *Industries of Glasgow*, 239 (Anderston); Murphy, 181–5; the Minerva Street foundry had a ten ton air furnace

[9] *Some of the Leading Industries of Glasgow and the Clyde Valley*, 127–9; *Industries of Glasgow*, 126 (Lancefield); *Stratten*, 160–1, refers to Blair, Campbell & McLean, when in Scotland Street, with two illustrations of products

[10] *Some of the Leading Industries of Glasgow and the Clyde Valley*, 72–4; *Stewarts & Lloyds Limited 1903–1953* (London 1953), 20–1, Tollcross was actually built for the Clydeside Tube Co. Ltd, for making seamless tubes up to four inch diameter

[11] *Industries of Glasgow*, 99 (Braby's)

[12] *Some of the Leading Industries of Glasgow and the Clyde Valley*, 74–6; *Industries of Glasgow*, 111 (Miller, ill of rivet machine); Murphy, 139–44 (Bilsland's); *Industries of Glasgow*, 119 (Clyde), 222 (Crosher)

[13] *Industries of Glasgow*, 97 (Riddell, Springfield Road); *Note it in a Book: the Story of Begg, Cousland & Co. Ltd, 1854–1954* (Glasgow 1958); Moray McLaren, *The History of the United Wire Works* (Edinburgh 1947), 37

[14] *Post Office Directory 1801–2*; Harvey, Robert, 'The History of the Sugar Machinery Industry in Glasgow', *The International Sugar Journal* (1916), 57–9; Cook bought a Watt engine in 1800, and probably based his early engines on it, BRL, B & W MSS, Engine Book, 2, Portfolio 202; *Engineering*, 1 (1866), 103, obituary of David Elder; MacLehose, James, *Memoirs and Portraits of 100 Glasgow Men* (Glasgow 1886), vol 2, 267–8 (Charles Randolph)

[15] *Post Office Directory 1801–2*; an en-

graved letter-heading in the Old Glasgow
Museum shows Dunn's (or Dun's) factory,
which was not demolished until the 1950s,
see photographs in Andersonian Library
Archives, University of Strathclyde; *A
Short History of the Scottish Coal-Mining
Industry* (London 1958), plate 3 facing 53,
shows the 80 inch beam pump made by
Girdwood for Newcraighall Colliery in
1828; Napier, J., *Life of Robert Napier*
(London 1904), 115, and Smith, E. C., *A
Short History of Marine Engineering* (1938),
44; Anderston Foundry looms are still in
use at Glenruthven Mill, Auchterarder,
Perthshire (NN956129) and Kilwuddie
Weaving Factory, Strathaven, Lanarkshire
(NS701448); a wire loom from Begg,
Cousland & Co. is now stored for eventual
display by the Glasgow Corporation
Museum Department; *Some of the Leading
Industries of Glasgow and the Clyde Valley*,
119; *Pigot & Co.'s Directory*, 1825, 498-9,
512

[16] A Duncan Stewart stenter (for drying
finished cloth to width) worked at Nether-
place Bleachworks, Newton Mearns
(NS522557) until c1968; some Pollok,
Macnab & Highgate beetling machines
are still in occasional use at Luncarty
Bleachworks, near Perth (NO100298);
*Some of the Leading Industries of Glasgow and
the Clyde Valley*, 121-4; an exterior view of
the Howe factory is illustrated in Butt
et al., 76; there is a Kimball & Morton
'Lion' sewing machine in the Old Glasgow
Museum, while Singers have two of
K & M's industrial machines at Dalmuir;
McLean, 79 (Kimball & Morton)

[17] *The Engineering Times Record of the
Glasgow Exhibition, 1901* (London 1901),
79, 81, 90, 92 (Sharp, Stewart); *Engineering*, 1 (1866) 331, 403 and 2 (1866), 74;
*Some of the Leading Industries of Glasgow and
the Clyde Valley*, 77-8, 89-90 and *Industries
of Glasgow*, 147 (Dron & Lawson);
Harvey, 'History of the Sugar Machinery
Industry', 116 (Smith firms)

[18] Napier, 31; the Cowlairs incline
engine was made by Mitchell & Neilson,
illustrated in Ellis, C. Hamilton, *The
North British Railway* (London 1955),

48, and another engine by that firm is
depicted in Scott, David, *The Engineer and
Machinist's Assistant* (London 1849), vol 2,
plates 19, 20; P. & W. McOnie, MS
Engine Book No 1, in possession of
Messrs A. & W. Smith, Eglinton Engine
Works; *Some of the Leading Industries of
Glasgow and the Clyde Valley*, 117; McLean,
60-1 (Duncan Stewart); Murphy, 123-6
(Alley & MacLellan); *The Engineering
Times Record of the Glasgow Exhibition,
1901*, 5-9, 18-22; Howden high-speed
engines were recently in use at Pullar's
Dyeworks, Perth, Seedhill Finishing Co.,
Paisley, and at a paper mill in West
Calder. One from Netherplace Bleach-
works, Newton Mearns, Renfrewshire,
has been taken into store by Glasgow
Corporation Museums Department.

[19] Harvey, 'History of the Sugar
Machinery Industry', passim; McLean,
57-9 (Mirrlees Watson Co.); a Yaryan
evaporator was in operation at Gorgie
Glue Works, Edinburgh, until closure in
1970; the first Mirrlees diesel engine is
preserved in the Science Museum, South
Kensington; McLean, 61-3 (Watson,
Laidlaw & Co.)

[20] Harvey, 'History of the Sugar
Machinery Industry', passim; *Industries of
Glasgow*, 261 (Aitken, McNeil & Co.)

[21] Bell, 85, 104, 118, 36; Napier, passim;
Robert Napier's first marine engine, now
preserved in Dumbarton, is illustrated in
Butt *et al.*; *Some of the Leading Industries of
Glasgow and the Clyde Valley*, 155-60;
Randolph & Elder's Centre Street engine
shop was surveyed in detail by the Royal
Commission on the Ancient and Historical
Monuments of Scotland and the survey is
lodged with the Scottish National Build-
ings Record, 52 Melville Street, Edin-
burgh; the shop is illustrated in Butt *et al.*,
78; *The Building of the Ship* (London 1891),
(Fairfields); *The Marine Number of Cassier's
Magazine* (London 1897), 453-5, two
illustrations of triple-expansion engine

[22] Simpson, plate 32, illustrates Wingate's engine works; Bell, 120-1, a large-
scale model of an early screw engine by
Tod & MacGregor is in Kelvingrove

Museum; Murphy, 117–21 (Ross & Duncan); *A Hundred Years of Howden Engineering* (Glasgow 1954), passim; Carvel, John L., *Stephen of Linthouse, 1750–1950* (Glasgow 1950), 64–5, and *The Engineer*, 34 (1872), 125

[23] A Kelvin marine engine is on display in Kelvingrove Museum; the AEG turbine factory is illustrated in Winter, John, *Industrial Architecture* (London 1970), 46

[24] Other firms who made water tube boilers before 1914 were Fairfield, the London & Glasgow Engineering & Iron Shipbuilding Co. and Duncan Stewart, McLean, 43; Murphy, 166–70 (Penmans)

[25] A handbill of Murdoch & Aitken, showing the works and its products, is reproduced in Thomas, John, *The Springburn Story* (Newton Abbot 1964), 37, which is the best account yet published of locomotive building in Springburn; *An Account of the Manufactures of the North British Locomotive Co. Ltd 1914–19* (Glasgow 1919); *A History of the North British Locomotive Co. Ltd* (Glasgow 1953); McLean, 67–8 (Dübs), 68–70 (Sharp, Stewart); *Industries of Glasgow*, 110 (Dübs)

[26] Abbot, R. A. S., 'Vertical Boiler Locomotives', *The Engineer*, 199 (1955), 727–8; Alliez, G., 'Dugald Drummond and the Glasgow Gas Works Locomotives', *The Journal of the Stephenson Locomotive Society*, 17 (1941), 54; photograph albums in the possession of P. & W. MacLellan

[27] *Industries of Glasgow*, 277 (North Street); *Stratton*, 63–5 (St Vincent St)

[28] Macdonald, A. Craig, and Browning, A. S. E., 'History of the Motor Industry in Scotland', *Proceedings of the Institution of Mechanical Engineers, Automobile Division* (1961), 319–36; Clark, R. H., *The Development of the English Steam Wagon* (Norwich 1963), 32–4 (Halley), 130–1, 133 (Alley & MacLellan), 138–9 (Duncan Stewart), Clark claims that a 'one-off' wagon built by John Yule in 1870 was the 'first true and successful steam wagon'; the interior of the

original Albion works is illustrated in Butt *et al.*, 81

[29] Simpson, plate 34, shows the Stobcross yard, and there are other views in *Development of Shipbuilding on the Upper Reaches of the Clyde* (Glasgow 1911), (Barclay, Curle); Napier, 149 et seq; Carvel, *Stephen of Linthouse*, 33–66; Murphy, 111–15 (Seath), 91–5 (Inglis); *Half a Century of Shipbuilding* (London 1896), 5–7 (J. & G. Thomson); *Fairfield 1860–1960* (Glasgow 1960) and Murphy, 83–9; Barnes, E. C., *Alfred Yarrow, his Life and Work* (London 1924), 192–7, and Borthwick, Alastair, *Yarrows: The First Hundred Years* (Glasgow 1965)

[30] An exception to the use of Clyde Trust cranes or sheer legs was at Stephen's Linthouse yard where an overall gantry with a steam crane was built for the installation of machinery during the construction of the ship on the berth, Carvel, *Stephen of Linthouse*, 65–6; Butt, 171, shows the Pointhouse woodworking shed; *Bridges, Structural Steel Work and Mechanical Engineering Productions* (London 1909) gives details and illustrations of workshops built by Sir William Arrol & Co. for Clyde yards; Tod & MacGregor had covered building berths at Meadowside until a great storm in 1856, Bell, 120, also *Glasgow Herald*, 8 February 1856, sheds 340′×60′×60′ and 280′×50′×60′, built 1853, timber with iron framed roof, 34,000 sq ft of corrugated glass; the overall gantry at Fairfield's yard is shown in aerial views taken in the early 1930s; the offices at Fairfield's are shown in *The Building of the Ship*, 15–17, 26, see also *The Builder* (9 July 1898)

[31] *Some of the Leading Industries of Glasgow and the Clyde Valley*, 96–8; *Stratten*, 224–5 and McLean, 74–5 (P. & W. MacLellan); *Bridges, Structural Steel Work &c*; McLean, 75–6 (A. & J. Main); *Industries of Glasgow*, 258 and McLean, 73–4 (Germiston); *The Engineer*, 102 (1906), 480 (Glasgow Steel Roofing Co.)

5 *Miscellaneous Industries and Warehouses*

Besides its staple trades, any sizable community generates subsidiary and service industries, mainly of local importance. Some of these have already been mentioned, for example in the chapters on engineering and chemicals. This chapter will attempt to indicate the wide range of Glasgow's industrial concerns which cannot be classified under the major headings already discussed.

Woodworking

Perhaps the most important group is the woodworking trades. The shortage of timber in eighteenth-century Scotland was acute, and the importation of timber for building and cabinet making, mainly from the Baltic and North America, expanded in that period. Deals, battens and boards could be used without much further processing in building construction, but for the manufacture of furniture and utensils additional finishing was naturally required, and in the eighteenth century this was done by hand. The low capital requirements of much 'secondary' wood processing led to a proliferation of small workshops, but the advent of woodworking machinery during the nineteenth century led to the creation of larger factories for bulk production. By the end of the century some of these were both sophisticated and extensive.[1]

For long the conversion of logs to useful sections was done by pit-sawyers, and saw pits are marked on the first edition of the Ordnance Survey maps in many country districts. Probably the earliest sawmill in Glasgow was one erected on the Molendinar in 1751. Reciprocating saws were almost certainly used here. It was a three-storey building, apparently with two wheels, and processed both Scottish and imported timber. By order of the Town Council it was pulled down in 1764, owing to the nuisance caused by stagnation of water in the mill dam. Little is known of other sawmills until the nineteenth century, but the rapidity with which buildings were erected suggests that mechanical (probably circular) sawing must have been used. The opening of the Forth & Clyde Canal, with the facilities it gave for the import of Baltic timber, encouraged the setting up of sawmills on or near the canal banks. The construction of timber basins at Firhill (for storage of logs) in 1788 and 1849 illustrates the importance of this trade. The City Sawmills (C19) founded in 1849, is the oldest surviving sawmill in the city, and was a pioneer of mechanised wood processing. Sited on the canal at Port Dundas, it had its own little timber pond off the canal. New sawmills continued to be built on the banks of the canal until the end of the period, at Temple (1874, A2), Ruchill (c 1885, B8), Firhill (c 1893, B22) and Phoenix (Townhead) (1911, C89). These sawmills were steam powered, with the possible exception of Phoenix. The other sawmills imported their timber through Glasgow harbour, and most were situated close to the docks, at Ballater Street (1875, G156), Kelvinhaugh (c 1892, H5), Byron Street (1899, L15), Shieldhall (1899, M87), Drumoyne (1903, M77), South Street (1905, L10) and Lancefield Street (1907, H105). The others had rail links with the harbour, as at Park Sawmills (1897, K39) and the Maxwell Road group of mills (H226–8 and I6), of which Muirhouse (1886, I6) had its own sidings.[2]

Most of these mills were sawmills *per se*, but some so-called sawmills also made finished products. Greenhead Sawmills (1877, F150) made turned goods, such as stair railings and legs for furniture, and the Waterloo Sawmill (1895, H74) specialised in box and packing case making. The City Sawmills had a joinery department from 1873. Secondary woodworkers as such were very numerous. Wrights and joiners were perhaps the commonest, their workshops normally being quite small, and often situated in the centre of tenement squares or in lanes behind residential property, which they serviced. There are, or were, examples in Kersland Street (1903, B45), Dunn Street (c 1876, F141), Kilbarchan Street (1904, G190) and North Gardner Street (1905, L6). Some joinery works were, however, large, notably those in Arcadia Street (1889, F69), Hydepark Street (late 19th century, H98) and Forth Street (c 1894, I14). Typically these workshops were brick-built, with timber floors on cast-iron or timber columns. They were usually very plain, built as cheaply as possible, and frequently had outside wooden stairs. They were normally two or three storeys high, though Waterloo Sawmill had four storeys, the top one with ornamental detail.[3]

Cabinet makers were also numerous, often doubling as upholsterers. Some cabinet works were very large, as in Otago Street (1887, B64), Couper Place (c 1876, C90), Salamanca Street (1896, E21), Orr Street (1876, F49) and Kent Road (1879, H13), though there were also smaller ones, such as those in Ladywell Street (c 1893, D23), Craignestock Street (c 1870, F60), and Reid Street (c 1886, F156). The Orr Street and Reid Street factories were termed 'Steam Chair Works'. Cabinet works were usually brick built, construction being of better quality than in wrights' and joiners' workshops. Stone facings are found in part of the Glasgow Cabinet Works, Darnley Street (1877, I12) and in James Sellars's Kent Road factory for Wylie & Lochhead. The latter is of 'fireproof' construction, and is a listed building. Other specialist factories associated with the furniture trade are hair works in Cavendish Street (c 1855, G194), Summerfield Street (1881, F185) and Gallowgate (1877, E17). The last named also made bedding, while the Campbellfield Bedstead Works (1876, F35) made iron bedsteads on a large scale. The Cavendish Street and Summerfield Street premises are one and two storeys high; the other two works had quite impressive three-storey red and white brick buildings.[4]

The significance of exports in the late nineteenth-century Glasgow economy is reflected in the number of factories making boxes and packing cases for products ranging from confectionery to heavy machinery. Several firms were tenants of flats in general-purpose buildings, but there were specialised box factories in Port Dundas Road (1897, C114), Major Street (1898, F51) and William Street (1911, H33). A very specialised type of box was made by the Acme Tea Chest Company in Polmadie Road (1896, I21), which had its own aluminium rolling mill to produce foil to line the chests. The British Basket and Besto Company made chip baskets and punnets for fresh fruit from wood veneers at their Crownpoint Road factory (1896, F31) until closure in 1969. All these were brick built, with no special architectural features.[5]

Other woodworking factories of interest included the Calton

Bobbin Works in Tobago Street (c 1850, F63), a lath-splitter's workshop in Commerce Street (1878, G184) and a hammershaft factory in Fairley Street (1892, K32). The Commerce Street building has a handsome stone frontage, and was probably intended for multiple occupation. The bobbin works resembled a cotton mill of the period, while the hammer-shaft factory is a neat brick structure with crow-stepped gables.[6]

Barrel and vat making was, of course, closely linked with brewing and distilling, but paint manufacturers, provision merchants and ship chandlers also used casks. A cooperage in Ruchill Street (1900, B14) which still operates was owned by Alexander, Fergusson & Co. Other cooperages were close to the river, as at Commerce Street (1900, G187), Lancefield Street (1907, H105) and Eastvale Place (1889, K10). Tennents also made barrels at their Wellpark Brewery. In recent years coopering has been carried out in second-hand premises, such as stables (G48), an iron store (H95) and a wright's workshop (G190). The trade is now confined mainly to barrel repair and is operated almost exclusively in connection with the whisky industry, as whisky must still be matured in barrel. Though cooperage buildings are in general nondescript, those in Commerce Street (which incorporated warehouse accommodation for letting) and Washington Street (1872, H79) were of stone, with some architectural pretensions.

Building

Builders' workshops have, as might be expected, not survived in any numbers. Often they were temporary wooden structures demolished on completion of a contract. The buildings that have lasted are those of firms which supplied builders with finished or part-finished components. Galbraith & Winton in Balnain Street (c 1849, C40) made the marble staircase of the City Chambers, while from Mossman's works in Cathedral Street (1864, G23) came statuary, monuments and other sculpture for many Glasgow public and commercial buildings. These are both brick buildings, the former very plain, but the latter resembling a small railway terminus with its open wood-valanced front. An early wood-framed gantry crane still survives out of use at Mossman's factory. More mundane were a slater's workshop in Milton Place (1897, C116) and a house-factor's workshop in Ladywell Street (1904, D22). The City Improvement Trust works in King Street (1896, G106) has crow-stepped gables to harmonise with the adjacent Trust houses. Currie & Co., cement merchants, had an unusual store in Wallace Street (1875, H141), part of which was constructed in imitation of a lime-kiln, and a more orthodox warehouse in Weir Street (1893, H181).[7]

Papermaking

Papermaking has been practised in Glasgow since about 1690, when Nicholas Deschamps, a Huguenot refugee, went into partnership with some Glasgow merchants with a mill at Woodside. He then set up a mill of his own at Langside (NS610576), and his son-in-law built another upstream at Millholm (NS587597), which by c 1790 was employing eight men making coarse paper. Other paper mills in operation by that time were on the Kelvin at Balgray (A27) and Dalsholm (1790, A6), and in 1812 another hand mill was started at Cathcart (M59). Papermaking machines were introduced about 1850 at Dalsholm, Balgray (now Kelvindale) and Millholm, with a rapid expansion in size. Other machine mills, using Clyde water, were set up at Springfield (1868, F189) and Govanhaugh (c 1858, G161). Remains of the earlier mills are naturally scanty, but most of Cathcart Mill, a one-storey rubble building, survives and old buildings are incorporated in Dalsholm and Kelvindale (now the only operating mill in the city). The Millholm buildings were demolished by the mid 1950s, but the weir still exists, as do parts of the two Clyde mills.[8]

Printing

Though there are some large firms, printing has never attained in Glasgow the importance it has in Edinburgh. The first printer, indeed, came from Edinburgh in 1638, and in 1661 the Town Council agreed to pay Robert Sanders a retainer of forty pounds a year, to keep him in the city. In return, Sanders was 'to print gratis any thing short the toune sall imploy him to print'. In the eighteenth century printing received encouragement through the appointment of a University printer (in 1713) and the establishment of a type foundry (in 1718). The first Glasgow newspaper, *The Glasgow Courant*, was published in 1715 by the second University printer. Equally significant was the work of the Foulis brothers, who gained a high reputation for the quality of their printing, especially of classical texts. Eventually the University acquired its own press buildings, located by 1826 in Dobbies Loan. Advertised for sale in that year, they consisted of ware-rooms, press rooms (with eighteen presses), composing rooms (with thirty-five frames), offices, type foundry and 'necessary house'. The buildings were of one storey, roof lit and were subsequently occupied by Blackie's Villafield Press (*c* 1830, G22). Extended in 1838, the one-storey buildings were replaced in 1841 by a three-storey block, still standing. The Villafield works eventually became the largest in Glasgow, covering most of an island site. Part of the offices were designed by Alexander 'Greek' Thomson, the leading Glasgow architect of his day. Across the road the Herriot Hill Works was started by William Collins about 1861 (G21, G26) and eventually outgrew Villafield in size. When Blackie's moved to Bishopbriggs in 1931, Collins took over the Villafield buildings.[9]

Blackie and Collins were basically book brinters, but although other Glasgow firms, such as MacLehose & Co., Foulis Street (1903, A24) and Brown Son & Ferguson, Darnley Street (1903, I9) also print books, most of the other Glasgow printers were engaged in newspaper or general work. Some of the general printing works are very large, for example McCorquodale in Maxwell Street (1868, G90), and Aird and Coghill's old works in Cadogan Street (1899, H46), but many of them were small. Indeed most jobbing printers occupied part of multiple-occupied buildings, or second-hand premises. Medium-sized firms sometimes specialise, such as Gilmour and Dean in North Hanover Street (*c* 1871, G37), but now out of Glasgow, who are colour printers, and Miller and Lang in Darnley Street (1901, I8) who make greeting cards.

Though the University press mentioned above was only one

storey high, the majority of recently surviving printing works were multi-storey buildings. Curiously, the present University press (1903, A24) is an exception. The large Blackie and Collins complexes contain three-, four- and five-storey buildings in both stone and brick. McCorquodale's two-, three- and four-storey buildings, of brick and stone, conform to the city centre pattern of 'anonymous' architecture – resembling offices rather than workshops. Aird and Coghill's Cadogan Street works is a handsome example of 'modern movement' architecture, while Miller and Lang's Darnley Street premises are a more striking, though perhaps less tasteful essay in the same style. The warehouses built for printers were on the whole plainer, unless they formed part of a larger complex. That at the rear of the Darnley Street block is absolutely plain, though stone-faced; the four-storey brick Blackie warehouses in Milnbank Street (1906, D7) are equally functional.

While some of the book and general printing works are physically impressive, the newspaper offices are singularly solid and imposing. Glasgow, like most large cities, at one time supported several independent daily papers. As their offices and presses occupied valuable central sites, and because their proprietors wished to impress, their buildings were normally large and ornate, and often by fashionable architects. The *Glasgow Herald* employed James Sellars to design their Buchanan Street block (1879, G72), while both the *Herald* and the *Daily Record* had buildings designed by Charles Rennie Mackintosh for their Mitchell Street (G72) and St Vincent Lane (1900, G35) premises respectively. The Mitchell Street building has a novel system of water jets designed to play on the windows facing a narrow lane, to prevent the spread of fire from premises opposite. The *Citizen* building in St Vincent Place (1885, G36) is remarkably ornate, and unusual in the early use of red sandstone as a facing material. This stone was also used in the *Daily Record*'s tall narrow block in Hope Street (1899, G75). The long-extinct *North British Daily Mail* had ugly but impressive headquarters in Union Street (1898, G73). More modest are D. C. Thomson's Port Dundas Road works (1906, C110) and the *Govan Press* building in Govan Road (1888, K22). The latter is ornamented with busts of such figures as Caxton, Gutenberg and Scott, as well as of the former proprietor and his wife.[10]

As well as printed material, the business community in Glasgow required stationery of all kinds. Most of the stationers, like the jobbing printers, occupied second-hand premises, such as cotton mills, or flats in multiple-occupation buildings, and indeed many firms described themselves as 'printers and stationers'. Of the specialist stationers, possibly the largest were Alex. Baird & Son of the Kelvinbridge Artistic Stationery Works, Herbert Street (*c* 1890, B46), whose four-storey and attic factory in the French Renaissance manner is particularly grand. Other stationery works were both smaller and plainer, such as those in Black Street (1910, C87), Robertson Lane (*c* 1893, H52) and Darnley Street (1903, I9).

Engraving

Linked with printing, both on paper and on cloth, were the various engraving works in the city, of which the St Mungo Engraving Works in Cathedral Street (1883, G24) and another in McAslin Street (*c* 1888, G19) both supplied blocks for calico printing. The Duke Street Engraving Works (1878, D18), which is still in operation, makes paper printing blocks, as do several other firms occupying flats in commercial buildings. The St Mungo works has a stone front and brick body, while the McAslin Street factory was all brick. The most interesting of the three is the Duke Street complex in Ark Lane, which has classical details and a fine ornamental chimney.

Warehouses

Warehouses perform a vital function in any commercial and industrial centre, and in the past, when communications were not so rapid, larger quantities of goods were stored in city centres than at present, requiring more numerous and varied buildings. The term 'warehouse' can be applied to a wide range of premises, from one room in a tenement building to a vast store with seven or more storeys and a floor area of tens of thousands of square feet. The warehouses described here are either buildings designed for the storage of a single commodity, such as grain, or general stores, kept by storekeepers. The large number of wholesale warehouses in the city, which resemble retail department stores in their physical organisation, are specifically excluded, as are bonded warehouses built as such, which are discussed in Chapter 1.

Eighteenth-century warehouses were often in the same building as the owner's house, a typical arrangement being to devote the lower floors to storage with the top floor a dwelling house, sometimes approached by a separate stairway. In the late eighteenth century some fine warehouses were built in Cochrane Street and John Street (G71) with plain, but well-proportioned frontages and access through arched 'pends' to rectangular and octagonal wells from which goods were loaded or unloaded by wall cranes or by simple pulleys. What might be called the 'traditional' warehouse, with small windows, often barred, and hoist doors in vertical rows, was developed by the end of the eighteenth century, and the type continued to be built until hydraulic lifts were introduced at the end of the nineteenth century. By the middle of the nineteenth century such buildings were to be found in quite large numbers in streets off the Broomielaw, and round the canal at Port Dundas. Typically the larger warehouses were used as grain stores, though tea and tobacco were also stored in bulk. Most of these buildings were stone-built, often with a dressed frontage, and rubble side and rear walls, though from the 1820s brick frequently replaced the rubble. Warehouses built between 1890 and 1914 normally had terra-cotta brick facings, sometimes with ornamental features. Internally, construction resembled that of contemporary multi-storey factories. The majority had cast-iron columns supporting wooden beams and floors, though a few had fireproof interiors, sometimes only on the ground floor or basement. Buildings designed as grain stores often had columns with four projecting pairs of ribs into which boards could be fitted to form partitions for bulk storage of grain (Fig 15).[11]

The oldest 'traditional' warehouses in Glasgow probably date from the 1820s or 1830s, and others of that period have only recently been demolished, for example the canal warehouses in Tayport Street and Colinton Street (C54, C57) and an isolated three-storey building in Albion Street (c 1825, G64). The survivors,

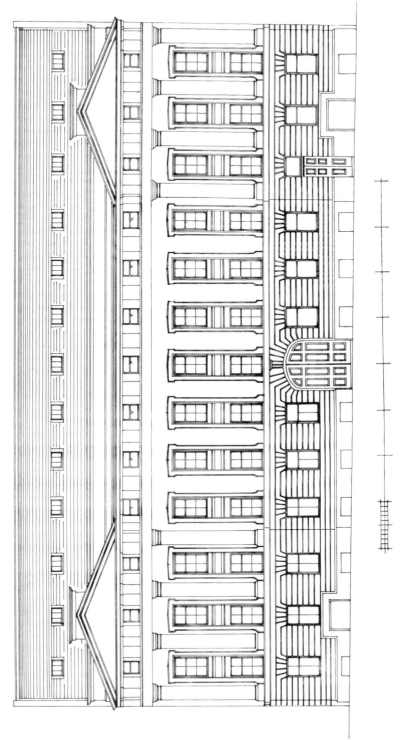

Fig 14

Elevation of Warehouse, 44–54 James Watt Street (H60), built for Thomas
Mann in 1861

in Robertson Lane (G79) and West Campbell Street (H50), appear to be contemporary with these, though they cannot be dated with precision. The finest group of warehouses in the city is undoubtedly in James Watt Street, where pairs of classical buildings face each other (H59, H60, H63 and H64). The earliest of these dates from 1847 and the latest from 1868, though one built in 1854 was extended in 1910–11 (Fig 15). Other mid-nineteenth-century

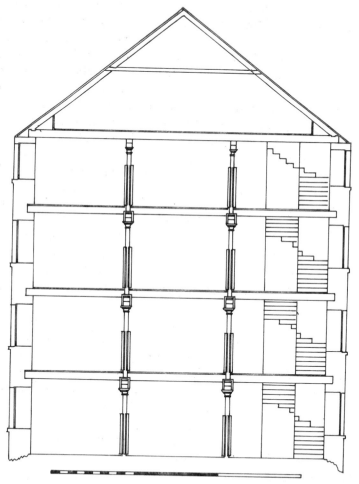

Fig 15

Section of Mr Huie's Store, Alston Street, drawn by J. T. Rochhead, architect. The original drawing was made for an enquiry into the partial collapse of the building, and the construction is typical of the period

warehouses are to be found in Fox Street (*c* 1857–9, G89) and James Watt Lane (*c* 1850, H55). One of the Fox Street group still has a handsome wall crane. Only slightly later were the fine Wallace Street warehouse of the Glasgow Storage Co. Ltd (1871–2, H140), designed by William Spence, and smaller blocks in Clyde-ferry Street (1875, H87) and Kingston Street (1878, H131). The five-storey and basement Wallace Street block could stand comparison with the James Watt Street buildings. All these later buildings, and the James Watt Street ones, had no hoists at the front of the building, access to upper floors being internal or from the rear. Other warehouses of the 1870s were less immediately recognisable as such. A large bag and mat warehouse in Cranston Street (1874, H30) was a striking example of the use of red and white brick, with an iron and timber interior, and could have been mistaken for a typical factory of the period. Some others were quite frankly designed for a range of possible uses, such as those in James Watt Street (1876, H61), Craignestock Street (1877, F65) and North Frederick Street (1881, G44), which were speculative building ventures. It is noteworthy that the two first named became common lodging houses for a period, before reverting to their original use. Both this trio and similar buildings used specifically as warehouses in Cathedral and Cunningham Streets (1869, 1882, G30–1), Montrose Street (1876, G68) and Broomielaw (1878, G83) are distinguished from earlier buildings by the greater size and number of windows and by the free use of Renaissance architectural motifs.[12]

The trend away from the traditional bulk store continued in the 1890s, after a lull in warehouse building during the 1880s, with the construction of several large warehouses to be let in flats, some financed privately and others by the City Improvement Trust. The Trust had allowed some of its land to be used for a privately built warehouse in 1873 (G118) but two blocks in King Street and Parnie Street (1899, G104; 1902, G105) were directly financed. The high site value deterred the Trust from building houses there, though in style the warehouses resembled adjacent residential tenements. Privately built warehouses included two enormous buildings in Dunlop Street, Clyde Street, Maxwell Street and Ropework Lane (1896, G98; 1901, G97) and the 'twin sisters' which faced each other across McAlpine Street (1899, H72, H73).

Warehouses for occupation by a single firm were also built in that period, for example in Brunswick Lane (1896, G109), Crimea Street (1896, H68), Clydeferry Street (1898, H88; 1900, H86) and Bruce and Hay's elaborate building for T. Hodge in Bishop Street (1894, H63). The construction of a group of three warehouses for a yarn merchant in Arcadia and Abercromby Streets (1891, F70; 1890, F71; 1892–3, F72) reflects the increasing use of imported yarn in the east end weaving factories. The few warehouses built between 1901 and 1914 were mostly small, as in Gorbals Street (c 1907, G170), Portman Street (c 1902, H151) and Sussex Street (1914, H155). A large block was, however, built in McAlpine Street in 1905 (H76), and was similar in style to W. P. Lowrie's bonded warehouse in nearby Washington Street (1897–1906, H82), though faced with terra-cotta brick rather than sandstone. Small single-storey warehouses had been built for many years, but J. & P. Coats' large single-level store in Durham Street (1907, H209) was a pioneer in that system of organisation, expensive in land but cheap in labour costs, that really came into its own after the Second World War.[13]

Co-operative Society Buildings

An important group of buildings – warehouses, factories and stables – which may be considered together are those put up by co-operative societies, both wholesale and retail. The co-operative movement from the 1860s grew in momentum, and rivalling capitalist enterprise in scale also competed in the commissioning of opulent architecture. The grandest buildings are those of the Scottish Co-operative Wholesale Society (scws) and the United Co-operative Baking Society (ucbs) (see p. 10), but most of the retail societies had buildings with some pretensions. The oldest surviving co-operative buildings seem to be the stores and stables of the Old Victualling Society at the back of 135 Main Street, Bridgeton (c 1865, F147), functionally built of brick. The Glasgow Eastern and St George's Societies had equally plain, though neater workshops in Baltic Street (1898, F139) and Glenfarg Street (1902, B57). The more ambitious buildings tended to be central warehouses, as most of the retail shops were on the ground floor of residential tenements. Both the Kinning Park and the St Rollox Societies had large central blocks, in Bridge Street (1902, G177) and Lister Street (1903, G14). The Bridge Street warehouse was designed by Bruce and Hay, who did much work for co-operative societies, and includes a retail shop. The Cowlairs and Shettleston Societies had extensive central premises in Angus Street (1895, C6) and Pettigrew Street (c 1910, M42) incorporating in both cases creameries, and in the latter a meeting hall.

The crowning glories of co-operative architecture and enterprise are to be found in the premises of the scws. From 1872 onwards a series of large warehouses and workshops was built in Kingston (H142; 1898, H192). The earliest, in Morrison Street, resembled contemporary grain and general stores, though at the west end decorative features were introduced. Successive warehouses became grander, culminating in the construction of the head offices to a design by Bruce and Hay, which, it was claimed, was that firm's unsuccessful entry in the competition for the Glasgow City Chambers. The architects strenuously denied this allegation, but it must be admitted that on appearances it was a reasonable assumption. Even after the First World War new premises constructed in the area were quite elaborate, but the detached brick-built range in Laidlaw Street, situated as it was amid factories, was much plainer. As well as fulfilling the function of a central store, the Kingston complex also housed manufacturing departments, including drapery, furniture, and boots and shoes. The growth in demand for scws products led eventually to the construction of factories elsewhere. Isolated examples have already been mentioned (see pp. 13, 14, 22) but the main manufacturing centre was at Shieldhall (M88). Built on a 'green field' site from 1887 the factory buildings were originally intended to be associated with a model village for the workers; the opening of an electric tramway rendered it unnecessary to build houses locally. The first block was completed in 1888, and by 1918 there were seventeen different departments. An impressive six-storey frontage to Renfrew Road was planned, but only the western half was completed to its designed height, owing to the outbreak of war in 1914. The majority of the buildings at Shieldhall are of red and white brick but the main block, as with most of the Kingston buildings, is of sandstone.[14]

Other Industries

It is obviously impossible to mention all the other industries to be found in Glasgow, but to round off this chapter a few of the more unusual will be mentioned. Morier's brush factory in Copland Road (1897, K37) was probably the largest in the city, while a firm in Barrowfield Street (c 1878, F94) made coir products, including mats. Window blinds were the speciality of James Meighan & Son, whose workshop was in Abercromby Street (1896, F74). Engine waste, a necessary requisite for manufacturing industry, as of railway operation, was usually processed in second-hand premises, but new workshops were built in Ladywell Street (D21) from 1889. Cork products were made by Symington & Co., who constructed a new warehouse in Clyde Street in 1914 (G95). The premises of boiler lagging compound (1910, H109) and engine packing makers (1907, H160) were conveniently near both docks and engine works. Adjacent workshops in Robertson Lane were used for japanning and pressure gauge manufacture (c 1874, G77; c 1876, G78). Perhaps surprisingly, only one tobacco firm's workshops recently survived: Stephen Mitchell & Co. had a large factory in St Andrew's Square, part of which was adapted from the terrace houses which originally lined the square (c 1875, G130).

[1] Clow, A., and N. L., 8, refers to shortage of wood

[2] There was a legal wrangle over the demolition of the Molendinar Mill, see Senex, *Old Glasgow*, 126–40, also a map produced in connection with the dispute, showing the north and south fronts of the mill, is reproduced in Gunn and Newbigin, as Fig 2; Singer, Charles *et al.* (eds), *A History of Technology* (Oxford 1958), vol 4, 437, states that the circular saw was probably invented in the third quarter of the eighteenth century by Walter Taylor (1734–1803) of Southampton; Carvel, John L., *One Hundred Years in Timber* (Glasgow 1949)

[3] *Industries of Glasgow*, 191 (Greenhead Sawmills)

[4] Ibid, 81–2 (Wylie & Lochhead), *Stratten*, 211 (Campbellfield Bedstead Works)

[5] 3rd SA, 296 (British Basket & Besto)

[6] Ibid, 296–7 (hammer shaft factory)

[7] *Industries of Glasgow*, 263 (Currie & Co.)

[8] Clow, A., and N. L., 30 (note that account of Deschamps in Gartshore, A., *Cathcart Memories* (Glasgow 1938) is confused); Thomson, 37–9; Gartshore, 21–8, 36–41; *Industries of Glasgow*, 139 (Springfield) and 124 (Govanhaugh); parts of Millholm illustrated in Gartshore, 28, 59

[9]Marwick, J. D. (ed), *Extracts from the Records of the Burgh of Glasgow 1630–62* (Glasgow 1881), 469; McDowall, J. K., *The People's History of Glasgow* (Glasgow 1899), 44, 49; *Plan, Front View, Specimens of Types and Inventory of Printing Materials* (Glasgow 1826), of University Press, copy kindly supplied by Mr J. Robertson; Blackie, Agnes A. C., *Blackie & Son 1809–1959* (London 1959), 15, 29, 58

[10]The *Herald*'s Mitchell Street block is illustrated in Young & Doak, plate 141

[11]Guildhall Library MSS 11937/36 Sun Insurance CD series, policy 710934, 14 November 1800, Robert and William Dalgleish, £2300; Robert's household goods were in the fourth storey and garrets, with stock and utensils in the third floor of a building in Bell Street (I am indebted to Dr John Butt for this reference); the panoramic views drawn for the *Illustrated London News* by McCulloch (1853) and Sulman (1864) show 'traditional' warehouses round the site of Central Station, and the first edition (1859) of the 1:500 Ordnance Survey of Glasgow confirms that a large area of that part of the city was devoted to storage; *The Scottish Wine, Spirit and Beer Trades Review* (12 January 1888), 171, describes and illustrates a partly fireproof warehouse

[12]The best of the James Watt Street warehouses is illustrated in Young & Doak, plate 45

[13]One of the City Improvement Trust warehouses is illustrated and described in *Municipal Glasgow: its Evolution and Enterprises* (Glasgow 1914), 65, plate facing 66

[14]The SCWS Head Office is illustrated in Young & Doak, plate 118; Flanagan, passim

6 Transport

Bridges

As early as 1285 the first bridge over the Clyde at Glasgow was
built, and the city's position as the lowest bridging point on the
river was maintained until 1971. The thirteenth century bridge was
replaced in the early fifteenth century by a structure that lasted,
with modifications, until 1850, when it was demolished to make
way for Victoria Bridge (1851-4, G139), reckoned the finest of the
Clyde road bridges. Before then, however, Glasgow's growing
importance as a trading centre, coupled with developments on the
south side of the river, had led to the construction of four more
bridges within the present boundary. The first was William Milne's
bridge at Jamaica Street, opened in 1771, followed by the first
Rutherglen (1776) and Dalmarnock Road (late 1790s) bridges. The
ill-defined community known as Bridgeton derived its name from
Rutherglen Bridge. An attempt was also made in the 1790s to
build a bridge at the foot of Saltmarket, but the works were swept
away in 1795, and not until 1830 was Hutchesontown Bridge
completed on this site.[1]

Even these five bridges were inadequate to deal with the city's
growing trade, and Milne's bridge was rebuilt between 1833 and
1836 by Thomas Telford. With a width of sixty feet Telford's was
the broadest river bridge in Britain, and its designer's last major
work. During reconstruction a temporary wooden bridge was
provided at South Portland Street, and proved so useful that it was
replaced by a suspension footbridge (G140) in 1853. A second
suspension bridge farther upstream (1853, G135) replaced a ferry
between Hutchesontown industry and Calton housing. Owing to
scouring of the foundations, Hutchesontown Bridge was superseded in 1870-1 by the cast-iron Albert Bridge (G137). Pressure on
river crossings then eased with the slowing of industrial expansion
after 1873, but in the late 1880s demand for improvement began

again. Dalmarnock Road bridge was replaced in 1889–91 (F183) and after much debate Jamaica bridge was rebuilt between 1894 and 1899, using the original facade of Telford's bridge, but with the width increased to eighty feet (G141). The temporary bridge this time was used to provide crossings at Ballater Street and Polmadie Road, which were later rebuilt in reinforced concrete (1933, G134). Rutherglen Bridge was also renewed in the 1890s (1896, F154).[2]

The other rivers of Glasgow, the Kelvin and the White Cart, were also spanned many times in their serpentine courses. A few eighteenth-century bridges survive, but, as on the Clyde, there has been a succession of new bridges at major crossing points; for example, there have been three Kelvin bridges at Hillhead since 1800.[3]

Changing techniques in bridgebuilding are well represented in Glasgow bridges. The fifteenth-century Glasgow Bridge resembled those still existing at Ayr and Stirling, with semicircular arches necessitating a steep rise, while eighteenth-century design improvements are apparent in Milne's bridge with its flattened segmental arches and small rise, and in Hutchesontown, Telford's Jamaica and Victoria bridges. Lesser bridges, with the exception of John Adam's Nether Pollok House Bridge (c 1750, M71), were conservative, those at Netherlee Road (M60), Dalsholm Road (M11), Kelvindale (A30) and Partick (L45) all having semicircular arches.

As far as is known iron was first used in a little bridge over the Molendinar (1826, G128), and in a slightly larger one in Linn Park, over the Cart (c 1835, M61). A vogue for cast-iron arch bridges started about 1870, with Albert Bridge's three flattened spans and an approach span to Belmont Bridge (1870, B37); followed by the skewed Partick (1878, L44), Kelvin (1891, B61) and Eldon Street (1895, B66) bridges. However, masonry continued to be used, in the third Jamaica and second Rutherglen bridges, and in minor bridges at Kirklee (1899, B30), Cart (1901, M55), Langside (1898, M64) and Kelvingrove Park (1895, M85). Wrought-iron was used in the suspension bridges for both chains and deck, though the ironwork at South Portland Street had to be renewed in 1871. Iron trusses were employed in the first Queen Margaret Bridge (1870, B39) and at Dalmarnock Road. Plate girders, so common in railway practice, were used in minor bridges in Bantaskin Street (*c* 1871, A14) and Delvin Road (M57). Concrete, though used in buildings from the 1880s, was only adopted as a bridge-building material after 1920 when King George V (1924–8, G143), Riverford Road (1923, J15), Queen Margaret Drive (1926–9, B40) and Killermont (1925–9, M10) bridges were built with reinforced-concrete arches and King's Bridge (1936, G134) was constructed with reinforced-concrete girders.[4]

Ferries

On the Clyde, ferries complemented bridges, one of the oldest ferries being at Govan. In 1858 the Clyde Navigation Trust was authorised to provide ferry boats in the harbour, and by 1900 two types of service had evolved: vehicular ferries, at Govan (K5), Finnieston (1890, H123) and Whiteinch (1900, L11), and passenger ferries at intervals from York Street to Meadowside (*c* 1900, K2). The Govan ferry was chain operated until 1912, when a patent variable-level ferryboat was substituted as used at Finnieston and Whiteinch from the start. Rowing boats were used for the passenger ferries until 1865, when steam vessels were introduced. Fixed provision for ferries consisted of simple gated docking bays with chain operated metal flaps, for the variable level boats, and for the passenger ferries wooden stairways with wood or masonry walls, either set into quay walls, as at Finnieston, or projecting from the river banks, as at Meadowside. The only ferries surviving in 1972 were at Kelvinhaugh (K13) and Finnieston (H123).[5]

Tunnel

It is also possible to cross the Clyde underground, by the new Whiteinch Tunnel, or by the pedestrian tunnel constructed by the privately financed Glasgow Harbour Tunnel Company (1890–6, H119). This company controlled two other tunnels, two for vehicles (mainly horse-drawn), which gained access by hydraulic lifts, but development of motor lorries ended its popularity. The circular terminal buildings are still landmarks, and the tunnels are now used for water pipes.[6]

Roads and Streets

While it is convenient to consider river crossings as a group, they should be seen in the context of a growing network of roads linking Glasgow with other towns, and of streets serving new houses. Before 1753, road repair was undertaken by statute labour, but in that year two turnpike acts were passed for the improvement of the principal roads to aid commerce and, in the wake of the '45, 'the convenient marching of his majesty's troops'. These and succeeding acts were sufficiently successful for Gibson to write in 1777 'we are now blessed with good roads all round the city'. The rent for the city tollbars in 1816–17 totalled £20,198, which compared favourably with the £1,836 6s from Road Money (the payment levied in lieu of statute labour) in 1817. Turnpike survivals include the alignment of certain roads, such as Great Western Road, three tollhouses, in Parliamentary Road (G20), Dalmarnock Road (F178) and Pollokshaws (J22) and a few bridges, such as the two Kelvin bridges at Partick (L44, L45). All tollhouses were, of course, built to provide the tollkeeper with excellent visibility of the road. The Pollokshaws tollhouse, which has been preserved, exhibits this principle to a nicety, being completely circular.[7]

The laying out of new streets was part of the growth of the city, and starting from the High Street–Trongate axes of the old town, middle-class houses spread east and west, leaving the old core to the labouring poor. Miller Street, Ingram Street, George Square, Frederick Street, Cochrane Street and Buchanan Street were laid out between 1770 and 1790 while Bridge Street, opened in 1791 and St Vincent Street, formed in 1804, opened up large new areas. During the next twenty years not only were streets laid out on virgin ground, but new ways were cut through decaying properties, notably London Street (now London Road). By 1820 there were 125 streets 'paved with durable whin-stones, from the almost inexhaustible Quarries adjoining the Cathedral'. A major new project in the 1830s was Great Western Road, authorised in 1836, which is still one of the city's finest streets. Though the growth of long distance road traffic was curbed by railway development – the mail-coach service between Glasgow and London was cut back to Beattock in 1847 and abandoned altogether in 1848 – internal traffic was stimulated. Improved paving, by then urgently necessary, was authorised by the Glasgow Paving Act of 1856, and £150,000 spent on relaying streets with square-dressed granite setts, the standard surface for main roads until the 1950s. Two new factors which affected street layout in the late nineteenth century were the City Improvement Trust, which in clearing old properties opened up new streets, and the formation of street tramways, which required wider and straighter streets, and in some cases new bridges. Boundary extensions brought new areas into the city, and this, together with the abolition of turnpikes, helped to increase the mileage of roads and streets in the city to 214 in 1900.[8]

Tramways

The first street tramways, authorised by an act of 1870, were, owing to default by the original promoters, built by the Corporation and operated under lease by the Glasgow Tramways Company. The first route was opened in 1872, and thereafter expansion of the system was fairly rapid. By 1877 the Company had depots and stables in Whiteinch, North Street (1875, H40), Cambridge Street, Nelson Street, Tobago Street (c 1877, F68) and David Street. Others were added in Thurso Street, Partick (c 1883, L42) and in Duart Street, Maryhill (c 1883, A9), and existing depots were in some cases enlarged during the lease. This was due to expire in 1894, and the Corporation started negotiations about renewal in 1887. As no agreement could be reached, in 1891 the Corporation decided to take over. Logically the Corporation should have taken over the assets of the Company, but again the parties could not agree. The Corporation therefore decided to build depots, stables and cars and to buy horses before taking over operation of the system on 1 July 1894. The success of this early example of municipal tramway operation made it a model for other cities. Neat, standard horse-cars were housed in substantial new depots built for the opening at Coplawhill (I16), Kinning Park (H175), Partick (L23), Kelvinhaugh (H4), Maryhill, Cowcaddens (C118), Springburn (C13), Whitevale (F33) and Dalmarnock (F143). Another horse-tram depot was added at Dennistoun (D15) in 1895. Though horse operation was a success, mechanical propulsion had already proved its worth elsewhere. Glasgow, however, could not risk experiment during the crucial takeover, and it was not until 1898 that a trial electric route was opened from Mitchell Street to Springburn. A power station was added to the existing horse tram depot at Springburn; the building still exists (C13). This pioneer route was entirely successful, and electrification of the whole system was completed in 1901.[9]

From an early period, tramways had been built in adjoining burghs as part of the Glasgow system, and most of these came under civic administration through boundary changes. Two independent systems also operated within the present boundaries: the Paisley District Tramways Company, which spread one of its tentacles to Spiersbridge where a link was eventually made with the Glasgow system, and the older Vale of Clyde Company which ran a horse (later steam) service to Govan until 1893. These systems were absorbed by Glasgow Corporation in 1897 and 1923, the only surviving feature from either within the city being a concrete bridge at Darnley (c 1910, M69) on the reserved track between Spiersbridge and Barrhead.[10]

After electrification came expansion, both by absorption and by extension of existing routes, a process continuing into the 1940s. Longer routes required more cars and therefore greater depot accommodation. The first new electric depots were Langside (1900, M52) and Possilpark (1900, M20), followed by Newlands (1909, J17), Govan (1913, K26) and Parkhead (1921, M46). Some horse-tram depots were modified to take electric cars, as at Partick, Maryhill and Dalmarnock, while Whitevale and Cowcaddens became substations, Kinning Park a store, and Kelvinhaugh and Springburn were sold out of service. When the tram system was abandoned, Langside, Possilpark, Govan and Newlands depots became bus garages. Two new substations were built inside the boundary for the 1901 electrification, at Kinning Park (H175) and Partick (L40, rebuilt 1910), while the experimental Springburn generating station was replaced by Pinkston Power Station (1900, C71), which had good rail and canal access for fuel and cooling water. Large reciprocating engines installed at first were quickly replaced by steam turbines, and, after a second re-equipment, the station is still in use. It is now owned by the South of Scotland Electricity Board. Central workshops were built at Coplawhill, where most of the tram fleet was constructed; part now houses the Transport Museum. All these works were substantially built, and by 1914 the Corporation tramways were among the best in Britain.[11]

With cheapness in mind, most tramway buildings were brick built. The Company depots, usually three storeys high, were of red and white brick, though the Cambridge Street and Maryhill depots had stone frontages, the latter quite elaborate. Corporation depots were mostly red brick, one or two storeys high, but Cowcaddens, Springburn, Coplawhill, Govan and Newlands were faced with stone to harmonise with nearby buildings, as was the main frontage of the Coplawhill works. Pinkston, with its handsome twin chimneys and steel framed brick boiler and generator houses, became a well-known landmark.

Stables and Garages

Enormous numbers of horses were needed to operate a tram service – one Company depot had 436 stalls – but even more were required to haul lorries, vans, carriages and buses. Fifty-three stables are included in the inventory, most of them large, and including accommodation for vehicles on the ground floor, stables on upper floors (approached by wooden ramps) and hay and grain stores in the attic or top floor (Figs 16, 17). The largest group of stables was those of cartage contractors, such as Wordie & Co. (railway contractors), with stables in Paul Street (1861, G48; 1868, G50), West Street (1895, H138), and Calgary Street (1899, C96), James Bow & Son in Milnpark Street (c 1895, H154) and William

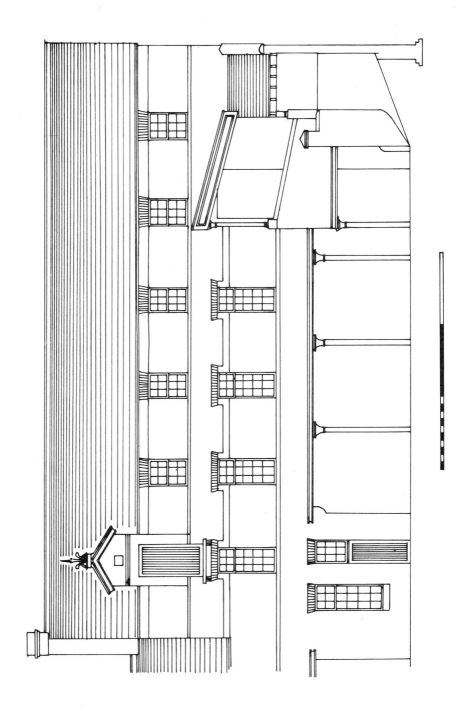

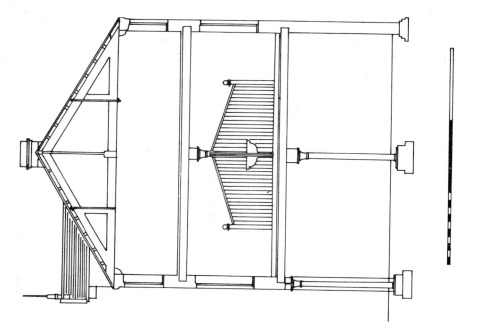

Figs 16 and 17

Elevation and section of stable, 32 Herbert Street (B47), built for Bishop & Henderson, grocers, to designs by Robert Duncan in 1890–1. Note that the cart shed is on the ground floor, stalls on the first floor and the hay store on the second floor. The ramp to the stalls is on the right of Fig 16

Bow in Martyr Street (1902, G17). Coach proprietors like Wylie & Lochhead, with premises in Berkeley Street (1870, H9) and Andrew Menzies with his St George's Horse Bazaar in St George's Road (1873, M84) had larger units, while the most elaborate stables in the city were probably the polychrome brick buildings of the Kinning Park Co-operative Society in Stanley Street (H206). The coach hirers' stables, with stone frontages, were also very grand, but some of the contractors' stables were handsome examples of brick building.[12]

Smaller stables abounded, often simple brick structures with an open yard for vehicles, such as those in Ravel Row (1906, E20), Tylefield Street (1897, F38), Baltic Street (1907, F187) and Fairley Street (1897, K30). One of the finest middle-sized blocks is 21–25 Carlton Court (c 1895, G147), where the ramps, and grain and hay hoists are still intact.

The successor to the stable was, of course, the garage, though since motor vehicles were relatively rare before 1914, so were garages. The earliest large examples seem to have been those in Hotspur Street (B28), Vinicombe Street (B44) and Berkeley Street (H8), but real expansion in services for motorists came after 1918.

Canals

The first serious proposals for a Forth–Clyde canal were made in the 1760s, and after much wrangling over route, depth and scale the first sod of the Forth and Clyde Canal was cut at Grangemouth in 1768. Under the guidance of John Smeaton, and the immediate supervision of Robert Mackell, the works reached Stockingfield (Maryhill) in 1775. Though finance was inadequate to complete the canal to a junction with the Clyde, it was continued to a basin at Hamiltonhill, opened in 1777, which immediately became a busier port than the Broomielaw, and a focus for industrial growth. Nine years later, with a new engineer, Robert Whitworth, and a Government loan of £50,000, work restarted on the main line of the canal to Bowling. Whitworth's locks and aqueduct at Maryhill (A11, A12) are particularly fine. The aqueduct became one of the sights of

Glasgow. At the same time a new Glasgow terminal (named Port Dundas after the chairman of the Company) was built, consisting of an oval basin with a granary, and a link at the east end – the 'Cut of Junction' – with the Monkland Canal. The main line, junction canal and new basin were all opened in 1790.[13]

Thus completed, a prolonged period of prosperity ensued, in which the loan was repaid, and further basins at Port Dundas and at Firhill were added. The Port Dundas district became heavily industrialised, with engine works, foundries, chemical works, grain mills and distilleries all receiving raw materials by canal and dispatching finished products by the same route. The handsome new canal offices (C46) built in 1812 are a tribute to the prosperity of the Company.[14]

Two years after the Forth & Clyde was authorised, an act was obtained for a second canal to serve Glasgow, the Monkland. With James Watt as engineer for this coal canal, enough money was raised to complete it from the Monklands to Riddrie (M34) in 1773. Construction was resumed in 1782, when the canal was extended to Blackhill, a detached length being built at a lower level to connect Blackhill with a basin at Castle Street (D2). The intermediate locks were not completed until 1793 (M33). From 1807, after the depth had been increased to five feet, the Monkland was very successful. Monkland coal could move via the 'Cut of Junction' to Glasgow industry and to Bowling for export, while the development of iron-smelting in the Monklands from the 1820s brought further lucrative traffic. Even the opening of the competing Monkland & Kirkintilloch and Garnkirk & Glasgow railways did not affect its prosperity, and a second flight of locks was added at Blackhill in 1841 to cope with increased traffic. To save water, an inclined plane, first proposed in 1839, was constructed at Blackhill in 1850 and remained in use until about 1887. The cutting made for it can still be seen. In the face of growing railway competition, the Monkland amalgamated with the Forth & Clyde in 1846, and the joint company was bought by the Caledonian Railway in 1867, largely to secure the port of Grangemouth as an outlet on the Forth. The Monkland was tied so closely to mineral traffic that inevitably the exhaustion of mineral fields resulted in closure, decline being hastened by railway development. By the 1920s the canal was virtually derelict. The Forth and Clyde, however, remained a useful sea-to-sea link, though traffic was light for several years before closure in 1962.[15]

The third Glasgow canal was, like the Monkland, designed for barge traffic. Promoted as the Glasgow, Paisley and Ardrossan Canal, the Act authorising construction was obtained in 1805. Excavation started at Johnstone, and the canal was completed to Glasgow in 1811; owing to insufficient funds this was the only part built. In any case the objective of linking Glasgow with harbour improvement at Ardrossan became unimportant once the newly formed Clyde Navigation Trust began to deepen the Clyde (see p. 125). Passenger traffic on this canal was heavy until the Glasgow & Paisley Joint Railway was opened, the subsequent competition being ended by agreement in 1843, whereby the canal company gave up passenger services for an annuity. The Glasgow & South Western Railway bought the almost derelict canal in 1869, and converted it to a railway between 1881 and 1885. The only substantial relic in Glasgow is the large warehouse at Port Eglinton, the city terminus (H215).[16]

Construction of all three canals was entirely orthodox. Basins were normally built with masonry walls and inverts (recently exposed at Port Dundas during road works), while private wharves, which abounded, were often simple, wood-piled structures. Private factory branches were rare, though the Monkland had one to Blochairn ironworks, there was one on the 'Cut of Junction' into St Rollox Works, and another to a colliery at Hamiltonhill (c 1875, C1). Also on the 'Cut' was an unusual branch between Charles Street and Garngad Road, serving several firms, which had passing places or docking bays at intervals. Of the city aqueducts, the two on the Glasgow, Paisley & Ardrossan Canal have disappeared, and of the five on the Forth & Clyde in 1790, four survive – a small aqueduct at Ruchill (c 1775, B5), Stockingfield (B3), Kelvin (A12) and Possil Road (C23), beside its successor (c 1880, C23). The Whitworth road aqueducts (B3, C23) have small semicircular arches, with spandrels curved in plan; the latter feature is also seen in the Kelvin Aqueduct, though here the arches are much larger. The original Maryhill Road aqueduct was demolished after replacement in 1881 (B1). A new aqueduct at Bilsland Drive (1879, B26) resembled these two replacements, with a segmental arch of heavy construction flanked by lighter semicircular arches carrying the banks and towpath. An aqueduct over the railway was built at Ruchill (*c* 1858, B4), and railways tunnelled under the Forth & Clyde at Temple (*c* 1885, A5), Maryhill (*c* 1894, B7) on the approaches to Buchanan Street (1849, C73) and Queen Street (1842, C72) stations, and under the Monkland at Barnhill (*c* 1875, D10). The only aqueduct on the Monkland in Glasgow is one over the Molendinar (D8) which resembles the later Forth & Clyde examples.[17]

Overbridges on the Monkland and Paisley canals were fixed, though all the Paisley canal bridges in Glasgow have gone. Monkland standard overbridges had wooden beams laid between stone abutments, with light wooden railings; five examples survived recently (M35–M39) but most have now been replaced. A cast-iron bridge at Roystonhill (1858, D1) has been demolished, but Robertson's Bridge (D3), a lattice girder structure, still spans the drained bed of the canal. The Forth & Clyde, as a ship canal, required opening bridges. On the first section built, swing bridges were apparently used, but later bascule bridges were used exclusively until railway bridges were needed. The original bascule bridges are distinctive, with cast-iron sector plates bolted to the abutments and to the opening wooden spans. Internal teeth on the latter engage with hand-cranked gearing (ratchet protected) on the fixed plate. Bridges of this type, varying in width, existed in recent years at twelve places in the city (A17, B21, C24, C48, C58, C64, C88, C98, M4, M5, M7 and M9) but almost all had disappeared by 1972. A programme of road improvement in the 1930s led to construction of electrically operated, steel, bascule bridges at Temple (1931, A3), Cloberhill (1928, M6) and Lambhill (1930, M14). The only swing canal bridges in Glasgow were two built *c* 1880 on the 'Cut of Junction'.[18]

Other interesting canal remains are a dry dock at Maryhill (*c* 1790, A10); a spillway at Ruchill (late 19th century, B6); stables at Lambhill (early 19th century, M13) of a standard Forth & Clyde type; and Cuilhill Basin (*c* 1847, M39), built in connection with the Drumpeller Railway, a horse-worked mineral line. In the centre of the basin is a loading island with masonry quays having curved depressions, probably for turning barges. The remains of the approach viaduct still exist.[19]

Railways

Cuilhill is a link with an early Lanarkshire railway, but there were railways in Glasgow much earlier, from Knightswood and Govan Collieries to wharves on the Clyde. Built by John and William Dixon, Tyneside men, in the late eighteenth century, they had wooden rails, presumably after the Newcastle pattern. The Knightswood line existed· to supply coal to the great Dumbarton Glassworks, eventually a Dixon enterprise. The Monkland Canal Act also included provision for a waggonway link from the Castle Street basin to the city centre, but this was never built. However, just as locomotive-worked railways were introduced there was a late development of waggonways; William Dixon II had rail-served coal depots in Hutchesontown and Tradeston, while a coal depot in Broad Street, Mile End, was served by a 'Rail Road', probably from Barrowfield Collieries.[20]

The introduction and growth of locomotive-worked railways in Glasgow have attracted the attention of both railway and economic historians for many years, much the best connected account being John Thomas's in his *Regional History*. In view of the wealth of published material the following account of railway development is deliberately brief.[21]

As with waggonways the Garnkirk & Glasgow Railway was built mainly to move coal to Glasgow, both for use there and for distribution farther afield. Opened in 1831, it was a valuable alternative to the Monkland Canal, but little else – the wretchedness of the passenger service was roundly condemned by Whishaw in 1842. The next three lines to enter the city were modelled on the Liverpool & Manchester Railway, and were intended primarily for passengers. Two of them, the Glasgow, Paisley, Kilmarnock & Ayr and the Glasgow, Paisley & Greenock, shared tracks from Paisley to the first Glasgow terminus south of the Clyde, at Bridge Street (1840, G146). The third, the Edinburgh & Glasgow, had a true city centre terminus at Queen Street, approached, like Euston, by a cable-worked incline (1842, G33). All three were promoted in the mid 1830s. As elsewhere, the mid 1840s mania produced many schemes for new lines and termini, and for new uses of existing railways. The most important completed projects were probably the Glasgow, Barrhead & Neilston Direct Railway, with its South Side terminus at Pollokshaws Road (1848); the General Terminus & Glasgow Harbour Railway, with the first modern mineral terminus on the upper Clyde; and the Caledonian Railway, which used the Pollok & Govan and Garnkirk railways to reach temporary termini at South Side and Buchanan Street (1849, G5). Beyond Glasgow, the expansion of the Glasgow, Paisley, Kilmarnock & Ayr as the Glasgow & South Western Railway in 1850, had important consequences for the city.[22]

The only railway of any significance built in the 1850s was the Glasgow, Dumbarton & Helensburgh, a revival of a Caledonian mania scheme, but linked with the Edinburgh & Glasgow. It opened in 1858. The 1860s, however, saw a revival of interest, and in the middle of the decade there were several proposals for new lines and terminals, the most interesting being the City of Glasgow Union Railway, a link between the terminal lines of the Glasgow & South Western and the Edinburgh & Glasgow (later North British). This scheme involved the first railway bridge over the Clyde in Glasgow, and a new central terminus on the site later occupied by St Enoch Station. More important in the long term were the amalgamations of the mid 1860s, which created greatly enlarged Caledonian and North British railways, and made possible the enormous capital investment of the period 1870 to 1906.[23]

The first phase of the expensive overhaul of the city's railways was the revival and revision of terminal schemes of the 1840s and 1860s, the first completed being a North British terminus at High Street for Airdrie and Coatbridge trains. Originally planned during the mania, the scheme lapsed owing to lack of funds, but after the payment of substantial compensation to Glasgow University the old College of Glasgow was demolished and replaced by College Station in 1871 (G57). More radical from a railway point of view were the other two terminals of the 1870s, which both involved Clyde crossings. The City of Glasgow Union opened a temporary station at Dunlop Street in 1870, though the permanent St Enoch Station was not completed until 1879. While this station was being built for use by the Glasgow & South Western, the Caledonian's scheme for an extension across the river from Bridge Street was under way. A high-level bridge was built and a station on Gordon Street – the Central Station – opened in 1879. Both Central and

St Enoch had large railway-owned hotels attached. Not to be outdone, the North British Railway enlarged its Queen Street station between 1878 and 1880.[24]

While terminal building characterised the 1870s, the 1880s and 1890s were years of suburban railway building, as the potential of the railways for cheap local transport was realised. The most spectacular feat of railway construction in the 1880s was the city's first underground line, the Glasgow City & District, a North British subsidiary opened in 1886, which cut through the city centre from Partick to Bellgrove to form, with existing lines, a circular suburban system on the north side of the river. The Caledonian-sponsored Cathcart District Railway, built in two stages, was a loop line through the southern suburbs. Both these lines carried a growing middle-class 'commuter' traffic, but the City & District also linked the expanding industries of the west with areas of working-class housing in the east. The reconstruction of the Glasgow, Paisley & Ardrossan Canal as a railway between 1881 and 1885 gave the Glasgow & South Western one of its few suburban routes.[25]

Developments farther afield also influenced city railways. The opening of the Caledonian's Gourock extension in 1890, which enabled that company to compete effectively for the steamer traffic to the Clyde coast resorts, was accompanied by the construction of a second Bridge Street Station. Rapid expansion of Lanarkshire coal mining and exhaustion of iron ore also led the Caledonian to back the Glasgow Central, Lanarkshire & Dumbartonshire and Lanarkshire & Ayrshire railways to give it links with Glasgow and Ardrossan coal exporting and ore importing facilities. The two former could also compete with the City & District for east–west passenger traffic. Situated nearer the river and at a lower level than the City & District, the construction of the Glasgow Central line involved underpinning many buildings and building a new intercepting sewer (see pp. 137–8). The Lanarkshire & Ayrshire passed through the outer suburbs, and gave impetus to their development as residential areas.[26]

By the end of the 1890s, increased traffic had made Central and St Enoch stations inadequate, and extensions to both, involving the elimination of Bridge Street Station, were the last major railway works to be undertaken in the city. In each case, a new bridge over the Clyde was required; that for St Enoch was a replacement of the City of Glasgow Union structure, while on the approach to Central the original bridge, raised to a higher level, was retained, and a much wider new one added to the west. In both cases the capacity of the station was approximately doubled.[27]

Other railway developments included the construction of central goods depots and other freight-handling facilities. The first central mineral depot was at the Glebe Street terminus of the Garnkirk line, and the first goods depot at Cook Street. These were followed by large goods depots at Buchanan Street (1850, G5), Sighthill, College (1874, G56) and High Street (1904, G54), while Queen Street also had a goods section (G33). Most suburban stations had their own mineral sidings, accommodating domestic coal retailers, a few had goods sheds and there were several goods-only lines, like the railways in the Port Dundas area. The movement of firms to the outskirts of the city was often motivated by a desire for a private siding, and by 1904 there were about 200 of these. Competition from road transport for freight traffic was in its infancy before 1914, but by then electrification of the tramways had made suburban railway construction unattractive. In railway development, more than in any other industrial activity, 1914 marks the end of an era.[28]

The oldest recently surviving railway buildings in Glasgow dated from the early years of the Garnkirk & Glasgow, consisting of the carriage shed at Glebe Street with dwelling house above, remains of staithes for land sale of coal, and a small crossing-keeper's hut built of stone sleepers, sometimes erroneously described as the line's first booking office (C97). Also recently demolished were the defaced remains of the first Bridge Street Station (1841, G146) and the Dundas Street entrance hall of Queen Street Station (1855, G33). The only surviving pre-1850 buildings are the Glasgow, Barrhead & Neilston Direct stations at Kennishead (c 1848, M66) and Pollokshaws West (c 1848, J7).[29]

Of the few stations built in the 1850s, Maryhill Park retained until recently its Glasgow, Dumbarton & Helensburgh building (c 1858, A8). The 1860s are also poorly represented. There are more relics of the 1870s, the first part of St Enoch (G88) and the roof of Queen Street (1880, G33) being the grandest. The different solutions to the problem of providing covered accommodation for trains are interesting. College passenger station (c 1871, G57) is an old-fashioned train shed, with a pitched roof supported on cast-iron columns and arches; St Enoch and Queen Street have arched overall roofs like those at St Pancras, Manchester (Central) and the original Charing Cross (London) stations. The original arch at St Enoch, unlike that at St Pancras, is anchored at each end below platform level, while that at Queen Street is tied above the platform, and is supported on cast-iron columns. Central has trusses in the older part (rebuilt in the 1880s) supporting glazed ridged roofing, which is easier to clean than an overall arch and gives more light (G74). Apart from terminal buildings there are fragmentary remains of two suburban stations of the 1870s, Strathbungo (c 1877, I29) and Cardonald (1879, M75), both with wooden buildings.[30] College Goods (1874, G56) also dates from this period.

The suburban lines of the 1880s and 1890s had new types of building and layout. The City of Glasgow Union and Glasgow City & District used both stone and wood buildings. Charing Cross (H11), Finnieston (H6), Alexandra Parade (D12), Springburn (C7) and Hyndland (L3) were examples of stone construction, with wooden platform shelters, while all-wood stations were to be found at Anniesland (A26), Jordanhill (A33) and Partickhill (L26), though all of these have recently been replaced. On the south side, the Cathcart District Railway introduced the island platform into the city, a layout ideally suited to heavy suburban traffic, as it resulted in major staff economies. Pollokshields East (I15), Queen's Park (I27) and Mount Florida (M50) on the first part of the railway (opened 1886) closely resembled all but two of the later (1894) stations (J3, J19, M63, M56) on the Cathcart–Pollokshields West section. The exceptions were unusual two-level wooden stations at Maxwell Park and Pollokshields West (J1, I28).

The architects of the majority of suburban stations are unknown, and they were probably designed in the respective Engineers' Offices. For the Glasgow Central Railway, however, and for certain of the stations on the Lanarkshire & Dumbartonshire Railway, established Glasgow architects were employed. Kelvinside (A31), Kirklee (B31), Anderston Cross (H44) and Glasgow Cross (G113) were designed by J. J. Burnet, while James Miller was responsible for Botanic Gardens (B42) and Kelvinbridge (B63). Botanic Gardens with its twin onion domes was a well-known landmark until its destruction by fire in 1970. Miller also designed the second Bridge Street Station (1890, G178) in French Renaissance style. The other architect employed on the underground lines was Robert Wemyss; Maryhill Central (B12), and probably also Possil (M15), Dalmarnock (F177), Bridgeton Cross (F106) and Glasgow Green (F110) were his work. Outside the central area some Lanarkshire & Dumbartonshire and Lanarkshire & Ayrshire stations had steel frames clad in wood, as at Whiteinch (L9), Scotstoun East (M91) and Muirend (M62a). In the turn-of-the-century enlargement of St Enoch a second, shorter arched roof was added, tied above train level. At Central, flattened steel arches were used to support ridged glazing. The stonework of the extension here was designed by Miller. In the construction of the new High Street Goods Station of 1904 (G54), the largest in the city, reinforced concrete was extensively used for the first time in a railway building in Glasgow.[31]

Evolutionary changes in railway bridge design were comparable to those discernible in road bridges. Masonry over- and under-bridges were extensively used in the early days, as in the Glasgow & Paisley Joint's now demolished King Street bridge and in viaducts at Pollokshaws (1847, J5) and Maryhill (c 1858, A7). Cast-iron arches do not seem to have been employed, but wrought-iron trusses were used in conjunction with masonry columns in the first Central Station bridge (1879, G142). Trusses on cast-iron columns were used at Dalmarnock (c 1858, F182), and in the first City of Glasgow Union Railway bridge over the Clyde. Wrought-iron was succeeded by steel as a structural material in the 1880s, smaller bridges being of the plate girder type and larger ones of truss, or truss and plate type, as in the new Central Station bridge. Steel arches were used in the second St Enoch bridge (1898, G138) and in the second Dalmarnock bridge (1893–7, F182). A curious hybrid is the junction viaduct at Garrioch Quadrant (B13) where one arm is of masonry and the other of steel.[32]

The first railway tunnels in Glasgow were those on the Cowlairs incline (1842, C72), followed by the Buchanan Street tunnel (1849, C73). No more were required until the City of Glasgow Union's line south of Springburn (c 1875, D10), and the approach to Central Station from Gushetfaulds were constructed. The great period of tunnel-building was in the 1880s and 1890s, when the

City & District, Glasgow Central and Lanarkshire & Dumbarton-shire lines were made. Not only were considerable lengths of these lines in tunnel, but there were also underground, or partly underground stations such as Glasgow Cross, Anderston Cross and Central and Queen Street Low Level, and even an underground junction, at Stobcross (H16).

Miscellaneous railway structures included signal boxes, ranging in size from tiny wooden boxes at Queen's Park and Crosshill to 'armour plated' giants at Central and St Enoch. Most have now been replaced by centralised control systems. Engine sheds were originally closely linked with repair works at Cook Street, Cowlairs (1842, C4) and St Rollox (1856, C75), but pressure on space eventually forced one or other to move. The Glasgow & South Western moved its works to Kilmarnock in 1856–7 and after St Enoch Station was opened a new engine shed was built there (1882, G88). Increasing traffic eventually necessitated construction of a new shed at Corkerhill (1896, M72), a move accompanied by the creation of a model village (M73), only recently demolished. Similarly, a new Caledonian engine shed was built at Eglinton Street when Central Station was opened, together with one at Polmadie (I30). On the north side of the city, the shed at St Rollox was abandoned when a new one was built at Balornock (1916, M30), while the North British shed was moved from Cowlairs to Eastfield in 1904 (M25). While the Glasgow & South Western was moving its works out of Glasgow, the Caledonian moved in from Greenock in 1856–7. The new St Rollox works was completely rebuilt in the 1880s (C75). The Cowlairs works of the Edinburgh & Glasgow was taken over by the North British, who decided to concentrate new construction there. The original works and shed lasted until 1968–9, when they and the many additions were demolished (C4). As at Corkerhill, workers were housed in railway terraces (M26) built about 1863. Other interesting railway buildings included the Glasgow & South Western's Bell Street warehouses (G58, G59) and stables (G116), and large grain stores at Buchanan Street (1870, G5) and Queen Street (1878, G33).[33]

Subway

The Underground remains as a part of Glasgow's way of life. First proposed in 1887, when congestion in the city streets was serious, an Act was obtained in 1890 by the Glasgow District Subway Company for a circular cable-worked line, the first of its kind in the world, with two four-foot gauge lines in separate iron-lined tunnels of circular cross-section. The railway was completed in 1896, and had a route mileage of six and a half, reaching a depth of 155 feet near Hillhead. The power station for the cables was in Scotland Street (H199); it was closed in 1935 when the line was converted to electric traction by Glasgow Corporation, who had taken it over in 1923. The fifteen stations are all underground, though some have natural roof lighting. The island platforms are linked to the surface by stairs, entrances being mainly in commercial or domestic buildings. Two, however, have original detached surface buildings, St Enoch, the headquarters of the company (G87) and West Street (H194). Repairs to rolling stock are carried out in ground-level workshops in Govan (K21), in which a pit gives access to the tracks.[34]

The Port of Glasgow

Throughout the eighteenth century, the port of Glasgow consisted of the Broomielaw Quay, described by McUre as the 'Bremmylaw Harbour and Cran . . . strangely fenced with Beams of Oak, fastened with Iron Batts within the Wall thereof that the great Boards of Ice in time of Thaw may not offend it'. Until 1818 no vessels engaged in foreign trade came up to the quay, their cargoes being discharged into lighters at Greenock or Port Glasgow for conveyance up river. Deepening and straightening of the river, however, started in the eighteenth century, and as it took effect in the early nineteenth century, widening and extension of the quays took place, most notably in the 1840s. While quay construction continued for several more decades, the provision of docks was the only way to ensure a sufficient number of berths near the city centre. As early as 1806 Thomas Telford had proposed the construction of wet docks, and a plan exists showing a large dock to be built in Anderston, with a curious curved entrance lock. A dock at Windmillcroft was authorised in 1840, but work did not start until the 1860s, and when it was completed in 1867, it was already inadequate. Known as Kingston Dock (1867, H126) it was a single, lockless basin with the entrance spanned by a steam-operated swing bridge. Queen's Dock followed (1872–80, H120) at Stobcross, with three basins and a hydraulic swing bridge. As at Kingston Dock, and at the quays, single storey brick transit sheds were provided. Dock development then ceased for fifteen years, though new quays were built, as at Stobcross, on the river side of Queen's Dock, completed in 1882. When dock-building resumed with the construction of Cessnock Dock (now Prince's Dock) between 1893 and 1897 (K25) the influence of the increased size of ships was apparent in the much wider, unbridged entrance, and in the two-storey transit sheds of heavy brick and steel construction. Later docks at Yorkhill (c 1908, K6) and Shieldhall (King George V Dock; 1931, M101) had completely unobstructed entrances.[35]

Responsibility for both river improvement and the provision of quays and docks was vested, from 1809, in the Clyde Navigation Trust, and during the nineteenth century its scope was widened to take in provision for special cargoes. Cranes of increasing capacity were provided for the export and installation of heavy machinery, coal hoists were built at General Terminus Quay and Prince's Dock, and coaling cranes at Queen's Dock. Live cattle were landed at Plantation, and from 1907 at Merklands where a large rail-linked lairage was built. Grain imports were eventually concentrated at Meadowside Quay, where the enormous granary (1911, L19) has been extended several times. Notably absent from the port of Glasgow are the multi-storey warehouses which are a feature of the ports of Liverpool, London and Hull. Transit sheds were used instead, with longer term storage in warehouses in streets near the quays and docks (see chapters 1 and 5).[36]

Ship-repairing facilities, necessary in any major port, were initially privately provided at the Kelvinhaugh and Stobcross slip docks, Tod & MacGregor's graving dock in Partick (1857, L28) and the Pointhouse patent slip of A. & J. Inglis (1865, L36). The

Clyde Navigation Trust entered this field partly in consequence of the growing size of ships. The first Trust dry dock was opened at Govan in 1875, and two others, each larger than its predecessor, followed in 1886 and 1898 (K14). Not until 1904 was another private dry dock built, at Elderslie, by Shearer & Co. (M99).[37]

Of early cranes in the port, little is known. McUre's 'Cran' or its successor was still the only one in 1778, but by 1848 there were several with capacities of seven and a half to ten tons, one of forty tons at Windmillcroft, and an almost completed thirty tonner at Finnieston, all hand operated. The heavy cranes, used mainly for installing engines and boilers in ships, required a large number of men to operate them – a forty-ton crane at Greenock needed thirty-six. That at Windmillcroft was converted to steam power in 1867, moved to the Graving Docks Quay in 1890 and not demolished until 1931. Large fixed steam cranes were used at Finnieston and Prince's Dock until quite recently, the last (1894, K24) was scrapped in 1970, together with a heavy mobile steam crane at Govan Graving Dock. Hydraulic machinery was introduced at Queen's Dock in 1877–8, with an Italianate pumping station (K12) powering a swing bridge, two large coaling cranes and at least one smaller mobile crane. At Prince's Dock there was a much larger hydraulic system, with large mobile hydraulic cranes built by Fullerton, Hodgart & Barclay of Paisley, which lasted until the 1950s. A hydraulic coal hoist was also installed, with its own accumulator tower. The main accumulator tower is Italian Gothic in style, and the nearby 'tower of the winds' was the base of a large chimney. All the cranes in the port are now electric, the largest being at Finnieston with a capacity of 175 tons, built in 1931 for installing and loading machinery.[38]

Quay wall construction also changed with time. McUre's 'Beams of Oak' gave way from 1828–9 to massive masonry blocks supported on wooden piles, the main load bearing piles being protected in front by wooden sheet piling. In the construction of Queen's Dock, concrete rafts were first used as a substitute for wood piling, and in the post-1914 reconstruction of Kingston Dock concrete was used for the quay walls.[39]

[1]The sections in this chapter on bridges and roads draw heavily on Marwick, J. D., *Glasgow: The Water Supply of the City* (Glasgow 1901), and specific reference to that work in these connections will not be made; the fifteenth century bridge is depicted before and during demolition in Simpson, plates 17, 18; GCA, T/CN uncatalogued, plan and elevation of Milne's bridge, which is illustrated in Oakley, *The Second City*, 31; the first Rutherglen Bridge is shown in Cowan, 48; Simmons, J., *Transport* (London 1962), plate 98 (from J. Weale, *Bridges*, 1839) shows Hutchesontown Bridge under construction

[2]Telford's bridge is illustrated in Oakley, 126, and Gibb, Sir Alexander, *The Story of Telford* (London 1935), 260, 261, described it as 'in many ways the most beautiful of all that were built by Telford'; the South Portland Street suspension bridge is shown in Young & Doak, plate 46; the temporary bridge provided during reconstruction of the Telford bridge is shown in one of Thomas Annan's photographs, and was a plate girder structure

[3]The Kelvin bridges at Hillhead are all illustrated in Cowan, 148–53

[4]Lindsay, Charles C., 'On the Design & Construction of Partick Bridge', *Transactions of the Institution of Engineers and Shipbuilders in Scotland*, 21 (1877–8), 85–104; the reinforced concrete bridges are described, and some illustrated, in *British Bridges* (London 1933), 464, 466, 468, 469

[5]Duckworth, C. L. D., and Langmuir, G. E., *Clyde River and Other Steamers* (Glasgow 3rd edn 1972), 138–47

[6]Marwick, *Water Supply*, 208–9, 226

[7]Gibson, 119; Cleland, *Rise and Progress* (Glasgow 1820), 184, 131

[8]Ibid, 108–9

[9]Map in *Acts of Parliament &c Relating to the Glasgow Corporation Tramways* (Glasgow 1877), shows lines and depots then in operation; Cormack, I. L., *1894 and All That* (Glasgow 1968); Lamb, J. M., *Glasgow: the Pioneer of Municipal Tramway Enterprise* (unpublished dissertation for the degree of BA, Strathclyde University 1972); Marwick, *Water Supply*, Appendix Ga, 79; the last horse-cars had disappeared by April 1902, *Municipal Glasgow, its Evolution and Enterprises*, 73

[10]Cormack, I. L., *Glasgow Trams beyond the Boundary* (Glasgow 1967); Coonie, Ian M., *Tramways of Paisley and District* (Glasgow 1954); the Vale of Clyde's steam service, inaugurated in 1877, was the first urban steam tram service in Britain, see Charles E. Lee's introduction to Whitcombe, H. A., *History of the Steam Tram* (Lingfield, Surrey 1961), 4

[11]*Glasgow Municipal Transport* (Glasgow 1934), passim; Oakley, C. A., *The Last Tram* (Glasgow 1962), passim; for a detailed description of Pinkston, see *Electrical Handbook Part I, Glasgow and Edinburgh and Districts* (London 1906), 17–32; the Transport Museum houses six Glasgow trams, including a horse tram, as well as a fine collection of locomotives, horse-drawn vehicles and cars

[12]*Industries of Glasgow*, 81, shows the original form of Wylie & Lochhead's stables

[13]This account of canal development owes much to Pratt, E. A., *Scottish Canals and Waterways* (London 1922) and Lindsay, Jean, *The Canals of Scotland* (Newton Abbot 1968), and detailed references to these works will not be made; on importance of the Hamiltonhill basin see Senex, *Old Glasgow and Its Environs*, 143–4

[14]Date for canal offices from Graham Mathieson, illustrated in Butt, 206

[15]Thomson, George, 'James Watt and the Monkland Canal', *The Scottish Historical Review*, 29 (1950), 121–33; British Waterways Board Plans, at Applecross Street, Glasgow, show inclined planes both proposed and built

[16]*The Glasgow & South Western Railway 1850–1923* (London 1950), 16

[17]GCA, TD146, Scroll Ground Plan of

St Rollox Chemical Works, by Andrew Thomson, 1834; SRO RHP125, Branch Canal at St Rollox, February 1836 by Andrew Thomson, the first edition of the six-inch Ordnance Survey (1858) shows an additional branch to a works on the north side of Charles Street

[18]The bascule bridges at Temple and Cloberhill are described in *British Bridges*, 466–7

[19] *The Book of Airdrie* (Glasgow 1954), 276, states that the Drumpeller Railway was opened in 1847, acquired by the Forth & Clyde Navigation in 1851, and the northern part closed in 1883

[20]Senex, *Old Glasgow*, 46, mentions wooden wagonways; Lewis, M. J. T., *Early Wooden Railways* (London 1970), 133; Monkland Act 10 George III, cap 105, the reference to a 'waggonroad' in the OSA, quoted by Lewis (287) is almost certainly to a road rather than to a railway; Map of the City of Glasgow, by George Martin (1842) and City of Glasgow and Suburbs corrected up to 1833, published by James Lumsden & Son, H. Wilson, Engraver (Glasgow June 1833)

[21]Thomas, John, *Regional History of the Railways of Great Britain: Scotland, the Lowlands and the Borders* (Newton Abbot 1971), see also especially Kellett, John, *Railways and the Victorian City* (London 1969) and Thomas, *The Springburn Story*; for additional works see bibliography

[22]Wishaw, Francis, *The Railways of Great Britain and Ireland* (London 1840), 111, 'these carriages are by far the most unsightly and uncomfortable we have met with on any passenger-railway in the United Kingdom'; the Pollok & Govan was an upgrading and extension of William Dixon II's colliery waggonways, authorised in 1830, but not completed till 1840

[23]Robin, G. H., 'The City of Glasgow Union Railway', *The Railway Magazine* (1960), 20–6; the proposed new station is described and illustrated in *Engineering*, 3 (1867), 50–1

[24]The 1846 scheme is described in Kellett, J. R., 'Glasgow's Railways, 1830–80: a Study in Natural Growth', *The Economic History Review*, 2nd Series 17 (1964), 360–2; Hogg, Charles P., 'On St Enoch Railway Station', *Trans Inst Engs & Shipbuilders in Scotland*, 25 (1881–2), 193–202 and 26 (1882–3), 33–4 (discussion); the Central Hotel is described and illustrated in *The Illustrated London News* (14 July 1883), 48, and a recent view is included in Young & Doak, plate 113, *The Builder* (9 July 1898), 23 commented that its architecture was 'thoroughly well adapted to the purpose of the building', but said of St Enoch that 'its pointed segmental arches and heavy mock machicolations now seem the acme of ugliness'

[25]Simpson, Robert, 'On the Construction of the Glasgow City & District Railway', *Trans Inst Engs & Shipbuilders in Scotland*, 31 (1887–8), 97–121; Robin, G. H., 'The South Side Suburban Railways of Glasgow', *The Railway Magazine* (1954), 9–15, 17

[26]Robin, G. H., 'The Lanarkshire & Dumbartonshire Railway', *The Railway Magazine* (1959), 19–26; Robin, G. H., 'The Lanarkshire & Ayrshire Railway', ibid (1961), 89–96; Barker, C. D., 'Methods adopted in Constructing the Glasgow Central Railway (Bridgeton and Trongate Contracts)', *Minutes of Proceedings of Institution of Civil Engineers*, 114 (1893), 340

[27]Nock, O. S., *The Caledonian Railway* (London 1961), plates between pages 120 and 121 shows extension works at Central; *Bridges, Structural Steel Work and Engineering Productions*, 4–5 (Old Central Bridge), 115–18 (New Central Bridge, illustrated); Melville, W., 'City Union Railway Widening and Extension of St Enoch Station', *Trans Inst Engs & Shipbuilders in Scotland*, 44 (1900–1), 222–62; the original St Enoch bridge, was a wrought-iron truss bridge, see *Glasgow Contemporaries at the Dawn of the 20th Century* (Glasgow 1904), 23

[28]*Railway Clearing House Official Handbook of Railway Stations &c* (London 1904), 219–27, lists private sidings

[29]A drawing of the carriage shed at Glebe Street, wrongly identified by J. R. Hume as the engine shed, is in Butt, 178;

the first Bridge Street Station is described and illustrated in Warden, J., *The Glasgow and Ayr and Glasgow and Greenock Railway Companion* (Glasgow 2nd edn 1842), frontispiece and 23, the illustration being reproduced in Highet, Campbell, *The Glasgow & South Western Railway* (Lingfield, Surrey 1965), facing 46; a plan of Queen Street Station in 1860 (showing the Dundas Street Hall) is in Thomas, John, *The North British Railway* (Newton Abbot 1969), vol 1, 117

[30]Meeks, Carroll, L. V., *The Railway Station* (London 1957) discusses overall-roofed stations, and reproduces a cross-section of the Queen Street roof (illustration 94)

[31]Botanic Gardens station was described in *The Builder* (9 July 1898) as 'a strange sight in Glasgow ... very well grouped and detailed, and looks too good architecturally for what it is', it is illustrated in Thomas, *Regional History*, 238

[32]The King Street bridge is depicted in Oakley, *The Second City*, 60

[33]Corkerhill village is illustrated in Butt, *et al.*, 99, and Beharrel, L. V., 'Disappearance of a Model Railway Village', *Glasgow Herald* (27 February 1971); information about Balornock kindly supplied by J. F. McEwan; the railway terraces at Cowlairs are described and illustrated in Thomas, *The Springburn Story*, 99–100, and Butt, 154

[34]*Glasgow Municipal Transport*, 81–6; Thomson, David L., and Sinclair, David E., *The Glasgow Subway* (Glasgow 1964), passim; St Enoch subway station is illustrated in Young & Doak, plate 167, and was described by *The Builder* (9 July 1898) as 'only a doll's house beside its big neighbour [the railway station] but it is simply charming'

[35]McUre, 285–6; Marwick, J. D., *The River Clyde* (Glasgow 1909) and *Water Supply* have been used extensively in the preparation of this section, and specific reference to these works will not be made; GCA, T/CN uncatalogued, A Rough Sketch of the river Clyde from Partick Ferry-boat to the Broomielaw Bride (sic) – with several intended improvements for the benefit of Commerce by Alexr Farmer, nd, probably *c*1815; Senex, *Old Glasgow*

[36]Baxter, George H., 'The Design and Equipment of the Clyde Trustees' New Granary at Meadowside', *Trans Inst Engs & Shipbuilders in Scotland*, 58 (1914–15), 302–39

[37]The Kelvinhaugh and Stobcross slip docks are illustrated in Simpson, plates 34 and 39; Pointhouse patent slip is described in *Engineering*, 4 (2 August 1867), 93; Baxter, George H., 'The Machinery of the Clyde Trustees' No 3 Graving Dock', *Trans Inst Engs & Shipbuilders in Scotland*, 42 (1898–9), 267–321

[38]McArthur's map (1778) reproduced in Gunn & Newbigin, facing 40; GCA, T/CN uncatalogued, Clyde Navigation Trust Plans 342/C, C616, and printed plan by David Bremner, 21 March 1848; information from Fullarton, Hodgart & Barclay, see also French, William, *The Port of Glasgow* (Glasgow 1947), 39; the complete pumping station chimney is shown in a photograph in the Clyde Navigation Trust Collection, Glasgow City Archives; for a description and illustration of the Finnieston electric crane see Cowan, 209–11

[39]Alston, W. M., 'The Old Quay Walls of Glasgow Harbour', *Trans Inst Engs & Shipbuilders in Scotland*, 46 (1902–3), 305–27; Donald, P. D., 'Kingston Dock: Its Improvement and Reconstruction', ibid, 60 (1915–17), 157–94

7 *Public Utilities*

The provision of piped water, of gas, and later of electricity, telegraphs and telephones, was in Britain normally initiated by private enterprise, and the Glasgow experience in these fields was entirely typical. Equally normal was the subsequent takeover of these community services by public authorities. In Glasgow, only the short-lived Corporation telephone system could be considered unusual, but though the organisation of other public utilities was orthodox, the quality and size of the equipment provided was invariably above average and in some instances exceptional.[1]

Water Supply

The first service to be taken over by the civic authorities was water supply. As in most cities, before 1800 water was drawn from public and private wells and from streams. In the eighteenth century both pump and draw wells were in use, and until it became excessively polluted, water was drawn from the Molendinar for both domestic and industrial purposes. Though London had had a piped water supply in the seventeenth century, it was not until 1807 that Glasgow followed suit. In that year the 'Company of Proprietors of the Glasgow Water-works' opened its pumping station at Dalmarnock, which raised Clyde water to a reservoir at Sydney Street, whence it was distributed by main pipes (Fig 18). The Cranstonhill Waterworks, a second company promoted in 1807 to supply the high ground to the west of the city, constructed under an act of 1808 a pumping station at Anderston Quay and reservoirs at Cranstonhill (Fig 19). Apart from the obvious industrial and domestic use of water an important consideration was the need for high pressure water in adequate quantities for firefighting.[2]

Neither of these companies gave an entirely satisfactory service,

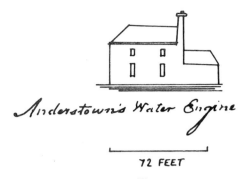

Anderstown's Water Engine

|— 72 FEET —|

Fig 18
Sketch elevation of the Cranstonhill Water Company's first pumping station at
Anderston

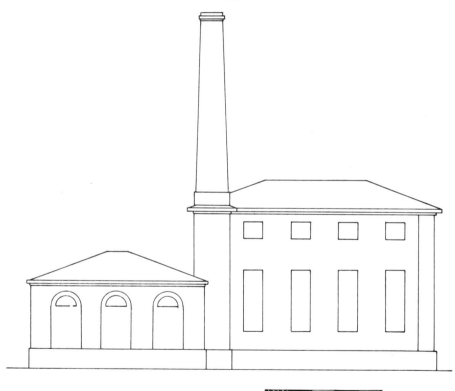

Fig 19
Elevation of engine house (right) and boiler house (left) for the Glasgow Water
Company, from a drawing dated 29 October 1818

and public wells continued in use. Cranstonhill Company was forced to build a new pumping station at Dalmarnock in 1819, owing to pollution of the Clyde at Anderston. Perhaps the inadequacy of supplies led to dwindling demand or there was competition from water carts but whatever the reason, neither company was profitable by the early 1830s, and in 1833 an attempt was made to amalgamate. This met with considerable opposition from private citizens and public bodies, and after further abortive attempts in 1835 and 1836 the Glasgow Company took over the Cranstonhill Company in 1838. During the anti-company agitation a proposal for a gravitation water scheme was put forward, and this was revived in the mid-forties by the Glasgow Company, but the project foundered owing to technical difficulties. However, in 1846 the Gorbals Gravitation Water Company was formed to supply suburbs on the south bank, and when it commenced services in 1848 it was an immediate success. Its works, now enlarged, still function.[3]

Municipal control of water supply came a step nearer with the formation in 1850 of a committee of the town council to consider the improvement of the supply. At first the committee proposed a simple takeover of the Glasgow Company, but in 1852 Professor J. Macquorn Rankine and Mr John Thomson suggested that supplies should be drawn from Loch Katrine. Despite opposition from the private companies and individuals, favourable reports from such eminent engineers as J. F. Bateman, Robert Stephenson and Isambard Kingdom Brunel confirmed the council in its view of the desirability of this scheme. In July 1855 an act was obtained authorising the acquisition of the private companies and the construction of a twenty-six mile aqueduct to link Loch Katrine with a reservoir at Mugdock, together with a further seven miles of aqueduct to the city. Work started in 1856 and the aqueduct was completed to Mugdock in 1859 and to Glasgow in 1860, at a total cost, including compensation, of £1,588,822 0s. 11d.

The demand for water increased with the growth of the city, and the aqueducts had to be enlarged in the 1860s. A second reservoir at Mugdock was authorised in 1882, and completed in 1896. A more radical improvement was the doubling of the aqueduct from Loch Katrine, authorised in 1885. This was accompanied by raising the level of the loch by five feet, and that of Loch Arklet by twenty-five feet. The outlet of the latter was changed to flow into Loch Katrine instead of Loch Lomond. These works were finished in 1900, and have remained more or less unchanged.

As well as supplying water by gravitation from Loch Katrine and from the Gorbals Water Works, the Corporation supplied water under pressure for hydraulic machinery. Before a system of hydraulic mains was laid down, firms used gravitation water, often with intensifiers, to power such devices as cranes, hoists, presses and gates, or had their own pumping stations. The Corporation pumping station in High Street, constructed under an Act of 1892, was opened in 1895 (G51). By 1900 seventeen miles of high pressure main had been laid, customers including the railway companies, warehousemen and engineering firms. The service ceased in 1964, but some of the machinery was sold to Manchester, where it was in use until 1972.

Cleansing

Since one of the motives of the Corporation in assuming control of water supply was the improvement of public health, it is not surprising that the next public service to be taken over was cleansing. The disposal of solid and liquid refuse was, of course, a pressing problem in nineteenth-century cities. Main drainage of streets through covered sewers did not begin in Glasgow until 1790, though the need to keep the streets clean was recognised in a seventeenth-century Council statute which required that no 'myddynnis' should be laid down on the front street. This injunction was not normally obeyed, but for special occasions, such as a royal visit, supervised cleaning was undertaken. In 1696 the Town Council passed an act prohibiting the custom of throwing excrement, dirt and urine from windows and of leaving such material in staircases, passages, streets or lanes. This custom persisted in Edinburgh, where the striking of ten o'clock from St Giles steeple signalled the discharge of night soil, with the cry 'gardyloo' to warn passers by.

Direct action by the council to clean streets seems to have begun in 1767 when a committee was appointed, with an annual budget of £30. By 1776 three men were employed in street cleaning; they were paid one pound a week in winter and ten shillings in summer. The introduction of covered sewers and of properly paved streets certainly improved standards, and by 1854–5 the annual expenditure on cleansing was over £8000. The supervision of cleansing was then the responsibility of the Police Board, but until 1866 its activities were confined to sweeping public streets. The sweepings, and domestic refuse were removed by a contractor, while courts and private streets had to be cleaned by the proprietors. The prevalence of diseases such as typhus, however, forced the council to remedy this situation, and from 1866 cleansing of private streets and courts was taken over by the Police Board. In 1868 a separate cleansing department was set up under a superintendent.

A complicating factor in both street cleaning and refuse removal for much of the nineteenth century was the commercial value of horse manure from stables and streets and human manure from houses. This made it difficult to enforce high standards of hygiene. Even after the introduction of piped water, and of water closets, many working class tenements relied on earth closets and chamber pots for sanitation, the contents of these receptacles being emptied into ashpits, ash from coal fires acting as a sterilising and deodorising agent. Ashpits were emptied on an irregular basis until the very late nineteenth century, when regular emptying was introduced. The contents were sold as 'urban manure'. Partly as a result of the reduction in the proportion of excrement consequent on the widespread use of water closets, sorting of refuse was introduced. The first sorting, or despatch, works was opened at St Rollox (1880, C77) and this was followed by Crawford Street (now Kilbirnie Street) in 1884 (H222), Kelvinhaugh (1891, K8) and Haghill (1897, E2). The procedure in these works was to riddle the refuse, the finer material being mixed with street sweepings (largely horse manure), excrementitious matter and fish refuse and loaded into railway wagons for transport to storage depots or direct to farmers. The remainder of the refuse was cremated and dumped, until 1896, when the crushing of clinker into aggregate for concrete was begun. The despatch depots had high-level access for carts, with railway sidings below, and were dominated by tall iron-bound brick chimneys. Some are still in use. In addition, the cleansing department had separate stables for the collecting carts, at Parliamentary Road (1873, G11) and Sawmillfield (1899, C35); a granary and stores in Bell Street (1896, G114); and repair workshops in Charles Street, St Rollox (C77).

Sewage Disposal

Between 1790 and 1818 over five miles of sewers were constructed. The agitation for sanitary reform in the 1840s led to increasing use of water closets, and the sewers came to be used as the outlet for these, as well as for surface water. As the sewers, which by 1849 totalled forty miles in length, discharged into existing rivers or streams, and ultimately into the Clyde, the city's rivers gained a reputation for foulness perhaps second only to that of the Thames. From the late 1850s proposals were made to replace this system of drainage by more hygienic methods. As with refuse collection, these were complicated by the potential value of excrement and urine as manure. The simplest way to make use of these substances was that advocated by Edwin Chadwick, irrigation of sandy soil on which crops would be grown. The Glasgow version of this was put forward by Bateman and Bazalgette in 1866. It involved the construction of intercepting sewers, leading to a pumping station in Pollokshields from which a twenty-eight mile conduit would lead the sewage to the Ayrshire coast near Stevenston, where the sandy soil was suitable for sewage farming. Other proposals included pneumatic or vacuum conveyance of excreta to manure factories.[4]

Fortunately sanity eventually prevailed, and the desirability of getting rid of sewage in the cheapest and most effective way became commonly accepted. Lengthy outfall sewers, proposed by Sir John Hawkshaw's Royal Commission in 1876 were expensive, though they had been successfully applied in London. Eventually, after years of talk, with the civic authorities too confused or too parsimonious to take vigorous action, the promotion of the Glasgow Central Railway in the 1880s led to the adoption of the latter solution. Construction of this line involved breaching some existing sewers and as part of the price of an agreement with the Corporation, the Caledonian Railway, sponsor of the scheme, agreed to finance rearrangement of these. Some were diverted to Dalmarnock, where the city's first sewage purification works was built. New sewers were designed by the city engineer, with Bazalgette as consultant, while the works was laid out by G. V. Alsing. Even when completed in 1894 the system of purification, batch precipitation, was conservative. The results must have been fairly good, for the same system was used at Dalmuir, opened in 1904 to serve the rest of the city north of the Clyde. The main sewer serving this works could not be arranged with an adequate fall, and so a steam pumping station was built at Partick (1904, L43). A third works at Shieldhall (M89) was completed in 1910, with an associated pumping station at Kinning Park (1909, H176). The precipitation method used at Dalmuir and Shieldhall produces quantities of sludge which is carried by two handsome vessels to a deep-water dumping area in the Clyde estuary. The Dalmarnock works has been modernised, but the other two are substantially as built. The two pumping stations are now electrically operated.[5]

Gas Supply

Municipal involvement in public utilities has been termed 'gas and water socialism', and Glasgow was as progressive in its attitude to gas as it was to water supply. As in other cities, the earliest experiments with the use of coal gas involved the lighting of private premises. In 1805 the shops of a bookseller and of a baker, a spinning mill, and the lecture theatre in the Andersonian Institution were lit by gas, and in 1807 a Pollokshaws weaving factory was lit by gas generated in an old steam engine cylinder. The Glasgow Gas Light Company, one of the first public gas companies in Britain, obtained an Act in 1817, and by the end of that year had twenty-five cast-iron retorts in operation at Townhead, in the angle between Castle Street and Parliamentary Road. District gas holders were built in Old Wynd, Broomward Street (Calton) and Hutchesontown, and demand grew so rapidly that by 1826 the authorised capital had risen from £40,000 to £150,000. The engineer of the company was James Beaumont Neilson, inventor of the hot blast process for iron smelting. Neilson's invention of the bats-wing gas burner, with its superior illuminating power, helped to increase demand. A second works was added at Tradeston (1835, H224) to supply the southern suburbs, and a third at Partick, for the West End. As with water supply, a rival concern, the City and Suburban Gas Company of Glasgow, incorporated in 1843 with a capital of £150,000, entered the field, with works at Dalmarnock (F171).[6]

The enthusiasm for municipal control which produced the Loch Katrine scheme is reflected in resistance to attempts at financial expansion by the private companies, and by moves towards municipalisation in the 1850s and 1860s. By 1869, when legislative powers were obtained, re-equipment was urgently necessary, and a new works at Maryhill was built to replace the Townhead Works. When under construction in 1872 Dawsholm (A16) was reckoned the second largest gas works in Britain with a designed output of nine million cubic feet of gas per day. Dalmarnock was at the same time rebuilt with larger clay retorts, so that by 1874 it had an output of five million cubic feet per day. Two recently existing gasholders, one of which is still in use, date from this reconstruction. Tradeston was also re-equipped, and these three works, with intermittent improvement, sufficed until the 1890s. Though the Corporation Gas Department had a monopoly of gas supply within the Glasgow boundary, there was competition in the communities to the north and west of the city from the Partick, Hillhead and Maryhill Gas Company, formed in 1871. Their works was built next to Dawsholm, at Temple (A18). Glasgow Corporation absorbed the Partick company in 1891, and the much smaller Pollokshaws works in 1892. To cope with steadily increasing demand from a growing area, a large new works was built at Provan (M32) between 1898 and 1904. This enabled Dalmarnock to be closed, though it was re-equipped and reopened in 1911 before final closure in 1956. Changes in the technique of gas production were naturally reflected in gasworks design. The early works had horizontal cast-iron retorts, the later ones fireclay retorts, which were replaced by vertical retorts at Provan and Dawsholm before 1914. More recently coal carbonisation has been completely displaced by the cracking of oil refinery waste, and the advent of North Sea gas will render even the latter process obsolete. The design of gasholders in the city also evolved from relatively small single-lift holders, through large holders with cast-iron guides to very large holders with steel girder guides. Neither waterless nor guideless holders have been used in Glasgow. The capacity has risen from the 25,000 cubic feet of the Glasgow Gas Light Company's 1819 holder to the 8,500,000 cubic feet of each of the Provan holders. Apart from the major works mentioned, there were central workshops in Walls Street (1881, G112) and in Milan Street (now closed), while there were chemical works at Dawsholm, Tradeston and Provan, originally leased to manufacturers, but operated from 1920 by the Corporation. The richly ornamented offices of the Glasgow Gas Light Company at 42 Virginia Street still stand.[7]

Electricity Supply

As with gas, the first electric lighting installations were privately owned. The earliest in Glasgow seems to have been at St Enoch Station in 1879, where six steam-driven Gramme dynamos, installed by Colonel R. E. Crompton, supplied current to six arc lamps. The first public supply was from a power station in the basement of 70 Miller Street, which was installed in 1885 by Muir and Mavor. This was such a success that a larger installation was made at 81 John Street in 1889 by the same firm. It consisted of a Ferranti alternator driven by a 400–500 horsepower tandem compound non-condensing engine, generating at 2400 volts AC. The Muir and Mavor venture was, however, short-lived, as in 1890 the Corporation obtained an Act to allow it to supply electricity throughout the city. Under the same Act the Kelvinside Electric Company received permission to supply the fashionable west end. No action was taken under this Act until 1892, when the Kelvinside Company started building a generating station (L2). The Corporation bought the Muir and Mavor stations for £15,000 and purchased land for a new generating station in Waterloo Street (H45). Shortly after this was completed in 1893, the original stations were closed. The demand for electricity grew so rapidly that within three years all available space at Waterloo Street had been used. Two battery substations, for peak loads, were a temporary palliative, but new plant was obviously essential.[8]

The new works, at Port Dundas and Eglinton Toll, were on a much larger scale. The former had a designed capacity of 30,000, the latter of 10,000 horsepower. The Port Dundas plant (C42) took coal and cooling water from the Forth & Clyde Canal, while the Pollokshaws Road station (G196) was rail-served, with wooden cooling towers on the roof. So rapid was the development of electric power engineering at that time that the reciprocating engined generating sets installed at first were superseded by turbo-generators before the stations were completed. The compactness of the latter meant that the designed output could be increased to 45,000 horsepower at Port Dundas and to 20,000 at Pollokshaws. The Kelvinside station was bought by the Corporation in 1899.[9]

The burghs of Partick and Govan received authorisation to supply electricity in 1893, but the Govan station (K50) was not opened until 1900. The first plant developed ninety kilowatts (120 horsepower), but by 1911 this had risen to 3150 (4200 horsepower). As in Glasgow, local distribution was at 500 and 250 volts DC. The Partick generating station (L21) followed in 1905, and was operated in conjunction with a refuse destructor – a popular combination at that time. These stations both came into the Corporation net in 1912, when the burghs were merged with Glasgow. Even with the addition of the burgh stations the Corporation Electricity Department was becoming hard pressed, and in 1913 ground was bought for a 100,000 kilowatt station at Dalmarnock. Construction was halted by the 1914–18 war, and the first part of this station (F184) was not opened until 1920. The increase in demand in the years immediately before the war came largely from factories where the electric motor was proving more convenient than steam engines or manual power. Mavor and Coulson, successors to Muir and Mavor, played a leading part in publicising the virtues of electric motors. By 1912–13 nearly two-thirds of the electricity generated by the Corporation was used for power. Another company operating within the present city boundary was the Clyde Valley Electrical Power Company, authorised in 1901, with works at Yoker (first part completed 1905) and Motherwell. The former is just inside the revised city boundary of 1912, though most of the present station is post-1914 in construction.[10]

The low pressure DC supply to houses was initially distributed direct from the generating stations, but after 1902 almost all new plant was designed to generate at 6600 volts DC. To lower the voltage, rotary converters were installed in substations. These formed a convenient location for transformers when alternating current supply was introduced, and hence most have survived. Their general appearance is similar to that of small power stations, with the exception of the Pollokshaws one in Haggs Road (1908, J4) which was designed to harmonise with houses nearby, and resembles a church. The Hillhead substation in Vinicombe Street (1912, B43) is sandstone faced, but the others, in Flemington Street (1906, C10), Alexandra Parade (c 1923, D5), Cathedral Street (1905, G46) and Osborne Street (1912, G101) are all of red brick.

The design of power stations was simple, consisting of large engine rooms, very tall in most cases, with lower boiler houses, initially housing banks of boilers. The Port Dundas station is a handsome building with a fine central tower. Construction was in all Glasgow cases of brick, with internal steel framing.

Telephones

The first telephone service in the city appears to have been provided by the National Telephone Company, while the Bell and Graham companies also operated in the 1880s. Certainly by 1893 the high cost and inefficiency of the National Company's service had encouraged the Corporation to seek authority to operate a telephone service. It was, however, only after a Government commissioner had conducted an inquiry, and the necessary general legislation had been passed that in 1900 the Corporation obtained a licence. Under this a central 'switch room' was constructed in existing premises in Renfield Street, linked with seven branch exchanges. As a consequence of improvement in national services, and of pressure from opponents of municipal trading, the system was sold to the Post Office in 1907. By that time there were more than 40,000 subscribers. As far as the writer is aware, no traces of this short-lived system survive, but the Post Office telephone service produced two interesting exchange buildings before 1914, in Highburgh Road (1907, L5) and Cubie Street (1910, F44).[11]

Other Services

Other amenities provided by the Corporation before 1914 included baths and washhouses, a fire brigade, street lighting (both gas and electric), public health services (including hospitals), model lodging houses, houses for the lower-paid, halls, libraries, parks, art galleries and museums. While lack of space prohibits discussion of most of these services, a mention should be made of the museums, which have for many years had links with industry. In 1870 a small City Industrial Museum was set up in Kelvingrove House, but industry soon took second, if not third place, and technology was not well represented in the museum and art gallery which replaced the house in 1892–1901. There are now in this museum, however, a notable collection of ship models, and an engineering gallery in which the most important exhibits are full-sized and model marine engines. In store are a number of significant relics including the parts of a side-lever marine engine (from PS *Industry*), a double-beam mill engine (from John Lean's Bridgeton weaving factory), a rotative Newcomen engine (from Farme Colliery), and the second British-built Diesel engine. The establishment of a transport museum in the former Coplawhill tramway workshops in Albert Drive (I16) followed closure of the tram system in 1962, and the opportunity was taken to include Scottish motor and horse-drawn vehicles, as well as trams, in the first stage. A second stage features seven full-sized locomotives. The Transport Museum has been a great success, and it is to be hoped that more adequate displays of other technological material will soon be provided.[12]

[1] Throughout this chapter, extensive use has been made of Marwick, *Water Supply*, and *Municipal Glasgow, its Evolution and Enterprises* and no specific references will be made to these works

[2] In 1804 William Harley piped water from Springs in Willowbank to West Nile Street, whence water was distributed by carriers: Burnet, John, *History of the Water Supply to Glasgow* (Glasgow 1869),

3; the engines for the Glasgow Water-works were obtained from Boulton & Watt, two in 1806, one each in 1815, 1817 and 1821 and two more in 1828. The 1817 engine was used to pump water from the reservoir at Sydney Street to basins at Rotten Row. BRL, B & W MSS, Engine book 281, Portfolios 1094–7

[3] In 1838 filtration of the supply was introduced. Before then water was drawn from wells close to the river at Dalmarnock, the gravel and sand of the river banks forming a natural filter. Some of these wells were on the bank opposite the pumping engines, the link being formed by a flexibly-jointed cast-iron pipe, designed by James Watt and built in 1811: BRL, B & W MSS, Portfolio 1095

[4] Fraser, J. McL., 'Glasgow and the River Clyde in the Context of River Pollution', *Journal and Proceedings of the Institute of Sewage Purification* (1963), part 5, 402–18, I am indebted to Mr Fraser for a copy of this article

[5] Ibid

[6] *The Gas Supply of Glasgow* (Glasgow 1935) was referred to extensively in the writing of this section

[7] For Dawsholm Gas Works see *The Engineer*, 33 (1872), 126, 161, 196; it is notable that both Dawsholm and Provan were planned to take advantage of existing canal and rail links

[8] Bowers, Brian, *R. E. B. Crompton, Pioneer Electrical Engineer* (London 1967), 21; 'C.J.G.', 'The Story of Mavor & Coulson', *M & C Apprentices' Magazine* (1960); Arnot, William, 'The Glasgow Corporation Electric Light Supply'; *Trans Inst Engs & Shipbuilders in Scotland*, 37 (1893–4) 145–77

[9] *Corporation of Glasgow Electricity Depart-ment, Description of Work for Lighting and Power* (Glasgow 1906), passim, see also *Electrical Handbook Part I, Glasgow and Edinburgh and Districts*, 53–82

[10] *Stothers's Glasgow, Lanarkshire & Ren-frewshire Christmas & New Year Annual 1911–12* (Hamilton 1911), 254–5; *Dal-marnock Generating Station: Official Opening of 100,000 kw Extension* 1 October 1937 (brochure); *Stothers's Annual*, 384–5

[11] The Highburgh Road exchange is illustrated in Young & Doak, plate 155

[12] Browning, A. S. E., 'The Museum of Transport, Glasgow', *The Journal of Industrial Archaeology*, 2 (1965), 7–12, plates 9–12

PART TWO

GAZETTEER

Notes on the Gazetteer

As stated in the introduction, to qualify for entry in this gazetteer, a site had to be inside the 1964 Glasgow boundary, to have been built, in part at least, before 1914, and to have substantial remains. A few post-1914 sites of particular interest have also been included. The inventory is not a complete one, but includes virtually all the major industrial buildings in the city and a substantial number of minor ones.

The reference numbers are to the key maps which are arranged so that areas with a large number of sites have individual maps; peripheral sites are included in a smaller-scale general map. The sites are numbered on the maps from north to south, giving easy location of a particular reference number on the map.

Each entry consists of the name or type of site; its street name and number (or Ordnance Survey Grid Reference); date of construction or foundation; party occupying the site; engineer or architect; and description. As space is at a premium, changes of ownership and use have in most cases not been included, unless such a change has been associated with additional building. The main sources for dates have been the Post Office Directories, the *Glasgow Herald* and *Evening News*, and Dean of Guild records (see bibliography for details). Where an approximate date is given, it is usually a directory date; for railways and canals, where precise date of construction (as opposed to opening) is not available, approximate dates have also been given. Considerable assistance was given with architectural descriptions by Frank Worsdall. Where possible, demolition subsequent to visitation has been noted, but destruction of industrial buildings is so rapid that no guarantee of accuracy in this respect can be given. There are photographs in the author's collection of virtually all the sites included in this inventory, though inclusion in the list does not indicate that a complete record has been made.

Section A
Anniesland, Kelvindale and Maryhill

1 Netherton Works, 290 Netherton Rd, founded in 1914 by the Ioco Proofing Co., the first part being designed by R. *Henderson*, architect (£660). An extensive complex of one, two and three storey red brick buildings, with a single storey windowless terra-cotta brick frontage to Netherton Rd.

2 Temple Sawmills, 349 Bearsden Rd, founded 1874 by Robinson, Dunn & Co., timber merchants. A large group of one and two storey buildings, some timber, some brick, on the banks of the Forth & Clyde Canal, which is used as a timber pond. Bearsden Rd was driven through the mills in 1931–2.

3 Temple Bridge, Bearsden Rd, built 1931–2, *T. Somers* and *Sir William Arrol & Co. Ltd* engineers (£65,624). A bascule bridge, electrically operated, with a 55 foot steel span, the abutments being of mass concrete faced with red sandstone. Replaced a wooden bascule bridge over the lower lock (A4).

4 Temple Locks, Crow Rd, built *c* 1790 for the Forth & Clyde Canal. A pair of standard locks, with a small lock-keeper's cottage between them. As usual, the lock gates have been cut down, though the lower gates on the lower locks still have their balance beams.

5 Tunnel, constructed *c* 1885 for the Glasgow City & District Railway by Hugh Kennedy & Sons, Partick. A short tunnel carrying the railway under the Forth & Clyde Canal, the Glasgow, Dumbarton & Helensburgh Railway and two roads. At the south end the entrance is spanned by a cast-iron girder.

6 Dalsholm Paper Mills, Dalsholm Rd, founded *c*. 1783 by William McArthur. A group of one and two storey buildings on the banks of the River Kelvin, the largest of which, containing a 100 inch Fourdrinier Machine, was built after 1934. Some of the subsidiary buildings probably date from the late eighteenth century. Closed 1970.

7 Viaduct, built *c* 1858 for the Glasgow, Dumbarton & Helensburgh Railway. A masonry structure, with seven semicircular arches, carrying a double line of railway over the River Kelvin.

8 Maryhill Park Station, built *c* 1858 for the Glasgow, Dumbarton & Helensburgh Railway. A two platform station, originally with a small goods yard on the south side. The platforms have been cut back, but the up platform building survived until 1972, a neat single storey structure on a T plan, with round-headed windows.

9 Horse Tram Depot, 28–32 Duart St, built *c* 1883 for the Glasgow Tramway & Omnibus Co. A three storey 5 by 16 bay red brick building with white brick string courses and a Renaissance sandstone facade. There are three large round-headed doorways with glazed fanlights, and a central pediment.

10 Kelvin Drydock, probably built *c* 1790 for the Forth & Clyde Canal Co. and let by them. A small graving dock with wooden gates. To the east is a slipway, where small steamers and barges were built and repaired.

11 Maryhill Locks, built 1787–90 for the Forth & Clyde Canal, R. *Whitworth*, engineer. A flight of five locks at the western end of the summit level of the canal. Between the locks are large oval basins with masonry walls, and there is a fifth basin between the bottom lock and the aqueduct (A12). The lock gates have all been cut down.

12 Kelvin Aqueduct, built 1787–90 for the Forth & Clyde Canal, R. *Whitworth*, engineer (£8509). Four heavy masonry arches, each 50 feet long carrying the canal over the valley of the Kelvin – only one pier actually stands in the river. The spandrels of the arches are also arched, with a buttress at each pier. The lower courses are rustic ashlar, the upper polished. The entire structure is 400 feet long and 70 feet high, and is SDD listed, category B, and scheduled as an Ancient Monument.

13 Railway Viaduct, built *c* 1896 for the Lanarkshire & Dumbartonshire Railway. A five span lattice girder viaduct on stone piers, over the River Kelvin. The girders have been removed since closure in 1966 but the piers are intact.

14 Bridge, Bantaskin St, probably built *c* 1871. A two span lattice girder bridge on stone piers, over the River Kelvin.

15 Kelvindale Mills, 80 Bantaskin St, founded *c* 1830 as Maryhill Printworks by John Barr, but converted *c* 1875 into a blacking factory by W. Cumming & Co. A large one storey, 11 bay rubble store with a Belfast roof was added in 1893, *Burnet & Boston*, architects (£3000), the prominent seven storey, 5 bay brick mill and chimney in 1900, *T. W. Copland*, engineer, Falkirk (£3000), and the bottom storey of the two storey 8 bay office block in 1902, *W. Reid* (II), architect (£400). Behind these blocks is a group of single storey sheds with Belfast roofs.

16 Dawsholm Gasworks, Skaethorn Rd, built 1871–2 for Glasgow Corporation Gas Department (£160,000) and rebuilt 1892, 1896, 1912, 1918 and 1927. The remains of a large complex of buildings, the most striking of which was a red brick retort house, demolished *c* 1968. The principal surviving structures are the one and two storey office block, and two rows of two storey houses in Skaethorn Rd. The plate girder railway bridge which linked the works with the Forth & Clyde Canal also survives.

17 Bascule Bridge, Cleveden Rd, of the standard Forth & Clyde Canal type, replaced by a culvert *c* 1968.

18 Temple Gasworks, Strathcona Drive, built 1871 for the Partick, Hillhead & Maryhill Gas Co., and purchased by Glasgow Corporation in 1891. Now used for storage only, there are two three-lift gasholders, built in 1893 (240 feet in diameter, capacity five million cubic feet) and 1900 (220 feet in diameter, capacity four million cubic feet).

19 Temple Works, 101 Strathcona Drive, built *c* 1913 for Gleniffer Motors Ltd, manufacturers of petrol and paraffin marine engines. A large single storey engineering shop, with a smaller two storey, 2 by 18 bay red and white brick block adjacent to the north.

20 Temple Iron Works, 1012 Crow Rd, founded *c* 1890 by William Baird, maker of iron and steel girders, roofs, etc. A two bay steel-framed, corrugated-iron clad engineering shop, built 1913 (£2500), and a one storey and attic, 7 bay office block.

21 Alexandra Park Laundry, 21 Hilton Gardens, built *c* 1901 for J. A. Ferrier & Co., dyers and cleaners, and extended by W. Beardmore & Co. Ltd as a service and repair depot for their motor vehicles. A 7 bay block of single storey, red brick, north light buildings.

22 Model Housing, Anniesland Rd, Munro Place, Greenlea St and Craigend St, built *c* 1877 for the Jordanhill Co-operative Buildings & Land Society Ltd. A group of five rows of single storey, red and white brick cottages, mostly two room.

23 Castlebank Laundry, 200 Anniesland Rd, built *c* 1896 for Alexander Kennedy. A two storey, 10 bay harled brick front block, set back from the road, with single storey workshops behind.

24 University Press, 15 Foulis St, built 1903 for R. MacLehose & Co., university printers, *A. N. Paterson*, architect (£12,200) and extended in 1914, *John Trail*, Edinburgh, architect (£2918). The 1903 portion consists of the two storey, 8 bay red brick neo-Georgian office block, with its sandstone facings, and the single storey workshops on the south side of the street. The 1914 addition is a 5 bay block of single storey buildings on the north side.

25 Patent Works, Caxton St and 920 Crow Rd, built from 1903 for Barr & Stroud Ltd, optical instrument makers, *A. N. Paterson*, architect, and *Sir William Arrol & Co. Ltd*, engineers (£39,698).

The Caxton St frontage is three storeys high, 27 bays long, and the Crow Rd frontage, built 1906, is also three storeys high, and 15 bays long, both terra cotta brick faced. On the other side of Crow Rd are later additions.

26 Anniesland Station, Great Western Rd, originally known as Great Western Rd Station, opened 1886 by the North British Railway. A two platform through station with two large wood and brick buildings of standard North British Railway pattern, replaced in 1969 by modern blocks.

27 Kelvindale Paper Mills, Kelvindale Rd, founded in the 18th century as Balgray snuff and paper mill, acquired *c* 1840 by Edward Collins & Son. An extensive complex of buildings, with a large chimney. The oldest part seems to be a three storey, 11 bay rubble building beside the river. There is a sizable lade, with V shaped weir. Within the works compound are three rows of workers' cottages, two single storey and one two storey. Between 1912 and 1914 £16,132 was spent on additions and reconstruction after a fire.

28 City of Glasgow Dyeworks, 160 Gairbraid Avenue, built 1901–2 for Brand & Mollison Ltd, cleaners and dyers, *J. Lindsay*, architect (£5600). A block of single storey workrooms, with a two storey, 4 bay office block, all red brick.

29 Kelvindale Laundry, 25 Gairbraid Place, partly built 1900, and completed to original designs in 1909, *James Ritchie*, architect (£4000). An 8 bay range of single storey sheds, with gable ends to the street. Three of the bays have recessed round-headed arches with circular ventilators, the arches being flanked by single round-headed windows.

30 Kelvindale Bridge, Kelvindale Rd, probably built in the 18th century. A neat masonry structure, with three semicircular arches. A western extension with wrought- and cast-iron parapet carries water pipes. The southernmost arch spans the lade from Kelvindale Paper Mills.

31 Kelvinside Railway Station, 1051 Great Western Rd, built *c* 1896 for the Glasgow Central Railway, *J. J. Burnet*, architect. A two platform through station in a cutting, with a two storey 3 by 3 bay Renaissance sandstone surface building, including a station house. There are the remains of stairways to the platforms. On the east side was a large goods yard. Closed to passengers 1 July 1942.

32 Model Cottages, Crow Rd, built *c* 1885 to house Scotstoun Estate workers. An interesting group of single storey red and white brick houses, some in rows, some detached.

33 Jordanhill Station, Crow Rd, built 1887 for the Glasgow, Yoker & Clydebank Railway. A two platform through station, with large wood and brick platform buildings of standard North British Railway pattern, replaced with modern structures in 1969.

Section B
Maryhill, Hillhead and Woodside

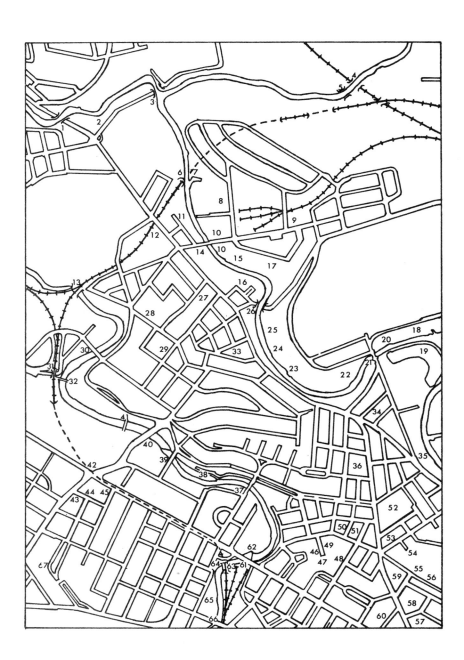

1 Aqueduct, Maryhill Rd, built 1881 for the Forth & Clyde Canal. A massive, rustic masonry structure, with a heavy segmental arch carrying the puddled bed of the canal and semicircular arches on each side supporting the towpath. This was a replacement of an earlier structure which was situated immediately to the north.

2 Maryhill Engine Works, 23 Lochburn Rd, built *c* 1873 for Clarkson Bros, engineers and machine makers. A three storey, 6 by 4 bay block, with an adjacent two storey, 10 bay range, facing the street. At the rear are one and two storey sheds.

3 Stockingfield Aqueduct, Lochburn Rd, built *c* 1790 for the Forth & Clyde Canal, *Robert Whitworth*, engineer. A semicircular ashlar arch, with curved abutments, the only original Forth & Clyde Canal road aqueduct still in use within the city boundary.

4 Aqueduct, built *c* 1858 for the Glasgow, Dumbarton & Helensburgh Railway. Two segmental masonry arches, with a brick parapet.

5 Aqueduct, built *c* 1775 for the Forth & Clyde Canal. A small segmental-arched structure, patched with brick, known colloquially as the Hallowe'en Pend.

6 Spillway, probably late 19th century, built for the Forth & Clyde Canal. A neat, three-arched, rustic masonry culvert, with a stone-lined water course leading to an older arched drain. The water level can be controlled by means of a sluice.

7 Tunnel, built *c* 1894 for the Lanarkshire & Dumbartonshire Railway. Carries the railway under the canal and through a hill. The western portal is set in a rock cutting, with a semicircular-arched tunnel mouth surmounted by a panelled ashlar entablature.

8 Ruchill Sawmills, 201 Shuna St, built *c* 1885 for D. McFarlane & Son. Now part of Bryant & May's Empire Match Factory, which also incorporates the former Corporation refuse destructor, built 1901, *A. W. Wheatley*, engineer (£10,250). The refuse destructor buildings consist of two, two storey blocks, one of 3 bays, the other of 5, and a single storey and attic, 11 bay stable block (16 stalls) with prominent ventilators, while the sawmill consists of a range of two storey buildings, much altered, with modern single storey additions.

9 Laundry, 221–31 Ruchill St, built 1909–10 for Baikie & Hogg, *James S. Hogg*, engineer, Edinburgh. A range of single storey red brick workshops, with one and two storey office blocks at the front, harled, with rusticated quoins.

10 Glasgow Lead and Colour Works, 50 Ruchill St, built from *c* 1874 for Alexander, Fergusson & Co. A group of two and three storey, red and white brick buildings on both sides of Ruchill St. The oldest part is on the south side, and is two storeys high, 9 by 9 bays, while on the north side are three storey, 3 by 3 bay; three storey, 3 by 8 bay; and three storey, 11 bay buildings. The last-named was probably built in 1904 as a white lead factory (£12,000). The works was originally served by a canal wharf.

11 Craighall Works, 46 Chapel St, built *c* 1879 for the Kelvin Chemical Co., match, blacking and chemical makers. A much-altered group of one and two storey red brick buildings, with a square-section chimney.

12 Maryhill Central Station, Maryhill Rd, built *c* 1896 for the Lanarkshire & Dumbartonshire Railway, *Robert Wemyss*, architect. A through and terminal station, with two island platforms, each having a glazed awning supported on pairs of cast-iron columns, and linked by a covered footbridge. The station offices were red brick with sandstone details, with the street entrance at first floor level. The goods shed, to the east, was a large red brick building. Closed 5 October 1964 and demolished *c* 1966.

13 Viaducts, Garrioch Quadrant, built *c* 1896 for the Glasgow Central and Lanarkshire & Dumbartonshire Railways. The eastern viaduct (GCR) has three large semicircular arches, in rustic masonry, with a small arch for a footpath on each side, while the western (L & DR) has plate girders on rustic masonry piers.

14 Cooperage, 30 Ruchill St, built 1900 for Alexander, Fergusson & Co., manufacturers of paint and lead products, *George Simpson*, architect (£1500). A two storey, 4 by 2 bay front block with a single storey, 8 bay range at the rear.

15 Glasgow Rubber Works, 125–9 Shuna St, built from *c* 1876 for George McLellan & Co., india-rubber, asbestos and waterproof manufacturers. Between 1895 and 1914 more than £14,382 was spent on buildings, mostly designed by *George Simpson*, architect. The most impressive of these is a high three storey and attic building of two wide bays, with five low-relief arches on the street side and four on the canal side. The canal-side range is continued by a two storey and attic 9 bay block, a two storey 3 bay link and a handsome two storey, 12 bay building with a central pediment, all red brick.

16 Kent Works, 36 Leyden St, built *c* 1885 for Blacklock, Goudie & Co., makers of waterproofs and india-rubber. A three storey, 9 bay red and white brick building, with large semicircular windows on the top floor.

17 Caledonia Foundry, 35–9 Shuna St, built *c* 1880 for Kerr & Co., ironfounders. The pleasing two storey, 3 bay office block was built in 1904, *Clarke & Bell*, architects (£500), while at the rear is a 6 bay range of single storey red brick moulding shops.

18 Phoenix Chemical Works, 70 Panmure St, built from 1886 for Paterson's Chemical Manufacturing Co. Ltd. Additions were made in 1893, 1905 and 1907 (R. T. *Napier*, architect, £1900). The only surviving buildings are adjacent one storey and attic, and two storey and attic, 9 bay red brick blocks.

19 Firhill Timber Basin, built 1788 and extended in 1849 for the Forth & Clyde Canal. A bend in the canal, widened to form a basin, with a second basin on the inside of the bend. At both ends of the island thus formed are light wooden footbridges, and in the stone abutments, grooves are cut for the insertion of planks to shut off the inner basin.

20 Firhill Ironworks, 180 Firhill Rd, built from *c* 1866 for Shaw & McInnes, architectural ironfounders. A complex of one and two storey, red and white brick buildings, much altered.

21 Bascule Bridge, Firhill Rd. A standard Forth & Clyde Canal bascule bridge, replaced by a culvert *c* 1969.

22 Firhill Sawmills, 19 Murano St, built from *c* 1893 for Graham & Roxburgh. A complex of one and two storeys, red and white brick buildings, with wooden drying sheds, added in 1900–2 (£4030). Demolished 1968.

23 Glasgow Glass Works, 99 Murano St, built *c* 1874 for the Glasgow Plate Glass Co., manufacturers of rolled plate glass. Additions were made in 1893 and 1896 (*William Tennant*, architect) and 1911, for Chance Brothers (*J. W. & J. Laird*, architects, £3870). A plain group of one and two storey red and white brick buildings on the banks of the Forth & Clyde Canal.

24 Caledonian Glass Bottle Works, 169 Murano St, built from 1892 for Scott & Co., *Alexander Petrie*, architect (£1000). A much altered group of brick buildings, with a plain, two storey and attic office block facing the street. There was a wharf on the Forth & Clyde Canal.

25 Ruchill Oil Works, 169 Murano St, built from *c* 1883 for John Sandeman, rosin distiller and oil refiner. Additions were made in 1894 (*Kyle, Dennison & Frew*, architects, £2000) and 1910 (£1590). A large complex of red brick buildings, dominated by a tall brick chimney (part of the 1910 addition). Old boilers, including some egg-ended ones, are used as storage tanks. As at B10, B22, B23 and B24, there was a works wharf on the canal.

26 Aqueduct, Bilsland Drive, built 1879 for the Forth & Clyde Canal. A massive rustic masonry structure, very similar to B1 and C23.

27 Stables, 26 Oran St, built 1901 for Donald McLean, *J. Cunningham*, architect (£1600). A plain, two storey, 11 bay red brick block, behind tenements.

28 Garage, 90 Hotspur St, founded 1906 by the Glasgow & Paris Motor Garage Ltd (first part *A. Nicolai*, architect £1785), added to in 1912 (*Warren & Stuart*, engineers, £1550). A wide single storey, single bay workshop, with a one storey, 7 bay office block in front, having a central segmental-arched entrance.

29 Stable & Dormitory, 91 Sanda St, built 1893 for the Sorn Dairy Supply Co., *William Ingram*, architect (£1000). A three storey, 5 bay red brick building, with stone quoins. At the rear, the words 'Sorn Dairy' are picked out in white glazed brick. Originally there were eight stalls and 16 beds.

30 Kirklee Bridge, Kirklee Rd, built 1899–1900 for Glasgow Corporation Highways Department, *Forman & McColl*, engineers. A high semi-elliptical masonry span with narrow semicircular arches on each side. The main span is flanked by pairs of granite Ionic columns, and there are low-relief carvings of the arms of Glasgow in the spandrels.

31 Kirklee Station, built *c* 1894 for the Glasgow Central Railway, *Sir J. J. Burnet*, architect. A two platform through station, with neat single storey red sandstone buildings. Though the down platform building was not particularly unusual, the up platform building was supported at the rear on massive rustic walls, with recessed arches and had a little semi-octagonal porch at the east end. Demolished *c* 1970.

32 Footbridge, Addison Rd, built *c* 1896. A light lattice-girder span with a simple wrought-iron railing, over the River Kelvin.

33 Kelvinside Bakery, 13 Arden St, built *c* 1893 for John Currie. A large four storey, 7 bay, ashlar-fronted brick building, with a row of pilasters at first floor level.

34 North Woodside Ironworks, 40 Springbank St, built 1867 for Thomas Allan & Sons, ironfounders. The only surviving part of this once large complex is a three storey, 14 bay block with round-headed windows on the first and second floors. The other buildings on this site have been added since 1893–4 for J. & A. McFarlane Ltd and consist of one storey, 6 bay and three storey, 6 bay blocks in Springbank St and two, two storey, 8 bay blocks and a three storey, 3 bay block in Firhill St. The 1893–4 additions were designed by *A. B. Dansken & Co.*, architects (£3500) and further additions in 1906–7 cost £2300.

35 Eglinton Chrome Tannery, 8 Firhill Rd, built *c* 1892. A complex of buildings between the street and the Forth & Clyde Canal, the largest of which was a four storey, 9 bay red and white brick building with an unusual 'semi-Belfast' roof. There was also a single storey, 17 bay, corrugated-iron clad drying shed with a Belfast roof, and a one storey workshop office on the street, built 1899, *H. K. Bromhead*, architect (£200). Demolished *c* 1971.

36 Workshop, Dalmally Lane, built 1892–3 for Alexander Stewart, *Thomson & Sandilands*, architects (£600). A plain two storey and attic, 3 bay red brick building with gable ends to the lane. Opposite is a four storey, 11 bay, red and white brick building of unknown origin.

37 Belmont Bridge, built 1870 to carry Belmont St over the River Kelvin. A high elliptical masonry arch, carrying an inclined roadway. The abutments are rusticated, and there are cast-iron parapets. A subsidiary span carrying the street over

Garriochmill Rd, of cast-iron, with six ribs, and lattice railings, was replaced *c* 1971 in concrete.

38 North Woodside Flint Mill, 125 Garriochmill Rd, built 1846 for Kidston, Cochran & Co. The ruins of a single storey mill and drying shed, demolished *c* 1964. The most substantial survivals are the square tapering kiln of stone and brick, the upper part of which is encased in concrete, and the weir and lade which supplied water to the wood and iron internal undershot wheel. When complete, the mill was SDD listed, category C.

39 Queen Margaret Bridge (1), built 1870 to carry Queen Margaret Rd over the River Kelvin. Two lattice girder spans carried on tall rustic masonry piers. Demolished *c* 1971.

40 Queen Margaret Bridge (2), built 1926–9, *Thomas Somers* and *Considére Constructions Ltd*, engineers (£108,424). A reinforced concrete segmental arch with small semicircular arches for footpaths on both sides. The concrete is faced with red Corncockle sandstone, and there are solid red Peterhead granite parapets. The main span is 135 ft 6 in long.

41 Footbridge, in Botanic Gardens, over River Kelvin, built *c* 1890. A neat three-span plate girder bridge, with elegant cast-iron railings.

42 Botanic Gardens Station, Great Western Rd, built *c* 1894 for the Glasgow Central Railway, *James Miller*, architect. An unusual and attractive station, with the platforms and waiting rooms underground. The booking office was in a red brick building with a steeply pitched roof having two towers with galleries, surmounted by gilded onion domes. The centre portion of the frontage was a verandah, and there were end pavilions. Destroyed by fire in 1970.

43 Electricity Substation, 21 Vinicombe St, built 1912 for Corporation Electricity Department (£1000) and subsequently extended. The 1912 part is a tall, single storey, red sandstone building with round-headed openings.

44 Botanic Gardens Garage, 16–18 Vinicombe St, founded *c* 1906 by A. K. Kennedy. The present two storey, 5 bay front building, which has large windows, and is finished in green and white glazed tiles, was added in 1911, *D. V. Wyllie*, architect (£3750). The steel roof trusses are of unusual design.

45 Joiner's Workshop, 6 Kersland St, built 1903 for John Orr's Trustees, *Andrew Balfour*, architect. A two storey, 6 bay brick building, with single storey extensions.

46 Kelvinbridge Artistic Stationery Works, 22 Herbert St, built *c* 1890 for Alexander Baird & Son, *Thomson & Turnbull*, architects (£2500) and extended in 1895 (£3500). The present four storey and attic, 8 bay Renaissance frontage was added in 1898, *Thomson, Turnbull & Peacock*, architects (£5600). This is constructed of sandstone, the body of the building being red brick.

47 Offices & Stores, 32 Herbert St, built 1890–1 for Bishop & Henderson (Cooper & Co.), grocers, *Robert Duncan*, architect. The office block is a two storey, 5 bay, terra-cotta brick building, with sandstone quoins; the centre 3 bays project slightly, and are surmounted by twin chimney stacks, linked by an arch. At the rear are three storey brick stores and stables.

48 City of Glasgow Steam Dyeing & Laundry Work, 27 Napiershall St, built from *c* 1873 for John Stewart. The older part is a single storey, 5 bay block, with round-headed openings, and the more modern part a single storey, 2 bay block, with gable ends to the street.

49 Jam & Confectionery Works, 17 Herbert St, extensively rebuilt, after a fire on 8 January 1907, for Thomas G. Bishop, (£15,000). A four storey, 10 bay red brick, flat-roofed building with terra-cotta brick frontage. The bays are separated by projecting piers. At the rear are the altered remains of the original three storey block (£14,000).

50 Workshop, 9 Mount St, built *c* 1877 for J. & J. Phillips, joiners. A small two storey and attic, 5 bay harled brick building. Demolished *c* 1971.

51 Glasgow Sausage Works, 240 North Woodside Rd, founded *c* 1888 by R. D. Waddell. The works was completely rebuilt in 1895–7, *James Lindsay*, architect. The 1895 additions are four storeys high, 10 by 14 bay, of red brick (£30,000) while the spectacular six storey and attic, 8 by 22 bay Renaissance corner block was added in 1896–7 (£15,000). A further small addition was made in 1900 (£2000).

52 Beehive Spindle Works, 57 Trossachs St, built from 1874 for Thomas Duff & Co. A block of red brick single storey, north-light workshops, with a more modern three storey, 7 bay flat-roofed reinforced concrete framed front building. Demolished 1972.

53 Garage, 31 Hopehill Rd, built 1913 for John Foster, *George Arthur & Son*, architects (£1570). A plain single storey red brick building with terra-cotta brick frontage. One bay had a Belfast roof. Destroyed by fire *c* 1971.

54 Grovepark Mills, 188 North Woodside Rd, built from 1857 for Mitchell & Whytlaw, power-loom manufacturers, and enlarged in 1878, 1888 (£1600), 1896 (£1000), 1897 (£1000) and 1900 (£2000), *John Gordon*, architect. The main block, built 1878, is on an L plan, four storey and attic, 8 by 13 bay (outside), with cast-iron columns supporting timber beams and floors. The walls are red and white brick, with curious moulded brick quoins. On the east side is a small single storey engine house, with a Flemish gable, and on the north is a larger engine house, 5 bays long, with round-headed windows. There are two associated blocks of weaving sheds, one 6 bays, the other 8 bays long,

with the normal timber north-light roofs supported on cast-iron columns. There is a tall iron-bound brick chimney, and a neat two storey villa, with pillared porch, which served as an office. Demolished in 1969.

55 Crown Ironworks, 156 North Woodside Rd, built from *c* 1869 for Thomson & Co., railway spring makers. Additions were made in 1871–2 (£2200) and 1874–5 (£3000), while the works was reconstructed in 1908 (£17,590). The range facing the street is two storeys high, 18 bays long, much altered, while there are single storey workshops at the rear.

56 Milton Ironworks, 142 North Woodside Rd, built from *c* 1856 for McDowall & Co., ironfounders. A large group of one, two and three storey buildings, the most interesting of which is a three storey rubble building on an L plan, 8 by 15 bay (outside), which was probably built in 1857. Additions were made in 1878 (£5500) and 1882 (£2200), including a two storey, 8 bay block to the north of the 1857 building, demolished *c* 1968. More recent additions include three bays of corrugated iron clad workshops and a three storey, 15 bay red and white brick building facing the street.

57 Workshops, Glenfarg St, built *c* 1902 (£1500) and 1905 (£6000) for St George's Co-operative Society, *R. W. Home*, architect. A group of plain two storey, red brick buildings, with flat roofs, and a square-section brick chimney.

58 Bakery, 37 Clarendon St, founded *c* 1887 by the Friendly Bread Association. A much-altered complex of buildings. The largest of which is a post-1914 six storey, 6 bay reinforced concrete building with red brick and sandstone facade, built 1926 for City Bakeries.

59 Bleachworks, 168 Maryhill Rd, founded *c* 1855 by the New City Road Bleaching Co., washers and bleachers, and extended in 1874–5 (£2500). An irregular group of two and three storey buildings running from Maryhill Rd to North Woodside Rd. The present front building, a single storey, 2 bay structure in Moorish style, was added in 1908 for Alexander Kennedy, cabinetmaker, D. V. *Wyllie*, architect (£1250).

60 Stables, 58 Cromwell St, built 1884 for Alexander Frew, coachbuilder and carriage hirer (£500). A plain two storey, 13 bay brick block, reconstructed as workshops in 1910 for the Apex Motor Engineering Co., *Honeyman, Keppie & Mackintosh*, architects.

61 Kelvin Bridge, Great Western Rd, opened 29 September 1891. An interesting cast-iron arch bridge, with two main spans over the Kelvin and a smaller span on each side. The eastern approach span crosses South Woodside Rd, to which it is linked by a stairway. The main spans have nine ribs each, the outer ones having the spandrels filled with Gothic tracery and decorated with the arms of Glasgow, while the subsidiary arches have six ribs each. This bridge replaced a three-arch stone high level bridge, opened in 1840, which was itself a replacement of a three-arch low level bridge; both survived until the construction of the new bridge.

62 Weir, South Woodside Rd, built *c* 1784 for William Gillespie, cotton spinner. The only surviving part of the South Woodside Cotton Mill, the first large cotton mill in Glasgow, which was demolished *c* 1894 to make way for the Glasgow Central Railway.

63 Kelvinbridge Station, Caledonian Crescent, built *c* 1894 for the Glasgow Central Railway, *James Miller*, architect. A two platform through station, partly built on a two span, plate-girder bridge over the Kelvin. The station was closed to passengers in 1952, and the platform buildings and awnings demolished. The offices, on a bridge over the tracks lasted until a fire

on 11 August 1968 forced demolition in 1969. The offices were two storeys high, red brick with sandstone dressings, in Renaissance style. Immediately to the north is Caledonian Mansions, designed by Miller, an elaborate three storey block of shops and dwelling houses, with a Mansard roof. There was a large goods and mineral yard to the east of the passenger station, with a brick goods shed, still surviving.

64 Warehouse & Workshops, 19–37 Otago St, built 1887 and 1897 for P. Hepburn, wholesale cabinetmaker and upholsterer. The northern block is three storey, attic and basement, 6 bay and the southern three storey, two attics and two basements, 6 bay. Both have ashlar fronts and red and white brick backs, while the second has a double mansard roof. At the rear is a triangular three storey garage, built 1913 for The Garage Properties Co., *William C. Boyd*, architect, £8880.

65 Hubbard's Bakery, 65 Otago St, built 1905–6 for Walter Hubbard, *Andrew Balfour*, architect (£14,000). A two storey, attic and basement building with a 7 bay frontage and a 6 bay rear elevation. The frontage has a central tower and three rusticated arches, and is finished in terracotta brick, with sandstone dressings. The rear is in red and white brick, with large round-headed windows at first floor level.

66 Eldon St Bridge, Eldon St, opened June 1895. A cast-iron arch bridge, with six ribs. The spandrels of the outer ribs are filled with Gothic tracery and carry the arms of Glasgow. The parapet is also of cast-iron, with panels of tracery. Similar in style to B61.

67 Workshop, 36 Ashton Lane, built in the late 19th century, and occupied from 1894 by Barr & Stroud, instrument makers. A two storey and attic, 7 bay red and white brick building.

Section C
Port Dundas

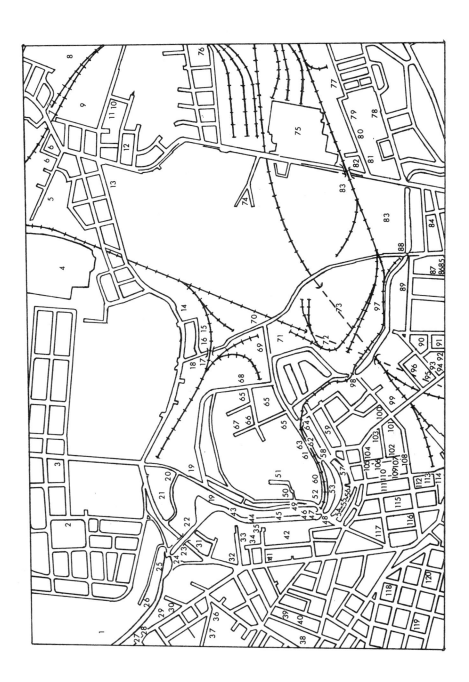

1 Canal Basin, Hamiltonhill St, probably constructed *c* 1875. A curved cut excavated from a hillside, about 200 yards long, built to link the main line of the canal with a colliery owned by the Strone Colliery Co.

2 Possil Engine Works, 97 Hamiltonhill Rd, founded on this site in 1876 by Hugh Smith & Co., machine tool makers. Additions were made in 1898 (£3400), 1906 (£410), 1911 (*C. J. McNair*, architect, £1340) and 1912 (£150). A large group of single storey engineering workshops, with two and three storey machine shops and a two storey and attic office block.

3 Warehouse, 111 Saracen St, built 1910–11 for Greenlees & Sons, boot and shoe makers, *Wyllie & Blake*, architects and engineers (£13,495). A six storey, 3 by 7 bay reinforced concrete building with two windows per bay. There is a central stair bay and clock tower in the Saracen St frontage. A single storey garage was added in 1913, *H. D. Walton*, architect (£108).

4 Cowlairs Works, Carlisle St, built from 1842 for the Edinburgh & Glasgow Railway and the North British Railway. A very large complex of workshops, stores and offices, forming the central locomotive, carriage and wagon works of both railways. The oldest parts, on the east of the site, were the light machine shop, a single storey ashlar building, 5 by 15 bay, the 2 bay old erecting shop and the former locomotive shed, a 7 by 8 bay structure. The new erecting shop was built in 1899 (£17,800). Other late 19th century additions were the brick carriage and wagon shops, with steel roof trusses, parts of the foundry and the two storey, 22 bay brick stores department (1897). Twentieth century additions were made in corrugated iron and asbestos clad steel. Closed 1968 and demolished 1968–9.

5 Springvale Mills, 73 Cowlairs Rd, built 1904–6 for Hutcheson, Main & Co., oil manufacturers and refiners and golf ball manufacturers, *G. Gibbs* and *J. & W. D. Hall*, architects (£9800). A two storey, 10 bay red brick building, recently extended to three storeys, with single storey workshops at the rear.

6 Warehouses & Creamery, Angus St & Kemp St, built 1895–1911 for the Cowlairs Co-operative Society. The main block, on the south side of Angus St, has three storeys and a basement, and is 11 bays long, of red sandstone, *Bruce & Hay*, architects (1895, £20,000). The creamery block in Kemp St is a two storey and attic structure with an ornamented gable. At the rear is a five storey and attic, 10 bay red brick building, constructed 1901 as stables, workroom and stores, *J. Lindsay*, architect (£4,550).

7 Springburn Station, Springburn Rd, built 1885–7 for the City of Glasgow Union Railway, *J. Carsewell*, engineer (£3000). A four platform station, with two through platforms and two bay platforms. A wooden shelter is provided on each platform, and there is a sandstone office block entered from street level, with stairs down to the platforms.

8 Atlas Works, Barcaple St, founded 1884 by The Clyde Locomotive Co. Ltd. Between then and 1914 £60,320 was spent on alterations and additions, mostly designed by *A. Myles*, architect, but the last additions were made by the Glasgow Steel Roofing Co. A large complex of red brick and corrugated-iron clad steel buildings. The older parts had round-headed windows and timber roof trusses. The erecting shop was a 15 bay brick building adjacent to the railway, with frame, tool and test shops at the rear. Immediately to the south of this group were the boiler and boiler mounting shops, 5 bays of brick and steel construction, much altered, while at the south end of the site were the Mons shops, two very large bays of steel framed corrugated-iron clad workshops. To the east was the office block, a two storey, 7 by 5 bay brick building with a corner clock tower. At the north end were the Marne shops, a single large bay and 4 smaller bays, built 1913–14

(£9330). The works was closed in 1963, and has been demolished.

9 Hydepark Works, 170 Ayr St, founded on this site in 1860 by Neilson & Co., locomotive builders, and subsequently greatly extended and rebuilt, for example between 1898 and 1910 £125,090 was spent on alterations and additions, while between the wars further reconstruction took place. The main office block, a two storey and attic, 17 bay brick building with round-headed windows at first floor level, and an ornamental gateway was probably built in 1885 (£5000). The oldest part of the complex was the pattern store – brass foundry – iron foundry block on the north of the site, a one and two storey, 45 bay red brick building. The rest of the buildings were single storey steel or iron framed engineering shops, with the exception of the castellated dining hall building in Flemington St, built in 1898. The works was closed in 1963 and demolished in 1969.

10 Springburn Electricity Substation, 136 Flemington St, built 1906 for Glasgow Corporation Electricity Department (£4990). A high single storey 4 by 5 bay terra-cotta brick building, with round-headed openings in the Flemington St frontage.

11 North British Locomotive Company Administration Block, 110 Flemington St, built 1909 for the company, *J. Miller*, architect (£64,000). An impressive four storey, 17 by 18 bay red sandstone building in the Renaissance manner. The end bays and the centre three bays project slightly, and the main entrance is surmounted by a broken pediment, with the front elevation of a North British 'Atlantic' locomotive in the tympanum. The pediment is flanked by single female figures.

12 Bakery, 7–11 Mollinsburn St, built 1891 and extended in 1902 (£120) for Thomas Miller, dairyman, *Burnet & Boston* and *W. B. Whitie*, architects. A plain two storey and attic, 3 bay, stone fronted brick building with brick extension at the rear.

13 Springburn Tram Depot, 81–3 Keppochhill Rd, built 1893–4 for Corporation Tramways Department, *William Clark*, engineer (£8000, 158 stalls). A 5 bay block of single storey red sandstone fronted brick car sheds and stables, with steel lintels over the doorways. The roof was raised in 1898, when a single storey corrugated-iron and brick engine and boiler house was added (£6000 total) for the experimental electric tram service between Mitchell St and Springburn. The buildings were converted to a laundry (the Springburn Steam Laundry) in 1904 for White Houses Ltd, lodging house keepers, *W. B. Whitie*, architects (£250), though there are still tram tracks in some of the sheds.

14 Keppoch Iron Works, 355 Keppochhill Rd, founded *c* 1875 by David King & Son, ironfounders, and subsequently extended by Allan Ure & Co. A group of single storey brick and steel sheds with a small office block. There was until closure in 1968 the last hoodless cupola in the city in operation.

15 Cooperage, 68 Coxhill St, built *c* 1906 for R. Williamson & Sons, coopers. A plain single storey red brick building.

16 Coxhill Ironworks, 60 Coxhill St, built 1907 for James Robertson & Co., smiths, railing, gate and asphalt cauldron manufacturers, *P. G. Macgregor*, architect, Bishopbriggs (£430) and extended 1913, *William Reid*, architect (£950). A block of single storey red brick engineering shops, with a two storey by 5 bay office building.

17 Clay Pipe Factory, 443 Pinkston Rd, built 1874 for Edward Feron, tobacco pipe maker (£700). A plain two storey red brick building on an L plan, partly harled.

18 Stables and Stores, 469 Pinkston Rd, built 1907–12 for J. Y. Alexander, cartage contractor. The 1907 block, consisting of a two storey office, store and house, was designed by *A. G. Macdougall* (£740), while the 1912 addition was a two storey,

4 by 16 bay flat-roofed range of stables, *F. Simpson* (£1650, 58 stalls).

19 City Sawmills, 119 Lower Craighall Rd, founded on this site in 1849 by James Brownlee, timber merchant, and rebuilt and extended several times. The mills are situated on both sides of Craighall Rd, and include a timber basin on the Forth & Clyde Canal (Glasgow Branch), with a gantry crane. The two storey, 2 by 8 bay Renaissance office block in polychrome brick was built in 1893, *George Bell*, architect (£3000). In Borron St is an 18 bay range of wooden stores with gable ends to the street, and in the yard behind several kilns and timber sheds. Between 1901 and 1914 additions costing £24,240 were made. A vertical, wall-mounted steam engine from the mills is now preserved by Mr T. B. Paisley of Huntingdonshire, and an early bandsaw is in the Birmingham Museum of Science and Industry. The complex incorporates J. S. Dunn & Co.'s Rockvilla Saw Mill.

20 Stables, Craighall Rd and Dawson Rd, built 1892 (£500) and 1899 (£2800, 40 stalls) for the St George's Co-operative Society, *Joseph Cowan*, architect. The older part is one storey and attic, and the newer a flat roofed, two storey, 4 by 7 bay block, both red brick. There is also a two storey ashlar fronted brick dwelling house.

21 Rockvilla Weaving Factory, 236 Possil Rd, built *c* 1850 for A. Mitchell, Jun. & Sons, power-loom cloth manufacturers. Cut down remains of a three storey rubble building.

22 Malt store, Dawson Rd, built before 1842 for Hugh Baird & Co., maltsters. The ruins of a large 9 bay rubble warehouse.

23 Aqueducts, Possil Rd, carrying the Forth & Clyde Canal (Glasgow Branch). The original aqueduct, with a small semicircular arch, is immediately to the west of the one at present in use, and can be seen from the north side. It was built *c* 1790 for the extension of the Glasgow Branch to Port Dundas. The newer aqueduct was probably built about 1880, and is similar to B1 and B26, with a heavy segmental arch carrying the channel and lighter semicircular arches carrying the towpaths.

24 Bascule Bridge, Baird's Brae. A standard Forth & Clyde Canal bridge, with a small square stone bridgekeeper's cottage.

25 Forth & Clyde Canal Workshops, Applecross St. A 21 bay range of whitewashed two storey buildings, with a detached single storey brick building having four lancet windows in the west end. The workshops are situated on the north bank of the Old Basin, the Glasgow terminus of the canal until 1790. At the rear is a two storey dwelling house.

26 Victoria Foundry, Canal Bank, Old Basin, founded *c* 1845 by G. B. Edington, iron founder. A plain single storey building with a round-headed doorway, and a two storey 8 bay structure, both red brick. Now used as a contractor's yard, there is an old crane on a new concrete base mounted away from the canal.

27 Store, 708 Garscube Rd, built 1911 for Charles Vaux & Sons, brewers, *N. C. Duff*, architect (£7250). A two storey, 10 bay terra-cotta fronted brick front block with four large round-headed openings on the ground floor. At the rear there are 4 bays of single storey sheds.

28 Aerated Water Factory, 706 Garscube Rd, built 1896 for J. Orr Comrie, aerated water manufacturer, *Burnet, Son & Campbell*, architects (£5000). A four storey, 7 bay red brick Renaissance building with sandstone dressings. At the east end of the frontage was a stair tower, while at the rear was a four storey wing and smaller outbuildings, including a two storey stable added in 1902 (£1200). Demolished after fire *c* 1971.

29 Great Canal Maltings, 580 Garscube Rd, built 1888 for Hugh Baird & Son, maltsters, *Russell & Spence*, architects

(£10,000). A five storey, 10 bay block of malt barns, with terra-cotta brick frontage, with a modern sixth storey. At the rear was a single kiln replacing the two kilns originally provided. As the name suggests, there was a rear entrance from the towpath of the canal. Demolished 1972.

30 Bottling Works and Store, 500 Garscube Rd, built 1907–10 for Whitbread & Co., brewers, *A. Dixon* (London), architect (£15,727). Two blocks, each 4 bays long and three storeys high, with neo-Georgian frontages to the street, with three storey plain red brick buildings at the rear.

31 Metal Cask Manufactory, 63 Wigton St, built *c* 1857–8 for Brown & Co., manufacturers of patent metallic casks, kegs, cisterns, etc. A four storey, 11 bay cement-rendered brick building with a projecting wing beside the canal.

32 Tower Buildings, 2–14 Possil Rd and Farnell St, built 1875 for James Allan, ironfounder (£6000). A four storey, 6 by 12 bay Renaissance building with arched windows on second and third floors. There is a corner tower with a cast-iron crown, and at the rear an external winch-type hoist.

33 Mineral Water Factory, 22 Farnell St, built 1897–8 for the British & Foreign Mineral Water Co. (£8200, not completed). A long two storey red brick building, with a small square-section chimney.

34 South Sawmillfield Mill, 6–12 Burns St, built *c* 1838 for Alexander Brown & Co., cotton spinners and weavers. A five storey and attic, 20 bay rubble building, with flanking rectangular stair towers, and a two storey engine house at the rear. Also at the rear was a range of single storey weaving sheds. The main block was converted to a model lodging house for George Young of Garscube Rd Home in 1891 (£3000). Demolished 1965.

35 Cleansing Department Depot, 21 Sawmillfield St, built 1899 for Glasgow Corporation, *A. W. Wheatley*, engineer (£8500). A block of one and two storey red and white brick buildings with a two storey, 10 bay frontage. Originally designed as a 38 stall stable, cart sheds and muster hall.

36 Furniture Factory, 37 Grovepark St, built *c* 1906 for Fred M. Walker Ltd, bedroom furniture manufacturers. A pair of two storey red and white brick buildings, one 4 by 4 bay, the other similar, but longer, with a circular-section brick chimney.

37 Violet Grove Mills, Grovepark St, built 1874 for Aitken, Wilson & Co., power-loom cloth manufacturers. A 14 bay block of north-light weaving sheds with roof ventilators.

38 Bakery, 322 St Georges Rd, built 1898 for John Neil & Son Ltd, bread and biscuit makers and confectioners, *D. V. Wyllie*, architect. A plain four storey, 8 bay flat-roofed red and white brick building behind a tenement.

39 Wright's Workshop, 144 St Peter's St, built *c* 1882 for George Ferguson, wright. A plain three storey, 2 by 9 bay red brick building with an outside stairway. Adjacent is a wooden timber shed.

40 Marble Cutting Works, 48 Balnain St, founded *c* 1849 by William Galbraith. The present buildings date from 1908 and were designed by *Clarke & Bell*, architects (£8335). A large 2 bay single storey brick building, incorporating an office.

41 Bakery, 12 Sawmillfield St, founded *c* 1855 by T. & W. Weir. A plain two storey, 9 by 2 bay red brick building.

42 Port Dundas Electricity Generating Station, Edington St, built 1898 for the Corporation Electricity Department, *Andrew Myles*, architect (£90,000) and extended 1903–9 (£71,900). A very large range of two storey red brick buildings, with round-headed windows. There is a fine French Renaissance tower projecting from the centre of the block, and a high boundary wall.

43 Wheatsheaf Mills, 65 Lower Craighall Rd, reconstructed 1931 for John M. White, miller, from part of the adjacent sugar refinery. A five storey, 3 by 8 bay rubble block, extended north by a three storey, 5 bay red brick building. To the south is a detached two storey kiln building.

44 Port Dundas Sugar Refinery, 256 North Speirs Wharf, built 1865–6 for Murdoch & Dodrell, sugar refiners. A seven storey, 16 bay ashlar fronted red and white brick building, dated 1866, linked to C43 by a three storey red and white brick block.

45 City of Glasgow Grain Mills & Stores, 204–44 North Speirs Wharf, built c 1851 for John Currie & Co., grain merchant, and extended in 1869–70. An impressive range of sandstone buildings. The northernmost is a six storey, 16 bay ashlar building with a pediment, dated 1851, then a five storey, 18 bay block, a six storey, 7 bay, and a five storey, 12 bay block, all rubble. When built had 20 pairs of stones and a 100 horsepower condensing engine.

46 Canal Office, 174 North Speirs Wharf, built c 1812 for the Forth & Clyde Canal. An attractive two storey, 5 bay Georgian building with a central pediment and a porch with Doric columns. SDD category B.

47 Collector's House, 158 North Speirs Wharf, built c 1790 for the Forth & Clyde Canal. A two storey, 3 bay ashlar building, with an arched iron lamp-holder over the gate. SDD category B.

48 Bascule Bridge, Ann St and Craighall Rd, built for the Forth & Clyde Canal. A standard bridge, demolished 1967. The canal at this point is now piped.

49 Warehouse, 51–7 High Craighall Rd and Lower Craighall Rd. An unusually sited wooden store, with a neat hand-crane

positioned to raise goods from Lower Craighall Rd.

50 Dundashill Bakery, 42–70 High Craighall Rd, built 1901 for William McDougall, baker, *J. Melvin & Sons*, engineers (£2600) and extended in 1908, *D. & A. Home Morton*, engineers (£8640). A large block of single storey red brick buildings, in two parts, one 13 bay, the other (1908) 9 bay.

51 Wellington Mills, 3 Mary St, built from 1882 by Edward Macbean & Co., brattice, oil clothing, cover, packing and tarpaulin manufacturers. Between then and 1906, £6920 was spent on buildings. The main body of the factory consists of three wide two storey bays, each with four windows per storey, and there is a two storey, 11 bay office block.

52 Dundashill Distillery, 2 High Craighall Rd, founded c 1811 by Daniel McFarlane. A heterogeneous and much altered group of one, two, three and four storey buildings, mostly sandstone rubble.

53 Warehouses, 60–74 South Speirs Wharf and 47–107 North Speirs Wharf. The Port Dundas Basin, between Tayport St and Colinton St, now drained, and part of a new road, was lined on both sides with single storey warehouses, with road access from the rear. Most of these were wood framed and planked, but on Carron Wharf there was a fine stone building (see *Industrial Archaeology of Scotland*, 165) and on North Speirs Wharf an unusual iron framed warehouse, with cruciform uprights, and arched ribs springing from a masonry base. This and several other of the warehouses had post cranes for unloading vessels. An aerial view taken in 1937 shows that at one time there were two four storey warehouses on the south side of the basin.

54 Warehouse, 40 Tayport St, probably built c 1830 for Carron Co. A three storey rubble building on a U plan, with a neat single storey, 11 bay frontage to Carron Wharf. There were pediments over the end three bays. Internally, cast-iron columns supported wooden beams and floors. Demolished 1967.

55 Warehouses, 30, 32 Tayport St, probably built *c* 1840. Two rubble buildings, one four storey and attic, 4 bay, with a pediment, and the other five storey, attic and basement, 5 bay. Demolished 1967.

56 Caledonian Grain Mills, 2–22 Tayport St, built 1862 for F. G. Perman, miller. A four storey, 4 by 12 bay square-dressed rubble building with a rounded corner and two large arched doorways having vermiculated quoins and voussoirs. The wooden floors were supported on cast-iron columns.

57 Warehouses, 7–39 Colinton St, probably built in the 1830s and 1840s. Two large five storey rubble blocks, one 10, the other 11 bays long, with a range of lower buildings along the street. Also included in this complex were a seven storey, 4 by 5 bay red brick building, and a five storey blue brick warehouse, both early 20th century.

58 Bascule Bridge, Portree St. Of standard Forth & Clyde Canal type, demolished in 1967.

59 Chemical Works, 31–3 Townsend St, founded 1856 by Joseph Townsend, the original buildings by *John Dingwall* of Helensburgh, architect. A rectangular block of red brick buildings built round a courtyard. On a sloping site, the front buildings were four storeys high, the rear three storeys, with entry from Payne St at top floor level. The front buildings were demolished in 1967, revealing the unusual construction of the rear blocks, with very massive cast-iron columns supporting heavy wooden frames, the spaces being glazed or brick filled. At one time this work boasted the highest chimney in Glasgow, built to rival Tennant's Stalk (see C83); known as Townsend's Stalk, it was 468 feet high, and was demolished in 1927.

60 Port Dundas Grain Mills, 88 North Speirs Wharf, built *c* 1843 for Andrew Hamilton, miller. A five storey, 5 by 15 bay rubble building, built into a hillside. On the west side is a beam-engine house.

61 Bonded Warehouse, 72 North Spiers Wharf, built *c* 1875 for W. N. Gemmill & Co., drysalters and oil merchants. A rubble three storey building with a 5 bay frontage and 3 wide bays, each with three windows per storey.

62 Port Dundas Goods Depot, North Speirs Wharf, built 1891 for the Caledonian Railway (£500). A small single storey, iron-framed wooden building, with two through tracks. A van body served as a store. Demolished 1967.

63 Eagle Foundry, 20 North Speirs Wharf, founded *c* 1820 by James Edington, and converted to a chemical works in 1872 for Alexander Cross & Sons. After a fire in 1889, the complex was extensively rebuilt (£15,000). The oldest building is a three storey, 4 bay rubble block with a wide segmental arched doorway and a moulding shop behind, and another early structure is a two storey, 8 bay block with an elliptically arched doorway. Recently the badly corroded stonework on this building has been harled. At the rear of the works in Harvey St is a three storey dwelling house and single storey stable added in 1901, *William Tennant*, architect (£1250).

64 Bascule Bridge and Railway Swing Bridge, Midwharf St. A bascule bridge of the standard Forth & Clyde Canal type, and a plate girder swing bridge, with hand operating gear.

65 Port Dundas Distillery, 76–80 North Canal Bank St, founded *c* 1820 by J. Gourlay & Co., and subsequently reconstructed and enlarged many times. A major rebuilding took place in 1913 after a fire, *Burnet & Boston*, architects (£27,640). The distillery proper is bounded by North Canal Bank, Borron St, Harvey St and Vintner St, and consists of a large block of buildings of two storeys or more. There are four malting kilns, with prominent vents, now disused. On the other side of Vintner St is a seven storey, 8 by 18 bay warehouse, built in 1899, *Campbell Douglas & Morrison*, architects (£29,500), while on the north side of Harvey St is a five storey, 15 by 20 bay store, built in 1889 (£15,000). Most of the buildings are of red brick.

66 Factory, 60 Vintner St, built 1890 for the Scottish Grain Co., and extended in 1905. The older part is a three storey, 3 bay red brick building with large segmentally arched windows separated by pilasters. Internally the building is iron framed. The 1905 block is five storeys high, 4 bays long, with an adjoining five storey, 3 bay kiln building. Badly damaged by fire in 1968.

67 Vulcan Maltings, 116 Vintner St, built from 1893 for Hugh Baird & Sons, maltsters, *Russell & Spence*, architects. A group of red brick buildings, the largest of which is a seven storey and attic, 11 bay block of malting floors, with more modern extensions at each end. There are also two storey and attic, 3 by 8 bay and four storey, 3 by 8 bay structures and a three storey, 3 bay office and dwelling house block.

68 Warehouses, Borron St, built 1897–1911 for Mackie & Co., distillers, *Burnet & Boston*, architects (£17,808). A group of one, two and three storey red brick buildings, with flat roofs.

69 Warehouses, 40 North Canal Bank St, probably built *c* 1860 for the Edinburgh & Glasgow Railway. A four storey, 7 by 2 bay building adjacent to a five storey, 5 by 9 bay block. Both are rubble built, with wooden floors on cast-iron columns.

70 Pinkston Iron Works, 328 Pinkston Rd, built from 1871 for J. & A. Law, ironfounders. The main block was two storeys high, 24 bays long, of red brick, and probably dated from 1877 (£8000). At the north end was a high single storey erecting shop added in 1898 (£1700). Cut down in 1968 to one storey.

71 Pinkston Power Station, North Canal Bank St, built 1900–1 for the electrification of the Corporation Tramways, *Harry B. Measures*, engineer, London (£100,000). An interesting red brick structure, with high single storey, 7 bay boiler house and engine halls side by side, and originally identical. The windows are round-headed with semicircular windows above and the wall tops are waved. Pilasters divide the bays, and are extended above the cornice, terminating in small pediments. At the north end are two large brick chimneys, with ornamental tops. The cooling tower, built 1952–4, was at the time of construction the largest in Europe.

72 Queen Street Station Tunnel, completed 1842 for the Edinburgh & Glasgow Railway. A double track tunnel on a 1 in 46 gradient, with a single ventilation point at Calgary St. At the Queen St end the tunnel mouth was set back when the station was enlarged in 1878–80, but the other end is as built.

73 Buchanan Street Station Tunnel, completed 1849 for the Caledonian Railway, though originally planned by the Glasgow, Garnkirk & Coatbridge Railway. A double track tunnel on a 1 in 79 gradient with a circular ventilation shaft about half way. The southern end has a spectacular facade, the northern is plainer. Just outside the south end, in the retaining wall can be seen a relieving arch over the Queen Street Station tunnel. The Buchanan Street Station tunnel has been disused since 1967 and the track has been lifted.

74 Contractor's Depot, 79 Fountainwell Rd, built *c* 1877 for J. & G. Hamilton, cartage contractors. A triangular single storey building with a two storey office block. Demolished 1967.

75 St Rollox Railway Works, 130 Springburn Rd, originally built for the Caledonian Railway in 1856–7, but completely rebuilt in the 1880s under the direction of Dugald Drummond, to designs by *Robert Dundas*, engineer. The buildings are mainly single storey, with round-headed openings and circular ventilators in the gable ends, and are of red and white brick. The two storey and attic, 3 by 17 bay office block on Springburn Rd was built in 1887 (£3500).

76 Petershill Sawmills, 172–8 Petershill Rd, built *c* 1900 for James Scott & Co., timber merchants and sawmillers. The main building is a two storey, 5 by 9 bay structure with a square-section chimney stalk, and there is a timber shed and a derrick crane. The office block is a plain two storey, 2 by 3 bay building, like the mill, of red brick.

77 Refuse Destructor & Workshops, 113 Charles St, built 1880 (£2000) and extended in 1895 (£800) and 1904 (£2500), for the Corporation Cleansing Department, *A. W. Wheatley*, engineer. A group of one storey red brick sheds, with a two storey, 3 bay gatehouse and a tall square-section chimney stalk.

78 Cotton Spinning Mill, 71 Royston Rd, built *c* 1845 for James Clark, cotton spinner. A four storey and attic, 2 by 12 bay rubble building with interior of jack arch construction. The top two floors were rebuilt in concrete after a fire. At the rear were single storey brick sheds. Demolished 1968.

79 Glasgow Pipe Foundry, 80 Charles St, part of a larger complex founded *c* 1852 by D. Y. Stewart & Co. A three storey, 12 bay red brick building with two elliptical-arched doorways. Demolished 1967.

80 St Rollox Ironworks, 28 Charles St, built from 1877 for Thomas Melvin & Sons, hydraulic, bakers' and general engineers. A large block of one, two and three storey buildings of various dates, incorporating premises built 1896–1902 for Murdoch & Cameron, engineers and Joseph W. Russell & Co., brassfounders. The oldest part is a three storey, 9 bay red brick building (1877, £2000) at the back of the site, and there is an interesting two

storey office block with round-headed windows.

81 Clay Pipe Factory, 18 Charles St, built *c* 1889 for D. McDougall & Co. A much-altered three storey, 7 bay red brick building, with two storey workshops extending to the rear, and a square-section brick chimney stalk. The last clay-pipe factory in Glasgow, closed 1967.

82 Workshops, 3 Charles St, built from *c* 1907 for T. D. Cowieson & Co., designers and erectors of portable buildings. The main frontage is two storeys high, 13 bays long, with a clock tower at the west end and a three storey, 5 bay block at the east end. To the rear are five wide bays. Most of the block was probably built after 1914.

83 St Rollox Chemical Works, 229 Castle St, founded 1799 by Tennant, Knox & Co., chemical manufacturers. A very extensive site, on both sides of the Garnkirk & Glasgow Railway. Latterly the oldest building was the neat one storey, 6 bay office block, though there were much-altered remains of other early structures. There was a modern Petersen sulphuric acid plant, which was demolished in 1964–5 with the rest of the works. The only surviving part is on the north of the railway, a two storey 12 by 6 bay red and white brick store at 11 Springburn Rd. At one time the works was renowned for 'Tennant's Stalk', a chimney 455½ feet tall, built 1841–2 and demolished in 1922.

84 St Rollox Flint Glass Works, 76 Kennedy St, founded *c* 1838 by Cochran & Couper. Two glass cones, both latterly truncated, with covered working areas, and three and four storey finishing shops and warehouses. Demolished 1966.

85 Store, 136 Kennedy St, built 1878 for Thomas Herbert, corn and grain merchant (£2600). A plain two storey, 4 bay red brick building.

86 Livery Stable, 138 Kennedy St, built *c* 1882 for George McKenzie. A plain three storey, 4 bay red and white brick building.

87 Warehouse, 54 Black St, built 1910 for John Watson & Co., stationers, printers and bookbinders, *C. A. Pattison*, architect (£1100). A three storey and attic, 3 bay red and white brick building.

88 Bascule Bridge, Glebe St, of the standard Forth & Clyde Canal type, spanning the 'Cut of Junction', with a single storey bridgekeeper's cottage. The cottage was demolished in 1965, the bridge in 1967.

89 Phoenix Sawmills, 28 Baird St, built from 1911 for J. B. Fraser & Co. A group of single storey red brick buildings, the oldest of which is a small 3 bay office block.

90 City Cabinet Works, 6–8 Couper Place, founded *c* 1876 by Cumming & Smith, wholesale upholstery furnishers, destroyed by fire on 22 November 1897, and subsequently rebuilt. An L shaped four storey, 7 by 14 bay red and white brick building with wooden floors supported on steel beams and columns. Demolished 1969.

91 Potato Store, 59 North Wallace St, built *c* 1907 for Wotherspoon & Donald, potato merchants. A two storey, 8 bay red brick building with an outside stair, at the rear of a block of tenements.

92 Stables, 43 Couper St, built *c* 1882 for Wordie & Co., carting contractors. Two, two storey, 2 by 6 bay red brick buildings, much altered, with a three storey, 15 bay block at the rear. The interior has wooden floors on cast-iron columns.

93 Oil Store, 22 Kyle St, built 1870 for P. W. Hall, and extended in 1909 and 1912 for M. Barr & Co., oilskin makers. A three storey, 8 bay red and white brick building (1870, £2300); a three storey, 2 bay red brick block (1909, *George Simpson*, architect, £830), with a mansard roof added in 1912 (£680, *Charles Henry*, engineer); and a

four storey, 10 by 4 bay flat roofed red brick structure.

94 Oil Refinery, 98 Dobbies Loan, built 1870 for J. V. Wilson & Co., oil merchants and extended in 1879 (£1200). A two storey, 6 bay red brick front block with a single storey back building and chimney stalk.

95 City Flint Glass Works and Hecla Foundry, 31 Kyle Street, founded *c* 1853 by James Couper & Son, and extended and rebuilt several times. The main buildings, one 2 by 10 bay, the other 14 bay, are two storey red and white brick structures, built 1900–1 (*Burnet & Boston*, architects, £10,700), and there are similar two and three storey blocks extending along Kyle St.

96 Contractor's Depot, 50 Calgary St, built 1899 (£2700, 58 stalls) and 1904 (£2000, 40 stalls) for Wordie & Co., cartage constractors, *William Tennant*, architect. A three storey building, one part 10 bay, the other 15 bay, in red brick, with projecting brick piers between the windows. Demolished 1967.

97 Glebe Street Station, built 1831 for the Garnkirk & Glasgow Railway. The most important recently surviving structure was the carriage shed, with arched doorways, and a dwelling house above (see *Industrial Archaeology of Scotland*, 179). Other interesting remains were the crossing-keeper's hut (not booking office), made of old stone sleepers, the coal staithes, and the stone piers of canal loading bays. Demolished 1967.

98 Bascule Bridge and Railway Swing Bridge, Canal St. The bascule bridge is of the standard Forth & Clyde Canal type, and the railway bridge a hand operated plate girder structure. Until *c* 1963 there was a single storey bridgekeeper's cottage on the east side.

99 Kelvin Motor Works, 254 Dobbies Loan, built 1909–14 for Walter Bergius, motor engineer, *Monro & Son* and *W. R.*

Watson, architects (£11,740). A large block of single storey brick and steel engineering shops, with a neat one storey and attic office block.

100 Engineering Works, 284 Dobbies Loan, part of Port Dundas Engine Works, founded *c* 1849 by William Forrest & Co., engineers & millwrights. A two storey, 13 bay ashlar building, partly cut down to one storey. Demolished 1967–8.

101 Alliance Foundry, 147 Milton St, founded *c* 1853. The most important remains are a 4 bay block of single storey workshops with circular and semicircular windows and a high single storey 2 by 7 bay red brick building with round-headed windows.

102 Port Dundas Pottery, 66 Renton St, founded 1831 by the Port Dundas Pottery Co. A nondescript collection of one, two, and three storey red brick buildings, much altered.

103 London & Glasgow Colour Works, 309–61 Dobbies Loan, built from 1889 for the London & Glasgow Colour Co., *J. Cairns*, architect. The main manufacturing blocks are a three storey and attic, 10 bay rubble block, from an earlier period, and a two storey and attic, 10 bay red brick building (1902, £2,000). A single storey block and offices were added in 1904 (£2000), and a three storey warehouse at the rear in 1911 (£1711).

104 Asphalt Works, 120 Renton St, founded *c* 1864 by William Neilson. The oldest part was a two storey ashlar fronted building, demolished *c* 1968, the largest a four storey and basement, 6 by 8 bay red brick block with a flat roof added in 1898 for Ferguson, Shaw & Sons, oil refiners, *James Thomson* (I), architect (£8000).

105 Stables, 127 Renton St, built 1906 for J. Menzies & Co., *Brand & Lithgow*, architects (£1650). A neat group of one and two storey red brick buildings round a small courtyard. As built it contained 14 stalls, a van shed and two houses.

106 Oil Works, 101–9 Renton St, built 1899–1900 for Rowley & Dick, oil merchants and refiners, *Burnet & Boston*, architects (£10,000). A four storey, attic and basement, 7 by 8 bay red brick building with a mansard roof over the front 4 bays.

107 Victoress Stove Works, 81–3 Renton St, built 1873–4 for Smith & Wellstood, ironfounders, *William Landless*, architect (£7000). A striking four storey, 5 bay Italian Renaissance building, with a cream sandstone frontage. There were round-headed windows on the first three floors, those on the ground floor having elaborate cast-iron grilles, and sculptured heads between the ground and first floors. Demolished 1968.

108 Glass Works, 97–9 Milton St, founded 1876 by John Baird, glass beveller and silverer. A high narrow four storey and attic, 12 bay red and white brick building on the street, built 1899 (*H. & D. Barclay*, architects, £3900), with an older four storey and attic, 5 bay extension at the rear. Demolished 1968.

109 Wright's Workshop, 100 Port Dundas Rd, probably built *c* 1853 for Peter McAinsh, timber merchant. A plain two storey, 4 bay red brick building, demolished in 1968.

110 Offices and Printing Works, 144 Port Dundas Rd, built 1906–11 for D. C. Thomson & Co., newspaper publishers, *Robert Gibson*, architect, Dundee. The first part of the printing works, built in 1906, was a single storey building (£3400). The ground floor of the 10 bay office block was added in 1907 (£280) and a second floor put on in 1911 (£240).

111 Oil Works, 82 Dunblane St, built 1904 for J. & D. Hamilton, oil importers, refiners and merchants, *Thomson & Sandilands*, architects (£4000). A four storey red brick building with a high ground floor having a large round-headed doorway flanked by pairs of pilasters. The top two storeys are a later addition, as is the office block, built in 1911 (£2660), a two storey and basement, 3 by 6 bay terra-cotta fronted brick building facing Port Dundas Rd.

112 Soap Works, 76 Milton St, built 1891 for Dick & Parker, soap manufacturers, *Russell & Spence*, architects and engineers (£3700). A 7 by 10 bay block of two storey red brick buildings on an L plan, with an arched doorway in Dunblane St.

113 Offices, 65 Port Dundas Rd, built 1910 for Lewis & John McLellan, oil importers and refiners, founded on this site c 1864, *Burnet & Boston*, architects (£2200). A plain three storey, 5 by 7 bay terra-cotta fronted red brick building.

114 Workshops, 41–51 Port Dundas Rd, part built 1897 for R. & J. Irving, wrights, trunk, packing box, zinc and tin case makers, *Joseph Cowan*, architect (£800). Two, two storey buildings, one 8 bay, the other 9 by 23 bay.

115 Cabinet Works, 63 Dunblane St, built c 1880 for Lee & Glendinning, cabinetmakers and upholsterers. A four storey, 4 bay red and white brick building, with wood floors on cast-iron columns.

116 Workshops, 5 Milton Place, built 1897 for James Barclay, slater, *William Tennant*, architect (£500). A plain two storey, 8 bay red brick block.

117 Buchanan's Confectionery Works, 35 Stewart St, founded 1869 by John Buchanan & Bros, incorporating nail-works built c 1865 for Motherwell & Lapsley. The Ann St frontage consisted of a two storey, 13 bay flat roofed block (*A. B. Dansken*, architect, 1902, £2500), a four storey and attic, 18 bay building, and a six storey, 4 bay reinforced concrete structure (*Wyllie & Blake*, 1907). The

Stewart St buildings were a four storey and attic, 11 bay block, a five storey and attic, 6 bay, and a five storey and attic, 11 bay structure, both extended from three storeys. On the corner with Maitland St was a five storey and attic, 6 by 10 bay building (*A. B. Dansken*, architect, 1897, £5000) and in Maitland St a six storey, 7 bay reinforced-concrete structure designed by *Wyllie & Blake*, architects, in 1907 (£10,400). In the interior of the hollow rectangle formed by these buildings was a five storey block built in 1898 (*A. B. Dansken*, architect, £4600) and a tall chimney stalk (1905, £300). This large complex was demolished in 1967.

118 Dalhousie Street Tram Depot, 65 Dalhousie St, built 1893–4 for Corporation Tramways Department, *William Clark*, engineer (£22,000, 286 stalls). A large 3 by 28 bay, two storey building, with three vehicle entrances at ground level, in Dalhousie St, and entrance to the first floor from West Graham St. It is of red sandstone, with seven small pediments on the West Graham St frontage, finished to harmonise with the surrounding residential buildings.

119 Coach Manufactory & Showrooms, 85 Buccleuch St, built 1869–70 for John Ewing Walker, coach builder. A three storey, 9 by 10 bay building with sandstone fronts to Buccleuch and Garnethill Sts, the other walls being of red brick. Above the main entrance are the arms of Glasgow in relief. Subsequently used as a veterinary college.

120 Workshop, 35 Buccleuch St, built c 1899 for George Walton & Co. Ltd, cabinetmakers. A two storey and attic, 7 bay red sandstone fronted brick building, with a brick extension at the rear.

Section D
Dennistoun and Milnbank

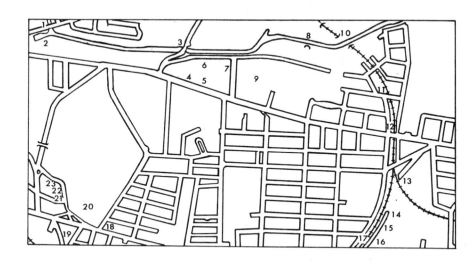

1 Canal Bridge, Roystonhill, built 1858. A small cast-iron girder bridge, with neat cast-iron railings, and masonry abutments. The castings were made at the Hydepark Foundry. Demolished 1966.

2 Canal Basin, Castle St, completed 1790 for the Monkland Canal. The Glasgow terminus of the canal, this once-important coal basin was filled in for road improvement in 1966.

3 Robertson's Bridge, Millburn Rd. A wrought-iron lattice girder, skew bridge supported off-centre by a row of five cast-iron columns. The bridge carries the road over the Monkland Canal.

4 Garage, 267 Alexandra Parade, built 1913–14 for Roberton & Stevenson, *J. W. & J. Laird*, architects (£800). A plain single storey, 3 bay red brick building, with gables to the street.

5 Substation, 287–9 Alexandra Parade, built *c* 1923. A high single storey, red brick building, with two large arched doorways, having glazed fanlights.

6 Craigpark Factory, 360 Townmill Rd, built 1860 for Rainey, Knox & Co., merchants, power-loom manufacturers and agents, and extended in 1861, 1865. A remarkable group of one and two storey, red and white brick buildings, with round-headed windows. There is a handsome engine house, with sandstone details. At the rear is an 18 bay range of conventional single storey weaving sheds. The factory was taken over by Dunlop & Twaddell, flax and jute spinners, in 1868, and a store was added for them in 1874 (£1500).

7 Warehouse, 87 Milnbank St, built 1906 (£7980) and 1912 (£5500) for Blackie & Son, printers and publishers, *G. Simpson*, architect. The older part is on the corner with Townmill Rd, an 8 by 5 bay block on an L plan, extended to south by a similar 7 by 5 bay block. Both are four storeys high, of red brick, with projecting piers separating the bays, each of two windows.

8 Aqueduct, Townmill Rd, carrying the Monkland Canal over the Molendinar Burn. A single span, rustic masonry structure with a semicircular arch carrying the towpath and a segmental arch supporting the canal bed. Similar to B1, B26 and C23.

9 Milnbank Bleachworks, 398–400 Townmill Rd, founded *c* 1828 by William Adam & Son as Burnbank Bleachfield, and subsequently much altered. The surviving buildings are plain, two storeys high, of red and white brick, and date from the late 19th century.

10 Tunnel, Barnhill, constructed *c* 1875 for the City of Glasgow Union Railway. This short tunnel carries the railway under the Monkland Canal, and has portals similar to D8.

11 Kennyhill Bakery, 10 Roebank St, built 1904 for George McAllister, *Crawford & Veitch*, architects (£1000). A two storey block, partly obscured by later additions.

12 Alexandra Parade Station, Alexandra Parade, opened 1 January 1881 by the City of Glasgow Union Railway. A two platform through station in a cutting, with access from a road overbridge at the south end. There is a combined single storey booking office and station house at street level, supported on round-headed arches (built 1888, £2000). The platform buildings have been replaced by modern steel and glass shelters.

13 Haghill Distillery, Birkenshaw St, built *c* 1837 for J. & W. Stewart, possibly a conversion from Haghill Brewery (*c* 1803 or earlier). The only surviving part is a two storey building on an L plan, the top part of which is a dwelling house, and the bottom a vaulted cellar, with two apartments at right angles.

14 Dennistoun Bakery, 116 Paton St, built from 1886 for William & David Beattie, *J. M. Monro* and *Munro & Son*, architects. Between 1886 and 1908 £58,700 was spent on buildings and ovens. A large group of one, two and three storey red brick buildings.

15 Dennistoun Tram Depot, Paton St, built 1895–6 for Glasgow Corporation Tramways Department, *W. Clark*, engineer (£26,000) and extended in 1903 (£4900), 1904 (£7500) and 1905 (£1500). A single storey red brick building, with a 5 bay gabled frontage to the street, and roof-lit extensions to the rear.

16 Factory, 34 Paton St, built 1904 for John Wallace & Sons Ltd, agricultural engineers, *Bruce & Hay*, architects. The first part was a block of single storey workshops, and an addition was made in similar style in 1907. The three storey, 16 bay block facing the street and the two storey, 9 bay office block (both red brick) were added in 1913–14, *William Baillie*, architect (£16,400).

17 Duke Street Station, Duke St, opened 1 Jan 1881 by the City of Glasgow Union Railway. A two platform station in a shallow cutting, with access from a road overbridge at the south end. The booking office, in a much modified wooden building (built 1883, £500), is at street level and an interesting wooden footbridge links the platforms.

18 Duke Street Engraving Works, 18–24 Ark Lane, built 1878 for David Fulton & Co., engravers (£7000). A pleasing group of two, and three storey and attic, ashlar-fronted red brick buildings with an ornamental square-section chimney. The main frontage consists of three storey, 6 bay and two storey, 6 bay blocks, in Classical style, with mansard roofs, and the frontage to Macintosh St consists of another 6 bay face of the three storey block, and a plain, three storey, 7 bay block, with three windows per bay.

19 Warehouses, 202–4 Hunter St, built from 1903 for J. & A. McArthur Ltd, grain millers, seed and potato merchants, *Monro & Son*, architects (£1500). A 5 bay range of one and two storey brick buildings, with an associated four storey and attic red sandstone tenement. There is an interesting low-relief sculpture on the tenement, composed of agricultural motifs.

20 Wellpark Brewery, 161 Duke St, reputedly founded *c* 1556 by the Tennant family. This extensive complex has been subject to alteration and modernisation at many different dates; for example, in 1873 a new group of malt barns, vaults, bottle stores and straw house cost £15,000, and between 1890 and 1911 £44,500 was spent on additions. The oldest part is a four storey range of malt barns, with two kilns, now used as stores and offices, while other 19th century buildings are in use as warehouses. At the rear are two water towers with machicolations.

21 Engine Waste Factory, 45 Ladywell St, founded *c* 1877 by James Paxton & Co. The back building was the oldest (1889) designed by *W. N. Tait*, architect (£1000). The southern front block, three storeys, 4 bays, with semicircular ground floor windows and a mansard roof, was added in 1900 and the northern part, 3 bays long, in 1909, both *Miller & Black*, architects (£1000, £1280). Demolished *c* 1971.

22 Workshops, 63 Ladywell St, built 1904 for Gossman & Smith, house factors, *MacWhannell & Rogerson*, architects (£600). A plain, two storey and basement, 4 bay building.

23 Furniture Works, 65–9 Ladywell St, built *c* 1893 for the Bennett Furnishing Co. A plain, three storey, 8 bay, red and white brick building, with two arched doorways. Demolished *c* 1968.

Section E
Parkhead, Carntyne and Shettleston

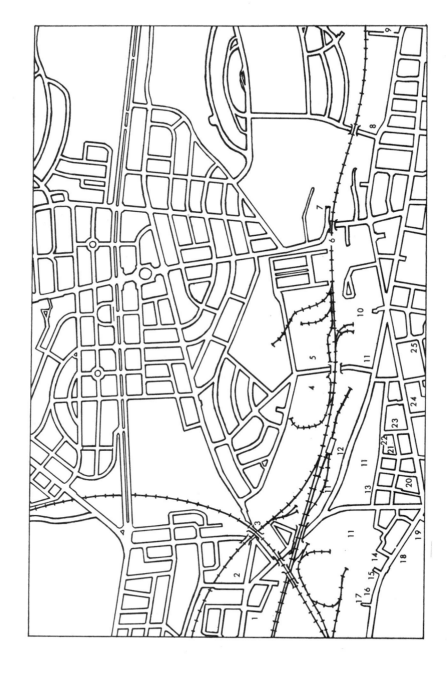

1 Netherfield Chemical Works, 694 Duke St, founded 1851 on this site by John Garroway. The works were split in 1873 when the North British Railway acquired land for their Coatbridge–Glasgow line. The fertiliser plant is on the north side and is housed in two storey brick and asbestos sheds of varying dates. There is a one storey and attic, 3 bay office block. On the south side is a modern contact sulphuric acid plant.

2 Refuse Destructor, 16 Haghill Rd, built 1895–6 for Corporation Cleansing Department, *A. W. Wheatley*, engineer (£9000). The main block is two storeys high, 4 bays long, with lorry access by a ramp leading to the first floor. There is a tall hooped brick chimney of circular cross-section, two dwelling houses, and single storey ancillary buildings.

3 Railway Bridges, Carntyne Rd, built *c* 1875 and *c* 1894 for the City of Glasgow Union Railway and the Caledonian Railway. An unusual example of two railways crossing each other and also a road. The rail crossing and one of the road crossings are plate girder bridges, the third being a truss bridge on a skew (CR bridge).

4 Wheel & Axle Depot, 139 Rigby St, built 1903 for William Beardmore & Co. (£25,000). Two groups of 3 bay, single storey workshops, with round-headed windows, and the remains of a neat 7 bay, single storey office. Much of the complex has been demolished.

5 Crane Works, 92 Rigby St, built 1903–4 for The Glasgow Electric Crane & Hoist Co. Ltd (£16,000) and subsequently extended. A large group of one, two and three storey buildings, the oldest of which have round-headed windows.

6 Carntyne Station, built *c* 1871 for the North British Railway. A simple two platform station on an embankment, with a disused goods yard at a lower level. The up platform building is of a standard wooden North British Railway type, modernised by the replacement of the platform facade, while the down platform shelter is modern.

7 Stanley Works, 29–41 Westerburn St, rebuilt 1926 for The Universal Casings Co. Ltd, sausageskin manufacturers. A group of one and two storey brick buildings with a two storey, 5 bay office block (built 1926) and an older two storey workshop block with a 7 bay gabled frontage to Westerburn St. The origin of this workshop is unknown at the time of writing.

8 North British Bottle Works, 515 Old Shettleston Rd, built from *c* 1904 for the North British Bottle Manufacturing Co. Ltd. A furnace house was added in 1912–13, *Hutton & Taylor*, architects (£5140). Facing the street is a single storey, 28 bay range of warehouses, decorated with low relief arches, and recently extended by the addition of a second storey. The machinery in the glasshouses behind is modern.

9 Shettleston Ironworks, 619 Old Shettleston Rd, built *c* 1874 for J. & T. Boyd, textile machinery makers. The main block is of red and white brick, 5 bays wide and 43 long, with upper floors supported on riveted beams carried by robust cast-iron columns. The windows are round-headed, as are those in the later adjacent block. There is also an extensive single storey foundry, with three cupolas.

10 Carntyne Dyewood Mills, 567 Shettleston Rd, built *c* 1883 for McArthur, Scott & Co., drysalters, dyewood and extract manufacturers, and added to in 1886 (£4500) and 1911 (*Honeyman, Keppie & Mackintosh*, architects, £2850). The two main blocks are 2 by 18 bay (1886) and 4 by 15 bay (1911). The former is of red and white brick, the latter red brick and concrete. At right angles to the 1886 block is a 10 bay block, possibly the original. All are two storeys high.

11 Parkhead Forge, founded *c* 1837 by Reoch Bros & Co. for the manufacture of scrap-iron forged work on a site to the west of Duke St, and subsequently greatly extended and rebuilt by Rigby & Beardmore and William Beardmore & Co. Between 1884 and 1914 £244,600 was spent on buildings alone. The buildings are mostly single storey, of brick or corrugated-iron clad steel, and some are very large indeed. The single storey G shop in East Wellington St is 72 bays long (built 1900–1, £33,000), and there was until 1969 a gun quenching shop 110 ft high, the highest building in Scotland when it was built in 1905 (£18,000). Large single storey machine shops on either side of Shettleston Rd date from 1905 (south side, £17,000, 19 bays added to in 1914, £10,130) and 1914–15 (north side, 20 bays and three storey, 13 bay office block, £13,970). The main office block, a three storey and attic, 17 bay Renaissance building in terra-cotta brick and red sandstone, was constructed in 1902, R. A. Bryden, architect (£14,000). The other two office blocks are post-1914.

The machinery in the works is of considerable interest, and includes two double-column and one single-column steam hammers, a late 19th century cogging mill driven by a two cylinder simple horizontal steam engine (built 1942 by Davy United in London Road Ironworks) and two large hydraulic presses. The machine shops contain many tools, some very large, designed for munitions construction and adapted for the manufacture of work rolls.

12 Carntyne Foundry & Engineering Works, 247–79 Shettleston Rd, founded c 1875 by Kesson & Campbell, engineers. Two blocks of two storey workshops, the western one with 12 bays, each having two round-headed windows at each level (1900, £11,500) and the eastern one with a 7 bay office (1901, £1500) and a 14 bay main section, similar in style to the 1900 building (1887, £3500). A single storey steel-framed corrugated-iron clad shed at the rear was added in 1907, *James Ferguson*, engineer (£1030).

13 Warehouse, 19–21 East Wellington St, built 1896 for John Fleming, ham curer and provision merchant, *A. R.*

Crawford, architect. A two storey and attic, 4 bay red and white brick building with gable end to the street.

14 Home Brewery, 7 Invernairn St, built 1865–6 for George Dalrymple & Co. and partly rebuilt in 1897 for Charles Blair, *P. L. Henderson*, architect, Edinburgh. The surviving buildings are one and two storeys high, round a small courtyard.

15 Van & Lorry Works, 15 Van St, built 1904 for J. H. Kelly, *Crawford & Veitch*, architects (£1100). A plain three storey, 9 bay red and white brick building. Its appearance has recently been altered by the use of coloured cement washes to give a 'modern' effect.

16 Parkhead Silk Factory, 1179 Gallowgate, built c 1899 for the Vanduara Silk Co. Ltd. A two storey and attic, 4 by 18 bay red brick building with prominent roof ventilators.

17 Hartshead Factory (Curled Hair & Bedding), 1141 Gallowgate, built from 1877 for Mrs C. McCrae and R. & J. McCrae, bedding manufacturers. The main block is three storeys high, 12 bays long, of red and white brick built 1880–3 (£2200). The one storey office block on Gallowgate, with a red sandstone Renaissance frontage, was designed by *N. C. Duff*, architect, in 1914 (£830) and has recently been extended by the addition of a second storey.

18 Aerated Water Factory, 1306–10 Gallowgate, built from 1889 for R. F. Barr, bottler and aerated water manufacturer. Between 1899 and 1914 £12,166 was spent on buildings, which were designed by various architects. The four storey tenement on the street was added in 1907, and has Renaissance features. It incorporates the office. The factory buildings at the rear are of one and two storeys, and are mostly red brick.

19 Parkhead Grain Mills, 1392–6 Gallowgate, built c 1897 and 1900 (£1000) for

John Kent, hay, grain and seed merchant. Two three storey red brick buildings with a single storey link block, at the rear of a residential tenement.

20 Stables & Workshops, 23–7 Ravel Row, built 1906 for John Roy. A single storey, 3 bay red and white brick office with a two storey, 5 bay red brick workshop and a yard at the rear. Part possibly dates from 1862.

21 Phoenix Cabinet Works, 121 Salamanca St, and 30 Nisbet St, built *c* 1896 for Crichton & Mooney, upholsterers, *A. R. Crawford*, architect (£4000). A four storey, 5 by 17 bay red and white brick building, with timber sheds at the rear.

22 Stables, 134 East Wellington St, built 1907 for Alexander Hart, cartage contractor. A group of single storey brick buildings round a small courtyard.

23 Parkhead Metal Refining Works, 16 Backcauseway, founded 1875 by Park & Paterson. A two storey, 5 bay red brick office block with single storey brick sheds at the rear, and a square section brick chimney. Additions were made in 1901–2, *A. R. Crawford*, architect (£3200) and 1907–9, *T. M. Scotland*, architect (£660).

24 Oil & Tallow Works, 270 Westmuir St, built *c* 1909 for Cardno & Co., oil and tallow refiners. A group of single storey red brick buildings, with an 8 bay frontage to Westmuir St. There is a two storey, 2 bay office and dwelling house at the rear, in a lane off Quarryknowe St, and an interesting chimney stalk.

25 Carntyne Rope & Twine Works, 16 Caroline St, built 1890 for H. Winning & Co., rope and twine manufacturers (£1750) and subsequently extended. A group of single storey, red brick buildings, lit from the roof, with a 6 bay frontage to the street.

Section F
Bridgeton and Dalmarnock

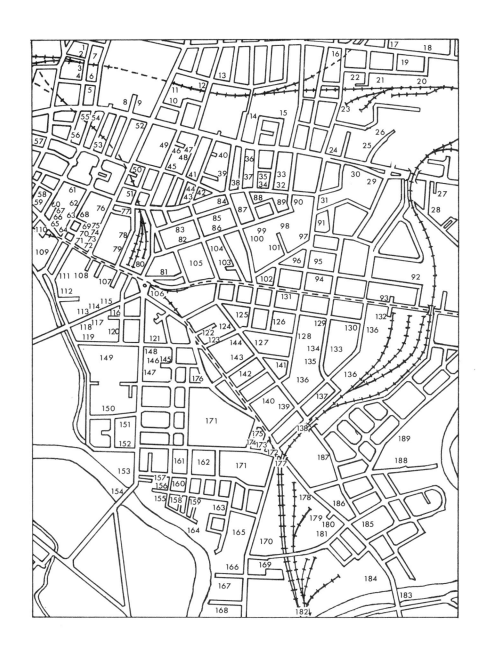

1 Stables and Cattle & Sheep Pens, 103 Sydney St, built 1908 for Brechin Bros, butchers, *Thomson & Sandilands*, architects (£2750). A two storey red brick block on an L plan, with semicircular windows on the upper floor and prominent louvred roof ventilators. Originally there were 13 stalls.

2 Sydney Street Soap Works, 87–9 Sydney St, built from *c* 1853 for Alexander Whitelaw, soap manufacturer. A high single storey and basement, 3 by 17 bay block, with round-headed openings, and a one storey, 5 bay office, both red and white brick, probably built 1869.

3 Engineering Works, 67 Sydney St, founded *c* 1889 by John Deas, blacksmith. The present building, a three storey, 4 by 7 bay red brick structure with round-headed windows at first floor level, was built in 1898 (£1250), R. *Miller*, architect. Damaged by fire in 1912, it was reconstructed to designs by *Miller & Black* (£1204).

4 Stables, 51 Sydney St, built 1897 for R. & D. Kelso, offal merchants, *D. V. Wyllie*, architect (£3000). A two storey and attic, 7 bay brick building, with red sandstone dressings, originally containing 51 stalls.

5 Wright's Workshop, 42 Sydney St, founded *c* 1834 by William Lightbody, wright and contractor. A three storey, 2 by 5 bay red and white brick building, with one and two storey red brick and timber outbuildings, and a small square-section chimney.

6 Cold Store, 39 Melbourne St, built 1913–14 for the Union Cold Storage Co., *J. W. & J. Laird*, architects (£22,080). A plain windowless brick building, of massive proportions. The exterior is relieved only by pilasters, while internally there are four storeys above ground and two below.

7 Water Depot, 118 Sydney St, on the site of the Glasgow Waterworks Co.'s basin. A large yard, used for the storage of pipe sections and valves, with one and two storey brick offices, built in 1896, *J. M. Gale*, city water engineer (£1200).

8 Weaving Factory, 11 Graham Square, built *c* 1825 for G. Grant Jun. as a power-loom factory, and occupied by them until *c* 1845. A six storey and attic, 3 by 9 bay red brick building, with a single row of slender cast-iron columns supporting wooden beams and floors. There is a small three storey, 4 bay block at right angles. Three tie rods, with cruciform washers, on each floor act as strengtheners.

9 Workshop, 38 Graham Square, built 1897 for John Wallace, agricultural engineer, *Bruce & Hay*, architects (£300). A three storey, 3 bay red and white brick building, with gable end to the square. At the rear are 6 bays of weaving sheds, built 1873–4 for John Brown & Son, cotton spinners and power-loom weavers (£1000).

10 Stables & Stores, 9–11 Brandon St, built 1896 for Mair & Dougall, bottlers (£2500). A two storey, 6 bay ashlar building, with a row of roof ventilators. Demolished *c* 1967.

11 Bellgrove Street Station, Bellgrove St, built 1883–9 for the City of Glasgow Union Railway, *J. Carswell*, engineer. A single island platform situated in a shallow cutting, with a glazed overall roof supported on cast-iron columns. Originally there was a single storey, 4 bay stone entrance in Sword St, built 1883 (£300); the present wooden building in Bellgrove St was added in 1889 (£1500). Cattle lairage was provided in connection with the nearby cattle market.

12 Box Factory, 79 Sword St, built *c* 1889 for J. G. Pratt, packing case and box maker. A plain two storey, 2 by 6 bay red brick building.

13 Cabinet Works, 107 Reidvale St, built 1900 for James Inglis, joiner, *J. Lindsay*, architect (£1200). A two storey,

3 by 8 bay red brick building, with a cart entry through the middle.

14 Ropeworks, 52 Bellfield St, built c 1884 for Andrew Brown, ropemaker. A plain two storey and attic, 3 by 5 bay red brick building, with gable end to the street.

15 Slatefield Brewery, Slatefield St, built 1881–4 for Gillespie, Gray & Co., brewers, *P. Henderson*, engineer and architect, Edinburgh. A neat group of two and three storey, red and white brick buildings round a rectangular courtyard. A circular-section chimney stalk rises through the former copper house.

16 Store, 16 Millerston St, built in the late 19th century. A two storey, 8 bay brick building with a Belfast roof, and three circular ventilators at first floor level.

17 Greenvale Chemical Works, 753 Duke St, founded c 1849 by C. F. Parsons & Co., Congreve match, paste and liquid blacking manufacturers. The oldest recently surviving part was a two storey, 10 bay rubble building, parallel to Duke St, and a later red brick addition, two storeys high, with two wide bays. Demolished 1967–8.

18 Glenpark Tan Works, 847 Duke St, built from c 1864 for Martin & Millar, tanners. A four storey red brick building, much altered, with parts of walls. The five acre complex was rebuilt in 1884–5 (£30,000).

19 Engineering Works, 25 Gateside St, built 1894 for Shiels, Elliot & Nelson, makers of milking machines, thermostats (£1000), *W. Stirling*, architect, Galashiels. Two wide single storey red brick bays behind a tenement, with offices on the ground floor of the tenement.

20 Avon Steel Works, Glenpark St, built c 1869 for M. W. Robertson & Co., crucible steel makers. A nondescript collection of single storey buildings, much altered.

21 Glasgow Oil & Chemical Works, 130 Glenpark St, built from 1883 for Hannay, Gourlie & Hinshelwood, chemical manufacturers, drysalters and oil refiners. A large complex of red and white brick buildings built up over a long period. The three storey office block with its tower was built in 1898, *R. Miller*, architect (£13,000).

22 Workshop, 34 Glenpark St, built c 1897 for G. Robertson, contractor. A two storey and attic, 6 bay red and white brick building at the rear, with a small two storey ashlar office block on the street.

23 Camlachie Goods & Mineral Station, 87 Millerston St, opened c 1875 by the North British Railway. The two storey, 3 bay red brick office block was built in 1914 (£400).

24 Crown Fireclay Works, Millerston St and Gallowgate, founded 1860 by James Shearer. The main survivals are two rectangular-section iron-reinforced brick kiln chimneys and a small single storey preparation shed. The kilns themselves were demolished c 1965.

25 North British Oil & Grease Works, 49 Vinegarhill St, built from 1875 for Joseph Jack, rosin, oil distiller and grease manufacturer (1875, £1000; 1881, £250). A large yard with low single storey buildings grouped round it.

26 Gut Factory, 61 Vinegarhill St, founded 1907 by John Noonan. A complex of one, two and three storey buildings, the largest of which is post-1914 in construction.

27 Contractor's Depot, 1064 Gallowgate, built 1889–1911 for Alexander Hodge, carting contractor. A three storey, 5 bay block, built 1889, *J. Higgins*, architect (£3000). This building originally contained 46 stalls. At right angles is a two storey, 10 bay block, part added in 1911, *L. B. Buik*, architect (£310).

28 Parkhead Factory, 49 Holywell St, built from 1865–6 for Clark & Struthers, gingham and pullicate manufacturers. A three storey, 20 bay red brick building with a six bay group of single storey weaving sheds at the rear (1897, £800). Projecting from the back of the main building are a brick water tower with an iron tank, and a circular-section chimney stalk.

29 Camlachie Distillery, 130 Camlachie St, built from 1853 for Bulloch & Co., later Bulloch, Lade & Co. Extensive additions were made in 1863, 1902 (£5000), 1903 (£16,000) and 1914 (£860), R. Ewan being the architect for the last three. A large group of two, three and four storey red and white brick buildings, including the stumps of two malting kilns. The largest block is three storeys high, with four wide bays extending back from the street.

30 Pyroligneous Acid Works, 100 Camlachie St, founded c 1813 by Turnbull & Ramsay, linen printers' colour makers. A nondescript group of single-storey red brick buildings with a three storey and attic, 4 bay red and white brick blacking mill and a tall rectangular section chimney. Some of the smaller buildings had pantiled roofs. The works operated until 1965, and was demolished in 1967.

31 Crownpoint Box Factory, 125 Fielden St, built c 1875 for E. W. Neil, cope tube maker, and considerably rebuilt and extended in 1896–7 (£4200) and 1910 (£2572) for George Pratt, boxmaker. A group of single storey red brick buildings with a circular-section chimney with a flared top, and a water tank on a brick tower. The office block includes a much altered 18th century private house 'Crown Point'. The factory closed in December 1969, and was the last chip-basket factory in Scotland.

32 Whitevale Foundry, 65–91 Rowchester St, founded c 1882 by David Auld & Sons, ironfounders. The two storey, 3 by 5 bay office block and two storeys of the 4 by 2 bay reinforced concrete building at the rear were designed in 1914 by

Brand & Lithgow, architects, in conjunction with *Mouchel & Partners*, licensees of the Hennebique system (£1490). A third storey was added to the workshops later.

33 Whitevale Tram Depot, 25–39 Rowchester St, built in 1893 for Glasgow Corporation Tramways Department (£10,000) and extended in 1899 (£1800), 1900 (£1800), 1906 and 1912 (£7458, substation). The Rowchester St frontage is in four sections, one of 3 bays and three of 2 bays each, all of red and white brick, with steel joists as lintels.

34 Express Oil Works, 177 Crownpoint Rd, built c 1890 for Patullo Bros, oil refiners. A two storey and attic, 4 by 7 bay red and white brick building, with an adjacent two storey, 7 bay office block, added in 1908, *W. R. Watson*, architect (£550).

35 Campbellfield Bedstead Works, 57–79 Campbellfield St and 53 Elgin St, built from 1876 for Andrew Sharp, iron bedstead manufacturer. The 1876 building (£4500) was badly damaged by fire on 30 November 1881, and restored in 1882 (£3500). At present there are two three storey blocks, one L shaped, 14 by 13 bay, and the other 12 bay, both of red and white brick. At the rear is a high single storey foundry building with a large round-headed doorway with iron-framed fanlight.

36 Campbellfield Twisting Factory, 18–34 Campbellfield St, built from c 1882 for Scott & McKillop, yarn twisters, and extended in 1891 (£2000), 1900 (£2500) and 1904 (£300), *Burnet & Boston*, architects. Two adjoining three storey, attic and basement red and white brick buildings, one 9 bay, the other 8 bays long. The northern part has round-headed openings on the ground floor.

37 Workshop, 74 Campbellfield St, built c 1875 for James Miller, harness, muslin and lappet cutter. A three storey and attic, 10 bay red and white brick building, with a

2 by 6 bay wing and a square-section chimney at the rear.

38 Stables, 7 Tylefield Street, built 1897 for Robert Robb, contractor, *A. Leitch*, engineer. A block of two storey red and white brick buildings on an L plan.

39 Bakery, 17–23 Soho St, built 1907 for W. & G. Muir, bakers, *Miller & Black*, architects (£8360). A two storey by 10 bay terra-cotta fronted brick building, with the end pairs of bays lower than the central part.

40 Grain Store, 17 Cornfield St, built from 1872–3 for John Cullen, grain merchant (first part £300). A group of two, three and four storey red and white brick buildings round a courtyard, with an ornamental twin-doorwayed entrance. The three storey block was built in 1882 (£1200) and the four storey in 1890.

41 Victoria Bread & Biscuit Works, 30 Wesleyan St, Forbes St and Cubie St, built from 1880 for John McFarlane & Sons. The oldest surviving part of this large block is a four storey and attic, 8 bay building with arched doorways (*McKissack & Rowan*, architects, 1886), extended to the south by a five storey and attic, 4 by 15 bay structure, with an attractive hoist tower at the rear (*J. M. Monro*, architect, 1895). The complex is completed by a two storey and attic, 5 bay stable block with a mansard roof, a two storey, 3 by 5 bay corner block, a single storey, 6 bay building, a three storey, 3 bay block, a five storey, 7 bay structure (*J. M. Monro*, 1890, top storey a later addition), a two storey 3 bay block, and a two storey, 6 bay range of north-light workrooms, all built by 1911. The administrative buildings in Wesleyan St are four storey, 4 bay and three storey, 3 bay. The main five storey block was damaged by fire in 1969, and the roof line has been altered.

42 Factory, 169 Crownpoint Rd, built 1874 for James Ormond, hosier (£3000). A three storey and attic, 12 by 3 bay, forming a triangle with some smaller buildings.

43 Engineering Works, 111 Crownpoint Rd, built 1862 for Farquhar, Knox & Co., engineers. A two storey, 12 bay red and white brick building, with round-headed windows on the first floor. At the rear is a single-storey range.

44 Telephone Exchange, 124–30 Cubie St, built 1910. A two storey, 7 bay brick building, with sandstone dressings, in French Renaissance style.

45 Workshops, 218 Orr St, built *c* 1880 for P. & J. Gaffney, cartwrights, spring van and lorry builders. A two storey, 6 bay red and white brick building. A similar three storey, 6 bay structure was added in 1889 for John Hughes, marine dealer (£2500).

46 Acme Machine Works, 2–8 Orr Place, built *c* 1886 for the Acme Machine Co., wringer makers. A striking red brick building, with white brick string courses, four storeys high, with 18 bays to Orr St and 15 to Orr Place. A mansard roof was added in 1909, *Burnet & Boston*, architects. The ground floor windows are round-headed.

47 Beehive Thread Works, 20 Orr Place, built *c* 1886 for A. Scott & Co., cotton spinners and doublers. A plain four storey and attic, 7 by 2 bay red and white brick building on an L plan. A water tower was added in 1906, *H. D. Walton*, architect (£130).

48 Wire Works, 47 Wesleyan St, built 1859 for W. Riddell & Co., wire manufacturers. A two storey, 5 bay stone fronted brick block with a two storey and attic, 4 bay brick and concrete addition at the rear. The buildings were altered to a grain store for A. Waddell, grain merchant, *W. Baillie,* architect (£270).

49 Victoria Steam Chair Works, 283 Orr St, built 1876–7 for A. & J. Harper, cabinetmakers (£10,500). A four storey, 7 bay stone fronted office block, with a four storey and attic, 10 bay red brick factory at the rear, with a circular-section iron-hooped chimney.

50 Calton Grain Mills, 193 Kerr St, built *c* 1878 for James Kerr & Co. Two adjoining buildings, one two storey and attic, 7 bay and the other three storey, 7 bay, both red and white brick.

51 Workshop, 24 Major St, built 1898 for the Eastern Packing Case & Washboard Co., packing box, tin and zinc case makers, *R. A. Wightman*, architect (£1100). A plain single storey building with a Belfast roof and a small yard adjoining.

52 Bakery, 522 Gallowgate, built 1897–8 for R. Nish, baker, *Bruce & Hay*, architects. A plain brick two storey building with a square-section brick chimney, behind a tenement.

53 Clydesdale Boot & Shoe Factory, 20–34 Elcho St, built *c* 1867 for A. & W. Paterson, wholesale boot, shoe and slipper manufacturers, and extended in 1873 (£700) and 1896 (£1000). A four storey, 4 by 12 bay building with the west and north walls stone and the others brick. At the rear is a water tower added in 1906 (£140). Inside, cast-iron columns support timber joists and floors.

54 Stables, 61–5 Elcho St, built 1890 for James Henderson, contractor, *Steel & Balfour*, architects (£4000). A three storey 9 bay red and white brick building with a flat roof, originally containing 51 stalls.

55 Gallowgate Central Station, 11 Lambert St, built *c* 1892 for the North British Railway. The surface offices were in a one storey by 7 bay, red sandstone building in the Renaissance manner, with round-headed openings. The large doorway is surmounted by a pediment. At this point the railway is in a cutting, with traces of platforms visible. The station was closed in 1917.

56 Stores, 44 Tureen St, built 1890 for

Thomas Spence & Co., *John Gordon*, architect. A neat two storey office block and gatehouse, with a two storey, 4 by 7 bay block extending through to Lambert St, both red brick.

57 Star Engine Works, 151 Moncur St, built 1880 for John Bennie, hydraulic and general engineer (£1200) and extended in 1883 (£3000). A two storey and attic, 8 bay ashlar fronted building, with three segmental-arched doorways. The interior was demolished in 1965, leaving the outside walls only.

58 Aerated Water Factory, 41 Bankier St, built 1907 for Joseph Dunn (£300), *J. W. Laird*, architect. A two storey, 4 bay painted brick building on the corner of Risk Street, demolished 1969.

59. Pleasance Leather Works, 381 London Rd, built from *c* 1861 for John Burt, machinery belt, lace and hosepipe maker. The entrance to the works was through a pend, and the main building was a four storey, 2 by 10 bay red brick building with wooden slatted drying sheds on the top floor. This block was probably built in 1868, and there was a later single storey office block.

60 Workshop, 31 Craignestock St, built *c* 1870 for Thomas Orr, cabinetmaker. A two storey, 4 bay red and white brick building, with an adjacent two storey wooden timber store.

61 Grocery Warehouse, 220–34 Stevenson St, built 1914 for Andrew Cochrane & Son Ltd, *J. Lindsay*, architect (£4065). A two storey, 7 by 5 bay terra-cotta fronted Renaissance red brick building, with a small three storey by 2 bay office block to the west.

62 Store & Stable, 75–7 Tobago St, built 1905 for James Fraser, rag and metal merchant (£2375), *A. Adam*, architect. A three storey, 3 bay red and white brick building, with a small square-section chimney at the rear. The frontage has two semicircular windows at second floor level, flanking a gablet with twin round-headed windows and a circular ventilator.

63 Calton Works, 45–51 Tobago St, built *c* 1850 for T. & J. Hamilton, bobbin turners. Adjacent, plain five storey, 7 bay and three storey, 12 bay red brick blocks. Demolished 1968–9.

64 Warehouse, 457 London Road, built *c* 1902 for Craig Riddell, wine and spirit merchant. A neat three storey, 8 bay red and white brick building, with large windows. Demolished 1970.

65 Workshops, Warehouses & Stores, 449 London Rd and Craignestock St, built 1877 for J. B. Herbertson & William Bremner, *John Gordon*, architect (£12,000). A four storey and attic, 13 by 12 bay sandstone fronted Renaissance building, with a mansard roof. Later occupied as a model lodging house.

66 Pipe Factory, 16–20 Craignestock St, built 1877 for William Christie, tobacco pipe manufacturer (£1500). A plain three storey and attic, 6 bay red and white brick building, with cast-iron columns supporting wooden joists and floors. At the rear is a square-section brick chimney.

67 Rockbank Works, 22 Craignestock St, built 1867 for James Hill, turner. A two storey and attic, 11 bay red and white brick building, with a four storey, 11 bay back building.

68 Tramway Stables, 58–72 Tobago St, built *c* 1877–83 for the Glasgow Tramway & Omnibus Co. An 1880 addition, in Arcadia St, cost £1000, while the large four storey, 5 by 12 bay building in Tobago St, which contained 436 stalls and a car shed, was added in 1883 (£8000). The date of the three storey and attic rear block, 7 by 13 bay, is unknown. The buildings were altered to a tobacco factory in 1901 for D. & J. Macdonald, *G. S. Hill*, architect (£950) and again in 1914 for the Imperial Tobacco Co., *Burnet & Boston*, architects (£1750).

69 Workshop, 1–9 Arcadia St, built 1889 for Robert Robertson, wright and wood-turner, *D. V. Wyllie*, architect (£700). A plain three storey, 11 bay painted brick building.

70 Warehouse & Stables, 13–19 Arcadia St, built 1891 for Alexander Raeside, yarn merchant, *D. V. Wyllie*, architect (£300). A striking five storey and attic, 9 bay red brick building with white brick string courses and a mansard roof. Immediately to the south are the cut-down remains of a large cotton mill (Bartholomew's), a seven storey, 8 bay front block, with a five storey, 10 bay wing projecting to the rear; both were demolished by 1965.

71 Warehouse, 41–3 Arcadia St, built 1890 for Alexander Raeside, yarn merchant, *D. V. Wyllie*, architect. A three storey and attic, 4 by 19 bay red and white brick building with a central pediment.

72 Warehouse, 352–72 Abercromby St, built 1892–3 for Alexander Raeside, yarn merchant, *D. V. Wyllie*, architect (£2500). A four storey, 7 bay red sandstone fronted building, with three windows per bay. There are pilasters rising from the second floor to the cornice.

73 Warehouse, 340 Abercromby St, built 1888 for Alexander Raeside, glass merchant and manufacturer, *D. V. Wyllie*, architect (£1000). A two storey and attic, 11 bay ashlar building with Greek central doorway.

74 Workshop, 328 Abercromby St, built 1896 for James Meighan & Son, blind-makers, *A. R. Crawford*, architect (£1000). A three storey and attic, 5 bay red and white brick building, with segmental-arched windows.

75 Bakery, 274 Abercromby St, built 1906–7 for John Dunn, *L. B. Buik*, architect (£7200). A plain two storey, 12 bay red brick building parallel to the street, with a single storey entrance block incorporating a retail shop. Originally there were 10 ovens, and a stable with 17 stalls.

76 Calton Brass Foundry, 246 Abercromby St, founded *c* 1876 by Allan & Bogle, brassfounders and brewery engineers, and rebuilt in 1894, *W. F. McGibbon*, architect (£1000). A two storey and attic, 4 bay ashlar fronted brick building, with a chimney at the rear.

77 Warehouse, 135 Kerr St, built 1899 for A. Denholm & Co., wholesale confectioners, *H. D. Walton*, architect (£2630). A plain two storey, 4 by 12 bay red and white brick building.

78 Broomward Mill, 63 Kerr St, built *c* 1867 for Henry Fyfe & Son, power-loom weavers, probably *John Gordon*, architect. From 1902–67 occupied as a carpet factory by James Templeton & Co. A three storey and attic, 4 by 15 bay red brick building with a prominent stone cornice and carved keystones in the first and second floor window arches. The second floor windows are round-headed, while the ground and first floor windows have flattened segmental heads. All the windows have the outer course of brickwork cut back for about two-thirds of their height. At the rear are 15 bays of single storey weaving sheds.

79 Broomward Cotton Work, 19–21 Kerr St, built *c* 1815 for James Dunlop & Sons, cotton spinners, *David Elder*, engineer. The remains of a five storey, 31 bay red brick mill, cut down to two and three storeys. Internally, wooden joists and floors are supported on slender cast-iron columns. The wall facing the street has recently been harled. At the rear are 13 bays of weaving sheds and a three storey, 10 bay red brick building.

80 Bridgeton Cross Station, 589 London Rd, built *c* 1892 for the North British Railway. The main office building is a two storey 9 bay red sandstone structure, with seven large round-headed openings at ground floor level, a heavy cornice, and

circular windows at first floor level at each end. The first floor consists of dwelling houses. The platforms have wrought-iron or steel glazed awnings carried on cast-iron columns.

81 Cotton Mill, Olympia St. Four bay portion of rubble wall, cut down to one storey from three, with margins round windows. Of interest as a fragmentary relic of one of the smaller early cotton mills.

82 Engineering Works, 47 Broad St, built 1896–7 for Mavor & Coulson Ltd, electrical engineers, *A. Myles*, architect (£10,000) and subsequently extended. The original building is a high single storey structure with side aisles and galleries. The roof is supported on cast-iron columns in the older part, on rolled-steel joists in the newer. In the gable end is a fine arched window, formerly a doorway.

83 Mile End Thread Works, Rogart St, founded *c* 1818 by John Clark Jun. & Co., cotton thread manufacturers. The surviving parts are a five storey and basement, 14 bay rubble fronted brick building, with wooden joists and floors supported on cast-iron columns, and a dimensionally similar 8 bay extension to the west, in red and white brick, with rolled-iron or steel joists. The older block was probably built in 1854, the newer in 1878 (£10,000). Until 1958, there was a large complex of multistorey mill buildings to the west, demolished to make way for extensions to Mavor & Coulson's works.

84 Bloomvale Carpet Works, 10 Fordneuk St, founded 1868 by J. & W. Lyle. The main block is three storeys and attic, 10 bays long, built in 1899, *A. Myles*, architect (£3100) flanked by a four storey 3 by 5 bay block, built 1872 (£1000), and a three storey and attic, 3 by 6 bay building, the original, built 1868–9. In Rogart St is a block of single storey weaving sheds, built 1909–11 (£2825), *G. Simpson*, architect, and a three storey, 6 bay block. All these, except the sheds, are red and white brick. In Crownpoint Rd are a three storey, 10 bay block and a post-1914 four storey 4 bay flat-roofed structure, both red brick.

85 Muslin & Tapestry Works, 72 Rogart St, founded *c* 1855 by T. & D. Wilson & Co., muslin, chenille and tapestry makers. A three storey and attic, 16 bay building, built 1880 (£1600) and a two storey and attic 8 bay block to the west (£1000), both originally red and white brick, now painted.

86 Sylvan Works, 57-9 Broad St, founded *c* 1854 by William Gibson & Co., shuttle and weaving utensil maker. A three storey, 5 by 13 bay red brick building, with round-headed windows in the 5 bay Broad St frontage. The door is flanked by sandstone pilasters, while the entablature bears the words 'SILVAN WORKS'.

87 Crownpoint Carpet Works, 14 St Marnock St, built from 1855 for J. & J. S. Templeton for the manufacture of Brussels carpets. The original factory appears to have been a block of single storey weaving sheds. These were added to in 1899 (£1700). In Crownpoint Rd was a three storey and attic, 19 bay office and preparation block, in red and white brick, built in 1886, *G. & A. Harvey*, architects and engineers, and demolished in 1968. On the corner of St Marnock St and Broad St is a two storey 9 by 14 bay reinforced concrete building built in 1912, *Wyllie & Blake*, architects (£4000). The works closed in 1967, and until closure power was supplied by a single cylinder horizontal Corliss engine built in 1900 by Fullerton, Hodgart & Barclay, Vulcan Foundry, Paisley, and a Bellis & Morcom vertical high speed compound engine (Works No 9211), both driving DC generators. The looms in use were made by William Smith & Bros Ltd, Heywood, Lancs, and the size tanks by T. Parkinson, Blackburn.

88 Crownpoint Boiler Works, 1 St Marnock St, founded *c* 1860 by Nicholson & Ferguson, boilermakers. At the front is a 4 bay, single storey building with round-headed windows, with a larger shed

behind, added in 1904 (£5000).

89 Fordneuk Factory, 96 David St, built *c* 1862 for George Grant & Sons, cotton spinners and weavers. A 10 bay block of single storey red brick weaving sheds, with a neat pedimented doorway. Formed a unit with F90 and F97.

90 Fordneuk Factory, 97 David St, founded *c* 1846 by George Grant & Sons, power-loom manufacturers. Fragmentary remains of a group of single storey weaving sheds with cast-iron columns, demolished 1967-8.

91 Crown Point Foundry, 145 Fielden St, built 1864 for William Ure, ironfounder, and added to in 1867, 1870, 1873 and 1887. The 1887 addition consisted of 3 bays of moulding shops, *R. A. Bryden*, architect (£1200). The older part is a high single storey red brick building with a large arched doorway. The whole complex has roof lighting only.

92 Chocolate Works, 100 Stamford St, built from 1899 for the Sweetmeat Automatic Delivery Co., *W. Ralph Low* of London, architect. The 1899 part cost £60,300, and there were additions in 1900 (compressor room, £1200), 1902 (£8000) and 1911 (£3470). A large group of one and two storey buildings, including a boiler-house with a tall chimney.

93 Workshop, 1009 London Rd, built 1889 for Duncan Buchanan, *J. Robb*, architect (£2500). A plain two storey, 2 by 3 bay office block, with single storey workshops at the rear.

94 Workshop, 100 Barrowfield St, built *c* 1878 for McFarlane & Co., cocoa fibre and mat manufacturers. A two storey, 11 bay red and white brick building, with single storey sheds, round a courtyard.

95 Fielden Mills, 199 Fielden St, built *c* 1860 for Alexander Paul & Co., power-loom manufacturers. A rectangular block of single storey weaving sheds, with two wide bays parallel to Fielden St and 11 narrow bays at right angles. There is a neat circular-section chimney, the remains of a high single storey engine house with three arched windows, a tall circular-section chimney and a two storey, 12 bay preparation block in Barrowfield St.

96 Howe Machine Works, 48 Avenue St, built 1872–3 for the Howe Sewing Machine Co., *A. Kennedy, Son & Myles*, architects (£15,000). A four storey and attic red and white brick building, 74 by 18 bay, on an angled plan, with one and three storey buildings forming a triangle. There was a large chimney, now cut down. The main block was demolished in 1969. It had wooden floors on cast-iron columns.

97 Fordneuk Factory, Fielden St and Avenue St, built 1871 for George Grant & Sons, cotton spinners (£2000). Eight bays of single storey red brick weaving sheds.

98 Cotton Mill, 358 Broad St, probably rebuilt *c* 1850 for Couper, Walker & Co., cotton spinners, after a fire in a mill built *c* 1840 (£50,000 damage). A five storey, 18 bay red brick building, with four rows of cast-iron columns supporting wooden beams, joists and floors. The building has apparently been cut back at the eastern end.

99 Barrowfield Weaving Factory, 260 Broad St, built *c* 1829 for the Barrowfield Weaving Co. A four storey building with two attics, 19 bays long, with two aisles of cast-iron columns supporting timber joists and floors. In several places tie-rods with cast-iron strengthening plates had been inserted. Modern additions included a fire escape, a sanitary tower with three wcs per floor, and a water tower. Additions at the back were made for Stewart & Young, confectioners, in 1886, *W. F. McGibbon*, architect (£2000), and in 1911–12 (a three storey block), *Miller & Black*, architects (£1870). The old block was demolished 1967–8.

100 Mile End Mills, 91–7 Fordneuk St, built *c* 1835 for Ferguson & Co., cotton spinners and power-loom cloth manufacturers. A three storey and attic, 12 bay red brick building with corner towers, at the rear, and on the street a two storey and attic, 11 bay painted brick block with low-relief arches framing the rectangular first floor windows. The latter building was built 1883 for William Tait & Co., wholesale stationers (£5000), while the older building was reconstructed for the same firm in 1914, *J. Lindsay*, architect (£810).

101 Brookside Weaving Factory, 15 Brookside St, founded 1862 by McMath & Pridie, power-loom cloth manufacturers. Eleven bays of single storey brick weaving sheds, probably dating from 1872 (£1200) and 1899 (£2600, for William Hollins & Co.).

102 Bon Accord Engine Works, 183 Fordneuk St, founded *c* 1870 by Marquis Bros, engineers, and added to for Drysdale & Co., in 1886, *J. Jamieson Young*, engineer (£1000), 1898 (£2000) and 1900 (£1200). The 1898 addition consisted of a large single storey brick engineering shop in Kirkpatrick St, and the 1900 addition was a two storey, 5 by 6 bay office block on the corner of Kirkpatrick St and Barrowfield St, with a neat pilastered doorway.

103 Weaving Factory, 55 Rimsdale St, built *c* 1878 for McLay & West, commission weavers. Nine bays of single storey weaving sheds, much altered, for example in 1889, when altered for William Roxburgh & Co., power-loom weavers (£800).

104 Burnside Works, 109–15 Brook St, founded *c* 1871 by Walker, Birrell & Co., power-loom cloth manufacturers. The main block, four storeys in height, 17 bays long, with a central pediment, was built in 1885 for J. W. Anderson (£3900), while at the side and rear are 5 bays of single storey weaving sheds, part added in 1885, *J. C. Rankin*, architect.

105 London Road Ironworks, 47 Summer St, built from 1865 for Duncan Stewart & Co., manufacturers of sugar machinery, steelworks plant and textile machinery. Five large bays of corrugated-iron clad engineering shops, part built 1882 (£6500), 1883 (£4000), 1887 (£1000) and 1906 (£14,000). In Summer St are two storey, 16 bay and three storey, 17 bay office blocks, the latter being added in 1892, *A. B. Dansken*, architect (£6000). The two storey block has a later mansard roof and round-headed openings, and the three storey block has round-headed openings on the ground floor only.

106 Bridgeton Cross Station, London Rd, built *c* 1896 for the Glasgow Central Railway. A small single storey red sandstone office block at street level, with stairs giving access to a four platform junction station. The Rutherglen line had independent platforms and the Coatbridge line an island platform, partly underground. The station was closed on 5 October 1964 and has become derelict.

107 Silvergrove Mills, 23 Silvergrove St, built 1873 for William Holmes, powerloom cloth manufacturer, as part of Greenhead Mills (£8000). A four storey, 5 by 13 bay red and white brick building. At the east end are an engine house and a neat tower with corner finials and Greek key pattern string course. There is a plain circular-section chimney.

108 Greenhead Brewery, 31 Blackfaulds Place, founded *c* 1800 by Robert Struthers, brewer, and reconstructed in 1887, 1892 (*John Cunningham*, of Edinburgh, architect) and 1914, *J. W. & J. Laird*, architects (£2860) for Steel Coulson & Co. A group of two storey, red and white brick buildings round a rectangular courtyard, with twin malting kilns adjacent to the south.

109 Carpet Factory, 62 Templeton St, founded on this site in 1857 by James Templeton & Son. The oldest part is a cut down cotton mill built *c* 1823, now only two storeys high. Subsequent additions were a three storey, 16 bay block at the south end of Templeton St, built 1868–9, a group of weaving sheds built 1881–9 (£6150), and most spectacularly *W. Leiper*'s Venetian Gothic block, faced in polychrome brick, with sandstone dressings. A four storey and attic, 4 by 11 bay structure, building commenced in 1888 and was almost complete when there was a partial collapse on 1 November 1889, killing 29 women in the adjacent weaving sheds. The building was eventually completed in 1892. It was designed for the manufacture of spool Axminster carpets and was originally to cost £20,000. Restoration of the collapsed part cost £1200, and of the weaving sheds £1800. The five storey, 14 bay red brick building, with vertically panelled brickwork, facing London Rd, was added in 1897 (£10,000). The Leiper building is category A (SDD).

110 Glasgow Green Station, built *c* 1896 for the Glasgow Central Railway. Situated partly in cutting and partly in tunnel, the station offices were in a single storey 8 bay red sandstone building, with round-headed openings, similar to the surface buildings at Bridgeton Cross (F105) and Dalmarnock Stations. Closed 2 November 1953, the platform buildings have been demolished, and the surface block is now derelict.

111 Greenhead Engine Works, 133 Arcadia St, founded *c* 1856 by Glen & Ross, engineers. Three two storey buildings round a courtyard, built 1859–63 and rebuilt in 1877 (£5000). The street frontage consists of the gable end, 5 bays wide, of a two storey building, and a similar two storey, 7 bay block at right angles, both cement rendered brick.

112 Greenhead Works, 45 Greenhead St, founded on this site in 1859 by R. & J. Dick, gutta percha manufacturers. The oldest part of the complex is a three storey and attic, 25 bay red brick building, built *c* 1840 for Messrs Bartholomew, and purchased in 1859 for £1000. The frontage to Greenhead St consists of two ashlar blocks, built to resemble tenements, one three storey, 3 by 3 bay built in 1886, with the adjoining single storey brick block (£4500, *G. F. Boyd*, architect), and the other four storey and attic, 5 bay, probably built 1872–3 (£3500). Further additions were made at the rear in 1888–9 (£3300), including a three storey and attic, 14 bay red and white brick building on McPhail St. The 1886–9 additions were required for the manufacture of balata belting.

113 City Machinery Stores, 81 James St, built 1889 for William Bennie & Sons, engineers and machinery providers, *W. Ferguson*, architect (£2000). A single storey building with two wide bays; recently extensively altered.

114 Greenhead Weaving Factory, 89–91 James St, built 1888 for Thomas Thomson, power-loom cloth manufacturer, *N. MacWhannell*, architect (£4000). A four storey, 4 by 13 bay red and white brick building, with gable end to the street. Adjoining to the south are 5 bays of weaving sheds, added in 1900 (£800), and occupied *c* 1906–7 by the short-lived All British Car Co.

115 Engineering Works, 119–23 James St, built 1888–9 for Smith & Christie, machinery merchants and mill furnishers, *MacWhannell & Rogerson*, architects (£2000). A four storey, 8 bay red and white brick building, similar in style to F112 with additions at the rear, built 1891 (£1000).

116 Sewing Machine Factory, 116 James St, built 1871–2 for the Singer Sewing Machine Co. (£8000). An imposing four storey, 6 by 22 bay stone fronted brick building on an L plan, with a cut off corner. At the rear is a circular-section chimney.

117 Stables & Carriage Shed, 76 James St, built 1889 for William Simpson, funeral undertaker and carriage hirer, *Bruce & Hay*, architects (£3500). A two storey and attic, 12 bay harled brick building, cut down from a four storey, 23 bay block.

118 'Wood's Mill', 60 James St, built *c* 1834 for Francis Wood & Co., cotton spinners and power-loom cloth manufacturers. A four storey, 22 bay red brick structure, with wooden beams and floors on cast-iron columns, and a prominent water tower. Altered to a cabinet works in 1888–9 for George Taggart & Co. (£1400). Demolished 1967.

119 St Ann's Leather Works, 78 Tullis St, founded 1869 by John Tullis & Son. The main block was five storeys high, built in two portions, one 8 and the other 10 bays long, both red and white brick, with the top floor fitted with louvred shutters for drying. Built 1899–1900 (£11,800), these and the more modern five storey block at the rear were demolished in 1967.

120 Grain Store, 100–2 Landressy St, probably built *c* 1890. A plain three storey and attic, 6 bay red and white brick building.

121 Muslin Factory, 21 Muslin St, built 1900 for Neilson, Davie & Co., muslin manufacturers, *McKissack & Son*, architects (£8000). A four storey, 8 bay red and white brick building.

122 Stables, 22 Pirn St, founded *c* 1882 by G. S. Munn, funeral undertaker and hirer. A three storey, 9 bay red and white brick building, built 1888, *James Waddell*, engineer (£2500), and demolished *c* 1967. To the west is a small single storey building with an ornamental gable, possibly built 1886 for Thos Simpson, starcher and dyer.

123 Part of Baltic Works, 47 Hozier St, built *c* 1866 for the Glasgow Jute Co. Ltd, *John Gordon*, architect, and occupied from 1902–7 by the Hozier Engineering Co. A three storey and attic, 8 bay building and a 7 by 8 bay block of single storey weaving sheds, both red and white brick. Demolished 1969.

124 Baltic Works, Baltic St, built from 1858 for W. & J. Fleming, linen manufacturers, *John Gordon*, architect. An 11 bay block of single storey weaving sheds, with a two storey block of preparation rooms. In Pirn St were altered remains of a three storey and attic, 8 bay building and a two storey and attic block, with gable end to the street. Demolished 1969.

125 Clyde Works, 1 Baltic St, built 1866 for W. & J. Fleming, jute manufacturers, *John Gordon*, architect. A triangular block of single storey weaving sheds, with a two storey, 6 by 20 bay block in Baltic St, both red brick with sandstone dressings. The latter has been cut down from a three storey and attic structure with a corner tower. There are round-headed openings throughout. Internally there are lineshaft supports dated 1866, cast by Thomson Bros, Dundee.

126 Marquis Street Weaving Factory, 55 Marquis St, built 1866 for J. & P. Wilson, lappet and muslin manufacturers, and extended in 1895, 1901 (£2000) and 1905 (£1200). Thirteen bays of single storey weaving sheds with a two storey, 8 bay red and white brick office and preparation block.

127 Atlantic Mills, 26 Walkinshaw St, built from 1864 for D. & J. Anderson, shirting manufacturers. A large complex consisting of 15 bays of single storey weaving sheds, a four storey and attic, 13 bay main block, a two storey and attic, 3 by 17 bay building, and several smaller two storey blocks, all red and white brick, with a circular-section chimney. Demolished 1967–9.

128 Shuttle Factory, 79 Dunn St, built 1871 for William Gunn, power-loom shuttle manufacturer. A tall three storey, 6 bay red brick building, with round-headed windows on the ground floor. An attic storey has recently been added.

129 Eagle Pottery, 60 Boden St, built from 1869 for Frederick Grosvenor, earthenware manufacturer; extensions were built in 1873 (£300), 1874 (£1500),

1875 (£7000), 1881 (£2500), 1885 and 1891, *J. M. Monro*, architect (£900). A three storey, 3 by 23 bay red and white brick block extending along Bernard Street. The gable end has a plaque with a monogram of 1869.

130 Bernard Street Mills, 244 Bernard St, built 1891 for the Broomward Weaving Co., and occupied since 1915 by James Templeton & Co. An 18 bay block of single storey red brick weaving sheds, with an engine house and chimney at the north-west corner.

131 Stable & Cart Shed, 856 London Road, built 1873 for Cowan & Co., carting contractors (£1200). A three storey, 8 bay red brick building, with a two storey office block at right angles. Wooden ramps for horses link the yard with the first and second floors of the building.

132 Factory, 1042 London Rd, built *c* 1891 for Moffat Bros, shoe accessory manufacturers. A plain two storey, 2 by 6 bay red brick building behind a tenement.

133 Boden Street Factory, 171 Boden St, built 1871–2 for Renison, McNab & Co., power-loom cloth manufacturers. There are two blocks of 8 bays of single storey weaving sheds, added to in 1889 (£2000), and 1906 (£4050), *McKissack & Son*, architects, with a two storey, 14 bay building facing Boden St, built 1877 (£8500). A two storey and basement, 4 by 19 bay block on the corner of Nuneaton St was added in 1907, *McKissack & Son*, architects (£7150).

134 Scotia Leather Works, 108 Boden St, founded 1873 by Hamilton Caldwell, currier. Between 1873 and 1893, £11,950 was spent on extensions and alterations, *D. Thomson*, architect, the present frontage being added in 1906, *J. C. Reid*, architect. The body of the building is five storeys high, 15 bays long, with a four storey, 10 bay frontage incorporating a seven storey tower. Immediately behind the main block is a cast-iron water tower with a railed gallery round it, added in 1904 (£300). All the buildings are of red and white brick.

135 Granary & Stables, 128 Boden St, built from 1873 for Gavin Wilkie, cartage contractor. A two storey by 3 bay dwelling house, built 1873 (£1500, including a stable and byre, now demolished), with a two storey, 3 bay red and white brick block added in 1890, *R. N. Crawford*, architect (£1200).

136 Dalmarnock Ironworks, 85 Dunn St, Bernard St, Baltic St and Nuneaton St, founded *c* 1868 by William Arrol. At the corner of Dunn St and Bernard St is a two storey, 4 by 26 bay red brick block built in 1889 (£4500), extended along Dunn St by four storey blocks, consisting of F128, the middle block, built in 1903 (£2160), and the southernmost, added by *Burnet, Boston & Carruthers*, architects, in 1906 (£2290). At the Baltic St corner is a two storey, 4 by 34 bay building built in 1898 (£10,000). Further additions, mainly single storey workshops, were made in Dunn St, Boden St, Nuneaton St and Baltic St between 1898 and 1911 (£67,190).

137 Aerated Water Factory, 165 Mordaunt St, built 1892–3 for G. & C. Moore, aerated water manufacturers, *Bruce & Hay*, architects (£2900). A plain two storey, 7 bay block, now cement rendered.

138 Stables, 74 Mordaunt St, built 1905 for J. & A. Donald, *L. B. Buik*, architect. A one storey and attic, 2 bay brick building, with a two storey, 2 bay office block.

139 Stores & Workshops, 254 Baltic St, built from 1898 for the Glasgow Eastern Co-operative Society. A one storey, 9 bay ashlar frontage with windows and doors blocked up.

140 Dalmarnock Flax & Jute Works, 275 Dunn St, founded 1863 by J. Y. Adams, sacking manufacturer, of Dundee, and originally known as Dundee Works. Additions were made in 1871–2 (£5000),

1877 (£2000) and 1898 (£2900). A range of single storey red and white brick weaving sheds, with a two storey, 3 bay office block and a tall red brick chimney stalk.

141 Workshop, 176–84 Dunn St, founded *c* 1876 by Robert Lyon, wright, and extended in 1883 (£200) and 1902–3 (£530), the last named for D. Wallace, wright. A plain two storey, 9 bay red brick block.

142 Workshop, 12–14 Ruby St, built *c* 1893 for Watson & Leck, cloth shrinkers. A plain two storey, 5 bay red brick structure.

143 Dalmarnock Tram Depot, 45 Ruby St, built from 1893 for Glasgow Corporation Tramways Department, *W. Clark*, engineer. The first part had 304 stalls and car sheds (£7000), and it was extended in 1895 by 84 stalls and sheds (£500) in 1899 (£16,400) and in 1903 (£10,000). Thirteen bays of red and white brick car sheds, with round-headed doorways and windows. Demolished 1967.

144 Part of Baltic Works, Hozier St and Baltic St (see F122 and F132). A 5 by 15 bay section of weaving sheds, with round-headed windows. Demolished 1967.

145 Workshop, 27 Savoy St, built 1898 for Neilson, Davie & Co., reed and heddle manufacturers, *J. McKissack*, architect (£2000). A two storey and attic, 9 bay red brick building with an integral square-section flared brick chimney stalk.

146 Tinsmith's Works, 111 Main St, founded *c* 1844 for Thomas Donald, and extended in 1881 (£300) and 1904 (£400) for Duncan Stewart. A group of one and three storey workshops behind a tenement.

147 Stables & Stores, 135 Main St, built *c* 1865 for the Bridgeton Old Victualling & Baking Society. A courtyard surrounded by two storey red brick buildings.

148 Bridgeton Brass Foundry, 16 Muslin St, built *c* 1830 for Thomas Wright, brassfounder. A plain two storey 3 by 4

bay red brick building, with a short flared square section brick chimney.

149 John Street Factory, 57 Tullis St, built from *c* 1836 for James and William Simpson and others. Thirteen bays of single storey weaving sheds, with a three storey and attic, 3 by 10 bay block, probably built in 1853 for W. J. Scott & Co., and a four storey, 13 bay 'fireproof' block. Purchased *c* 1920 by James Templeton & Co., and latterly used for chenille Axminster carpet weaving.

150 Greenhead Saw Mills, 38 Mill St, originally built 1877–8 for J. & D. McPhun, wood turners, and completely rebuilt 1888–93 to designs by *D. Thomson* and *J. McKissack* (£4750). An extensive complex of wood and brick buildings, with a three storey, 5 bay red and white brick office block on the street.

151 Weaving Factory, 252 Main St, built *c* 1860 for Henry Fyfe & Son, hand-loom cloth manufacturers and altered in 1906 for James Hendry, leather belting manufacturer. A small 6 bay block of single storey brick weaving sheds, with a three storey drying shed, a water tower on a brick pier and a square-section chimney stalk.

152 Newhall Street Weaving Factory, 16–22 Newhall St, built from 1859 for A. & J. Paterson, power-loom cloth manufacturers. A three storey and attic, 11 bay building, built in 1865, extended along the street by a three storey, 4 bay block added in 1882 (£800), both red and white brick. At the rear are single storey weaving sheds.

153 Clyde Thread Works, 342 Main St, built 1854 for J. Dick & Son, thread manufacturers, *Gildard & Macfarlane*, architects. The only fragment of the original factory is a neat engine house with round-headed windows, which was adjacent to a five storey, 12 bay mill, long since demolished. There are two blocks of single storey weaving sheds, one of 10, the other of 4 bays. The latter was probably

added in 1899 for Forrest, Frew & Co., power-loom cloth manufacturers, *John Cunningham*, architect (£1000).

154 Rutherglen Bridge, Main St, opened in 1896, replacing a five arched structure built in 1776. The present bridge has three flat segmental arches, faced in granite.

155 Barrowfield Leather Works, 129 Colvend St, built *c* 1878 for John Boag, tanner, currier and leather worker. A three storey and attic, 5 by 3 bay red brick building, with a later single storey addition.

156 Barrowfield Steam Chair Works, 228 Reid St, built *c* 1886 for Hugh Alexander. An L shaped block, one arm of which is a two storey and attic, 8 by 3 bay red brick building, and the other a three storey and attic, 8 bay structure, added in 1889 (£500).

157 Strathclyde Creamery, 26 French St, built *c* 1900 for the Strathclyde Creamery Co., margarine manufacturers. Three red brick blocks, the one on the street being four storeys, 4 bay, extended back by a three storey, 4 bay, and a two storey, 5 bay building.

158 Crown Chemical Works, 255 Reid St, built from 1879 for George Walker & Sons, manufacturing chemists, drug merchants and drysalters. Two four storey red brick blocks, one 6 bay, the other 7 by 5 bay, with a flat roof, designed in 1906 by *W. H. Howie*, architect.

159 Barrowfield Finishing Works, 87 Colvend St, built in 1907 for W. G. Mitchell, bleacher and finisher, *L. B. Buik*, architect (£1600). A 3 bay single storey harled red brick building with gable ends to the street, with a two storey, 9 bay office block at the rear.

160 Barrowfield Oil & Colour Works, 54 French St, founded *c* 1876 by James Storer & Co. A group of one and two storey red and white brick buildings round a courtyard. The most interesting is the two storey, 9 bay range facing Colvend St, which has arched doorways, now bricked up, while on the corner of French St and Reid St is a plain 6 by 6 bay two storey block.

161 Barrowfield Spinning Factory, 177 Reid St, built *c* 1846 for Peter Bogle & Co., cotton spinners. A five storey, 4 by 15 bay red brick building with a water tower, added in 1884 (£300) and a three storey, 4 bay extension to the south.

162 Barrowfield Weaving Factory, 103–5 French St, built from 1889 for John Brown & Son, power-loom muslin manufacturers, *M. S. Gibson*, architect. The French St range consists of a two storey, 4 by 12 bay block with polychrome brick decoration (1891, £700), a three storey, 7 bay building with a central pediment (1899, £2350) and a two storey, 11 by 2 bay structure in similar style. At the rear are 23 bays of single storey north-light weaving sheds. When completed, in 1899, the factory had cost £8300.

163 Clutha Weaving Factory, 62 Carstairs St, built in 1900 for John Brown & Son, power-loom muslin manufacturers, *G. & A. Harvey*, architects and engineers (£28,000), and added to in 1902–6, *G. & A. Harvey*, *M. S. Gibson* and *Duncan & Copland*, architects (total £10,390). The main block consists of 17 bays of single storey weaving sheds, and there are subsidiary blocks of 16 and 12 bays. Facing Carstairs St are two storey stores and offices and a single storey engine house.

164 Barrowfield Works, 49 Solway St, built from 1902 for Carsons Ltd, chocolate manufacturers. The main block is three storeys high, 32 bays long, and was built in two stages. The first two floors were constructed in 1904 (£6100) and a third storey added in 1910 (£1950), *Duncan & Copland*, architects. At the west end is a four storey attic and basement, 7 by 4 bay block, and at the east end a large circular section chimney stalk and a two storey,

3 by 7 bay office block with a pediment and pilasters.

165 Cotton Spinning Mills, 121 Carstairs St, built 1884–9 for the Glasgow Cotton Spinners Co. Ltd, *Joseph Stott*, of Oldham, architect. Two mills, one in Carstairs St five storeys high, 11 by 28 bay, built 1884–5 (£35,000), and the other in Swanston St four storeys high, 10 by 31 bay. Both have prominent stair towers, and are of red brick, with hollow tile floors on cast-iron columns. There is a tall circular-section chimney.

166 Dalmarnock Weaving Factory, 300 Swanston St, built from 1870 for George Wilson & Co., power-loom cloth manufacturers. Between 1872 and 1907 additions costing £7650 were made. An L shaped block of single storey weaving sheds, with a two storey, 4 by 9 bay red and white brick office block on the corner of Cotton St, and a circular-section iron-banded chimney stalk. The last additions were designed by *Brand & Lithgow*, architects.

167 Clyde Spinning Mill, 6 Cotton St, built from 1871 for the Clyde Spinning Co., cotton spinners. An irregular four storey block, red brick, with wooden beams and floors on cast-iron columns, completed in 1875 (£9000), *Clarke & Bell*, architects. The Swanston St frontage is 14 bays long. At the rear is a high two storey engine house, now roofless, added in 1910, *J. W. Laird*, architect (£900).

168 River Street Factory, 14 Shore St, built 1885–93 for George Wilson & Co., power-loom cloth manufacturers, *J. Hutchison*, architect (£6500). A block of single storey weaving sheds with an engine house and two chimney stalks, one square in section, the other circular.

169 Clyde Dye Works, 213 Strathclyde St, built from 1870 for W. & J. Bowie, dyers, extensions being made between 1882 and 1905, *MacWhannell & Rogerson* (£4950) and *Brand & Lithgow*, architects. A large group of two and three storey buildings, extending back from a three storey, 21 bay red and white brick block, built in three stages.

170 Glasgow Tube Works, 181 Swanston St, built from 1859 for William Wylie & Co., iron tube makers, and reconstructed 1903–8 for Mavor & Coulson, as a foundry. *The Arrol Bridge Co.* and *Alexander Findlay & Co.*, Motherwell, engineers (£16,000). A large rectangular block of single storey buildings, with roof lighting. There is a small two storey office block on Swanston St.

171 Dalmarnock Gas Works, 122 Old Dalmarnock Rd, originally built for the City & Suburban Gas Co. in 1843, *W. Spence*, architect, extended in 1856 and 1871, and closed in 1904. Reconstructed with vertical retorts in 1914 by Glasgow Corporation Gas Department, and closed again in 1956. The remains are scattered over a large area, and include the original two storey manager's house, the frontage of the original retort house – an Egyptian composition – two large gas holders with cast-iron guides, built in 1872, and some interesting footbridges over the level crossings, now removed, which served the works.

172 Contractor's Depot, 181 Poplin St, built 1897 for Malcolm Cunningham, cartage contractor, *J. Kellock*, engineer (£1700, 40 stalls). A plain three storey, 6 bay red brick building, with an earlier two and three storey block to the east. The windows in the newer block were very small, and are now bricked up.

173 Joiner's Workshop, 12 Playfair St, built c 1893 for James Laidlaw, joiner. A two storey, 13 bay brick and timber block, with timber sheds at the rear.

174 Workshop, 31–3 Bartholomew St, built c 1863 for James Reid, machine maker. A two storey, 6 bay ashlar building.

175 Workshop, 19 Bartholomew St, built c 1896 for Peter Davie, cartwright, van and lorry builder. A one storey and attic building with gable end to the street.

176 Baltic Wire & Metal Works, 81 Dale St, built from c 1894 for McCormack & Mills, paper machine wire and dandy roll makers, and general wire workers. Additions were made in 1897 (£3100), 1911 *Robertson & Gow*, architects (£1820), and 1913, *Clarke & Bell*, architects (£1870). A group of one, two and three storey buildings on an island site, some red brick, others red and white brick.

177 Dalmarnock Station, Dalmarnock Rd, built c 1896 for the Glasgow Central Railway. An underground station, with single storey red sandstone entrances in Dalmarnock Rd and Swanston St, giving access to separate platforms. Closed 5 October 1964, the surface buildings were demolished in 1968.

178 Tollhouse, Dalmarnock Rd, built c 1820. A small one storey and basement building with a semi-octagonal projection in the centre of the frontage.

179 Dalmarnock Dyeworks, Davidson St, built 1888–9 for William McConnell & Co., dyers, starchers and yarn polishers, *D. V. Wyllie*, architect (£2500). The main range is two storeys high, 30 bays long, of red and white brick.

180 Anchor Brewery, Davidson St, built 1889 for Thomas Gray & Co., brewers, *P. L. Henderson*, architect, Edinburgh (£8000). A group of one, two and three storey red brick buildings round a courtyard.

181 Caledonian Ironworks, 64 Strathclyde St, built 1889 for Penman & Co., boilermakers, *R. Dalglish*, architect (£7000). The frontage, of red and white brick, has a large arched doorway with a circular ventilator above, with high arched windows. At the rear there are extensions in corrugated iron clad steel.

182 Railway Bridges, Dalmarnock, built c 1858, *G. Graham*, engineer and 1893–7 for the Caledonian Railway. Two iron bridges, each carrying two tracks. The eastern one consists of three wrought-iron arches on sandstone piers with rounded cutwaters, approached on both sides by brick arches with sandstone soffits and parapets. The western bridge has three bowed lattice girder spans on triple cast-iron piers and approach spans of normal plate girder type.

183 Dalmarnock Bridge, Dalmarnock Rd, built 1889–91, *Crouch & Hogg*, engineers. A five span iron girder bridge on stone piers, with cast-iron quatrefoil panels hiding the structural members and a cast-iron balustrade of Gothic arches. The stonework of the piers is carried up to balustrade level and cast-iron lamp-posts are mounted on top.

184 Dalmarnock Power Station, Dalmarnock Rd, built from 1914 for Glasgow Corporation Electricity Department, *W. W. Leckie*, engineer (£74,000). The oldest part is a high single storey brick block with ornamental gable to the street, the first part of the turbine hall, but most of the work is post-1918.

185 Dalmarnock Hair Factory, 26 Summerfield St, built 1881–2 for Andrew D. MacNair & Co., curled hair manufacturers (£3500). The building facing the street is a two storey, 14 bay red brick block, and there are extensions at the rear, one dating from 1898 (£1600).

186 Workshop, 518 Baltic St, built 1904 for J. McCrindle, joiner, *Crawford & Veitch*, architects. A plain two storey, 10 bay red brick building behind a tenement, with a single storey extension at the south end.

187 Office, Store & Stable, 374 Baltic St, built 1907 for John Thomson, builder. A one storey red brick building with a 3 bay office portion and 4 bay store and stable.

188 Springfield Dyeworks, Springfield Rd, founded *c* 1826 by William Miller, and reconstructed as a bleachworks 1882–99 for John Blackwood & Son (£5260). An extensive group of buildings, the largest of which is a three storey red and white brick block, with a tall circular-section chimney at the east end.

189 Dalmarnock Paper Mills, 296 Springfield Rd, founded 1868 by Brown, Stewart & Co. A scattered group of undistinguished red brick buildings, now interspersed with modern structures. The most interesting is a high two storey building in Springfield Rd, with three low-relief arches in the gable end. Between 1891 and 1913 £7300 was spent on additions to the mills.

Section G
Central Glasgow

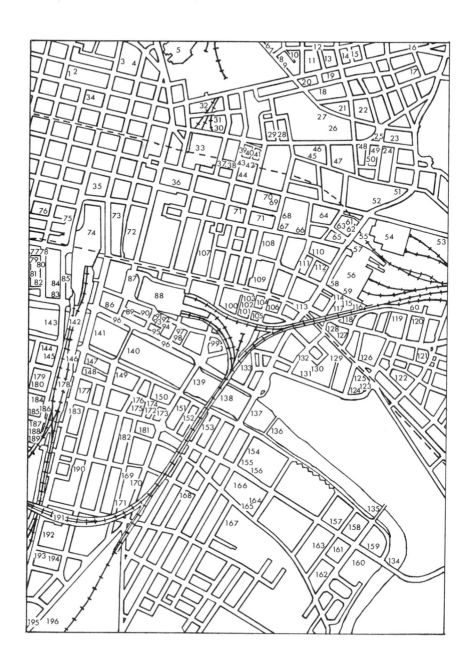

1 Warehouse, 18–20 Cambridge St, built *c* 1884 for James White, manufacturing optician and instrument maker, *D. Mac-Naughtan*, architect. A four storey, Italian Renaissance fronted, glazed brick building with 3 bays to the street, each of two windows. The first and third floor windows are round-headed, and there is a heavy cornice. At the rear is a five storey and basement block added in 1891 (£3500). SDD category B.

2 Warehouse, 105 Renfrew St, built 1901–2 for James White, instrument maker, *D. MacNaughtan*, architect (£7000). A six storey, attic and basement, 5 bay ashlar fronted brick building with a small tower at the south-west corner.

3 Stable, Rutherford Lane, built 1886 for Bishop & Henderson (Cooper & Co.), grocers, *Peat & Duncan*, architects (£470). A plain three storey, 3 bay red brick building with later additions.

4 Ice Factory, 8 Rutherford Lane, built 1899 for J. & T. Sawers, fish merchants, *Steel & Balfour*, architects (£6500), and extended in 1901–2. A three storey, 3 bay flat-roofed red brick building with two windows per bay in shallow vertical recesses. Demolished 1969.

5 Buchanan Street Station, Port Dundas Rd, opened 1 November 1849 by the Caledonian Railway, and subsequently rebuilt. The passenger station as it existed at closure (7 November 1966) had three island platforms with iron-framed, wooden terminal buildings. There was an awning over the main entrance, a carriageway on the south side, and separate iron-framed glazed awnings over the platforms (erected 1932). To the south and east was an extensive goods yard with sheds added 1891 (£15,000) and 1906 (£89,400), and a five storey, 5 by 20 bay grain store, probably dating from the 1870s. Part demolished 1967, rest by 1971.

6 Wire Rope Factory, 90 Dobbies Loan, built 1914 for Frew Bros, wire rope manufacturers, *Baird & Thomson*, architects

(£290). Facing the street is a two storey, 2 bay red brick block.

7 Milton Colour Works, 58–70 Dobbies Loan, built 1873 for James Steel Jun. & Co., oil and colour merchants (£8000). A two storey, 9 bay, red and white brick building with central entrance and tower. The ground floor windows are Gothic. At the rear, in Couper St and Kennedy St, is a later two storey, 7 by 9 bay, red and white brick block.

8 Stables, Kennedy St, built 1900 for J. M. Dawson, iron merchant, *G. N. Beattie*, architect (£250). A two storey, 3 bay terra-cotta brick fronted building with an adjacent, older, two storey, 5 bay red brick office block.

9 Stables, 36 Dobbies Loan, built 1880 for John Allan, horse dealer (£1700), and altered in 1914 by the roofing over of the central courtyard. The alterations were designed by *Burnet & Boston*, architects (£1630). A two storey, 5 bay, red and white brick building with the 1914 wooden addition visible over the central doorway. To the north, at the corner of Kennedy St, is a four storey wood store, with slatted wooden sides, built in 1887 for Wordie & Co., cartage contractors, *Baldie & Tennant*, architects.

10 Metallic Works, 23 North Wallace St, founded *c* 1894 by J. G. Carrick & Co., sheet metal workers, tinplate printers and makers of drums and kegs. Two red brick blocks, forming an L, one 14 by 4 bay, three storeys and attic, and the other 19 by 7 bay, three storeys high.

11 City Manure Office, 234 Parliamentary Rd, built 1873 as headquarters of city cleansing services. The principal survivals of the original complex are the two storey, 2 by 3 bay gatehouse and massive ashlar gateposts. The 6 by 11 by 7 bay, three storey block of stables at the rear was added in 1902 and 1910 for James Cowan & Co., contractors, *J. Lindsay* (£4000) and *Burnet & Boston* (£850), architects.

12 Sun Foundry, 280 Kennedy St, built 1870–1 for George Smith & Co., artistic ironfounders, and subsequently altered. A large two storey, 25 by 28 bay cement-washed red brick building, with a small tower at the south east corner.

13 Workshop, 14 Drummond St, built *c* 1893 for C. Lightbody, stair railer and turner. A plain, harled, two storey, 6 bay brick building.

14 Warehouse, Lister St, built 1903 for the St Rollox Co-operative Society, *C. J. Zamorski*, architect. A four storey, 3 bay red sandstone block, with rusticated ground floor.

15 Store, 16 Ward St, built 1878 for R. Stewart & Co., metal merchants. Adjacent two storey and attic, 5 bay and one storey, 4 bay red and white brick blocks.

16 St Rollox Spring Van & Lorry Works, 83–99 Kennedy St, built *c* 1877 for Alexander Grant, cartwright, spring van and lorry builder. A single storey red brick building, with two wide bays.

17 Stables & Store, 9 Martyr St, built 1902 for William Bow, contractor, *D. V. Wyllie*, architect (£3000). A four storey and attic, 3 by 9 bay, terra-cotta brick building, with Renaissance details in red sandstone. At the rear is a two storey, 12 stall stable built in 1900 for Sam Allsopp, brewer, *John Hamilton*, architect (£2000).

18 Contractor's Depot, 223 McAslin St, built *c* 1867 for McFadyen & Co., cartage contractors. An L plan block of two storey stables and a two storey office building, both brick, with a large open yard. Demolished 1968.

19 Engraving Works, 188 McAslin St, built *c* 1888 for James Gray & Co., calico printers' engravers. Formerly four storeys high, later cut down to a single storey building, 11 bays long, with round-headed windows. Demolished 1968.

20 Tollhouse, 255 Parliamentary Rd, built in the early 19th century. A single storey rectangular building, with a projecting circular wing giving visibility in three directions. Damaged by fire spring 1969. SDD category C.

21 Part of Herriot Hill Stationery & Printing Works, 136 St James Rd, built in 1902 for Collins & Co., *Burnet, Boston & Carruthers*, architects (£3500). A five storey, 4 by 5 bay red and white brick building, very plain.

22 Villafield Press, 15–17 Stanhope St, founded on this site as Glasgow University Press, and purchased by John Blackie *c* 1830. The two three storey blocks in St James Rd, were added in 1838 and 1841, one 5 bays, the other 9 bays long, and extended respectively by two and one storeys. Next to the west is a five storey, 3 bay building of 1890, designed by *A. Skirving*, architect (£1600), while on the corner with Taylor St is a five storey and basement, 3 by 8 bay red sandstone block built 1899–1900 to designs by *G. Simpson*, architect (£5000). The main office block in Stanhope St, now demolished, was built in two parts. The northern part was three storeys high, 9 bays long, built 1883, *A. Skirving*, architect, while the southern part, four storeys high, 7 bays long, was built in 1869, *A. & G. Thomson*, architects. Behind the street frontages is a complex of buildings of various dates.

23 Monumental Sculptors' Works, 60 Cathedral St, built 1864–5 and extended in 1876 (£350), for J. & G. Mossman, a firm founded in 1816. A high single storey, brick building on an L plan with the front and one side open. A gantry crane runs on rails supported by wooden frames, and there are the remains of an ornamental, railway-station-like, wooden valance at the front of the building.

24 St Mungo Engraving Works, 51–61 Cathedral St, built 1883 for Duff & Towart Ltd, engravers to calico printers (£2200). A four storey and attic, 12 bay ashlar fronted red and white brick building, with external stair tower and modern three storey lean-to at the rear.

25 Contractor's Depot, 84 Cathedral St, built 1872 for James Frew, contractor (£500) and extended in 1889, *W. F. McGibbon*, architect. A triangular block of one and two storey red and white brick buildings.

26 Herriot Hill Stationery & Printing Works, 135 St James Rd, Taylor St and 144 Cathedral St, founded *c* 1861 by William Collins & Co., printers and publishers. The main office block, in Cathedral St, is a four storey and attic, 25 bay building, probably built in 1872 (£1600) and extended in 1890 (£3000). The mansard-roofed attic was added in 1899, *Burnet & Boston*, architects, probably at the same time as the neat corner tower. The buildings in Taylor St (now partly a private street belonging to Collins) were added in 1878 (£5500), while the large group of buildings in the interior of the complex are of various dates, for example a four storey block at the west end was built in 1903, *Burnet, Boston & Carruthers*, architects (£15,000).

27 Provanside Engine Works, 181 St James Rd, built 1865 for A. & P. Steven, hydraulic engineers, the frontage being added in 1869. A fine 3 bay engineering works with gable ends facing the street. The frontage was of red and white brick, with a grey sandstone doorway flanked by Doric columns. On the centre gable was a neat belfry. The works was badly damaged by fire, and the frontage has been reconstructed.

28 Stirling Road Laundry, 6 Grafton St, built *c* 1885. A neat single storey, 5 bay ashlar building. Demolished November 1969.

29 Wright's Workshop, 9 Grafton St, built *c* 1874 for Archibald Cunningham, wright and builder. A group of small two and three storey buildings, the largest of which is a three storey, 3 by 4 bay red brick block with a modern flat roof.

30 Warehouse, 400 Cathedral St, built from 1869 for William Graham & Co., merchants, and extended 1876, 1880, *D. Thomson*, architect (£17,000), and completed in 1904 (eastern part, £11,000) by the same designer. A four storey, attic and basement, 6 by 16 bay sandstone building, demolished 1969–70. The interior of the 1904 part had steel beams on cast-iron columns, and of the earlier part wooden beams on cast-iron columns.

31 Warehouse, 38–44 Cunningham St, built 1882–3 for William Graham & Co., merchants (£4000). A three storey and basement, 8 by 11 bay ashlar fronted red brick building. Demolished 1970.

32 Livery Stables, 393–401 Parliamentary Rd, built 1877 for James Gilligan, carriage hirer (£3500). A three storey, 10 bay cement-washed building with central arched entrance leading to a small courtyard surrounded by three storey stables (total 53 stalls). Demolished 1971.

33 Queen Street Station, North Queen St, West George St, Dundas St, opened 21 February 1842 by the Edinburgh & Glasgow Railway. Nothing remains of the original station, though the offices at the corner of West George St and Dundas St were formerly a church ('Wardlaw's Kirk' built 1819 as West George St Independent Chapel to designs by *J. Gillespie Graham*, Edinburgh, SDD category C). This has a Doric terastyle portico at first floor level. The Dundas St entrance, which was demolished in 1968, was constructed in 1855–6, and had a frontage with five arches, three large ones flanked by single smaller ones, a heavy cornice and a five section balustrade. The roof was supported in the centre by a single cast-iron column, and consisted of a cast-iron frame braced with light wrought-iron tie rods and covered with wood and slates. Originally the tunnel mouth was on the south side of Cathedral St, but when the station was extended in the 1870s, the area to the north of Cathedral St was opened up, and the station boundary moved east to North

Hanover St. The present wrought-iron arched roof was completed in 1880, by P. & W. MacLellan, to designs by *James Carsewell*. It is carried on fine cast-iron Corinthian columns. At the corner of North Hanover St and Cathedral St a seven storey grain store on an L plan was built in 1878 to designs by the North British Railway Engineer's Office in Glasgow (£10,500). Built of ashlar, with classical four storey facades to the streets, the interior had cast-iron columns supporting wooden beams and floors. The building was demolished in 1966-7, but portions of the walls still stand.

34 Furrier's Workshop, 148 Wellington St and Sauchiehall Lane, built 1908 for H. P. MacNeill, *J. & J. W. Money*, architects (£490). A neat little two storey, 3 by 2 bay building with a single storey showroom at the front.

35 Daily Record Printing Works, St Vincent Lane and Renfield Lane, built 1900 for the Daily Record (Glasgow) Ltd, *C. R. Mackintosh* of *Honeyman & Keppie*, architect (£12,000). A notable building of the 'modern movement'. A glazed brick structure, with sandstone dressings, consisting of linked six storey and basement, 4 bay, and three storey and basement, 4 bay blocks. SDD category B.

36 Printing Works, 24 St Vincent Place, built 1885-7 for James Hedderwick & Sons, publishers, *T. L. Watson*, architect. A five storey, attic and basement, 6 bay red sandstone building in French Renaissance style richly ornamented, with crow-stepped gablets and a turret. The porch has two spirally fluted columns flanked by pillars with low relief carving. SDD category B.

37 Printing Works, 46-50 North Hanover St, founded *c* 1871 by Gilmour & Dean. The four storey and attic, 5 by 7 bay red sandstone Renaissance block on the corner with Frederick Lane was built in 1913, *Clifford & Lunan*, architects (£2030), while there is an earlier three storey and base-

ment, 2 bay red and white brick building to the east.

38 Calender Works, 4-6 Frederick Lane, built 1875-6 for James Anderson & Co., calenderers (£3000). An L shaped red and white brick building, four storey attic and basement, with a neat pedimented 5 bay ashlar frontage to the lane. The other wing is 5 bays long and 3 wide.

39 Oil Store, 62 North Frederick St, founded *c* 1855 by William Walls, oil merchant. Destroyed by fire in July 1866 and reconstructed 1866-7. A central three storey, 5 bay block, flanked by two storey, 3 bay units. The upper unit has a sunk ground floor. To the south is a similar three storey and basement, 4 bay block. The ground floor has a jack-arched roof. An interesting classical study.

40 Smithy, 12 Margaret St, established *c* 1851 by Peter McFarlane, smith. The two storey, 5 bay red brick building, with cast-iron window frames, dated from 1866 and was demolished in 1968.

41 Reed & Heddle Factory, 105-11 John St, built 1866-7 for James Neilson & Son, reed makers. An ashlar fronted four storey and attic red and white brick building. There are 8 bays to John St, each with two windows, 10 to Love Loan and 10 to Margaret St. Above the Margaret St frontage is a striking ornamental chimney in the form of a lotus flower.

42 Stables & Store, 11-13 Martha St, part built 1888 for John & James Fulton, potato merchants (£300). Two ranges of red brick buildings, one one storey, other two, with gable ends to the street, originally with seven stalls.

43 Engineering Works, 48 North Frederick St, built 1886 for James Ritchie, laundry engineer. A simple two storey, 6 by 5 bay red brick building.

44 Warehouses & Counting Houses, 34-6 North Frederick St, built 1881 for Daniel Paul, wright (£6000). A four storey and attic, 5 bay ashlar fronted brick building, with Corinthian pilasters running through first and second floors, heavy cornices above the ground, second and third floors, and a mansard roof with a balustrade in front of the attic windows.

45 Albany Works, 154 Rotten Row and 215 Cathedral St, founded *c* 1879 by J. McGlashan & Co., engineers and furnishers to the aerated water, wine, spirit and beer trades. A complex of two and three storey red and white brick buildings. Demolished 1967.

46 Electricity Substation, 199 Cathedral St, built 1905 for Glasgow Corporation Electricity Department (£5500). Two high single storey brick buildings, the original with three tall windows and a door, all round-headed, and the later building with a reinforced concrete lintel and a circular ventilator in the gable end.

47 Joiners' Shop, 14 Hopetoun Place, built *c* 1856 for McCraw & Kay, joiners. A group of two and three storey red brick buildings round a small cobbled courtyard. Demolished 1968.

48 Stables, 8 Paul St and Cathedral St, built 1868–70 for Wordie & Co., haulage contractors, and extended in 1881 (£350). A two storey, 15 by 16 bay block, with panelled brick walls. Demolished 1969.

49 Cathedral Works, 31 Weaver St, built 1908 for R. T. Paterson, *J. J. Waddell*, architect (£750) and extended in 1914 (£695). A two storey, 17 bay red brick building, partly fronted in red sandstone, with a single storey extension to the rear. Demolished 1969.

50 Stables, 11 Paul St, built *c* 1861 for Wordie & Co., haulage contractors. Two buildings, one two storey and attic, 8 bay, the other two storey, 4 by 5 bay, both partly stone and partly brick, with wooden floors on cast-iron columns.

51 Hydraulic Pumping Station, 295 High St, built 1893–5 for the Corporation Water Department, *J. M. Gale*, engineer. The retaining walls and chimney cost £3500. A large single storey rustic red sandstone ashlar building, in castellated style. There are three two storey crenellated towers. Originally there were three inverted vertical compound engines, each of 200 horsepower, but these were replaced before the station closed in 1964. Associated with the station is a three storey tenement in similar style, and a plainer two storey, 6 bay dwelling house. On the roof of the main block there are two large cast-iron storage tanks concealed by a crenellated wall.

52 Workshops, 263 High St, built *c* 1903 for the City Improvement Trust, and reinstated in 1905 after a fire to designs by *Burnet, Boston & Carruthers*, architects. A group of plain, flat-roofed, red brick blocks, the largest of which is six storeys high, 3 bays wide.

53 Cotton Mill, 100 Duke St, built 1849 for R. F. & J. Alexander, thread manufacturers, *C. Wilson*, architect. A six storey, 22 bay sandstone building in Italian Renaissance style with rusticated quoins and ground floor. The end bays project slightly. In 1909 the building was converted to a working-men's hotel, alterations including the central entrance. The interior is fireproof, of jack-arch construction. An outstanding industrial building.

54 High Street Goods Station, 208 High St, built 1904 for the North British Railway to designs by *James Bell*, engineer (£400,000). A very large red brick and concrete building, three storeys high, with 22 bays to High St and 20 bays to Duke St. The railway tracks are on the first floor. In front of the main block is a two storey, 13 bay office building with a small clock tower, and at the Hunter St end of the yard is a single storey shed added in 1905 (£10,000).

55 High Street Passenger Station, 198 High St (originally College Station), built *c* 1886 for the Glasgow City & District Railway, probably to designs by *James Carsewell*, engineer. The surface building is a single storey, 10 bay ashlar block, with a second storey over the southernmost pair of bays. Over the two doorways are entablatures with low-relief swags. Wooden stairways lead to two platforms in a cutting which has rustic masonry retaining walls.

56 College Goods Station, 172 High St, built from 1874 for the Glasgow & South Western Railway. A large range of one and two storey ashlar fronted brick buildings, with round-headed windows and doors. On the north is a two storey, 8 bay block with a single storey, 17 bay building to the south. The office block is a three storey and attic, 5 by 7 bay ashlar building, dated 1878. Much of the complex is built on a vaulted undercroft. The whole was fitted with hydraulic hoists and cranes, the latter now removed, supplied from a single storey pumping station in Bell St, with a neat Italianate red and white brick accumulator tower.

57 College Passenger Station, High St, built *c* 1871 for the North British Railway (opened 1 April 1871). An excellent example of a train shed, with wrought-iron roof trusses supported on the south side by a brick wall, and on the north side by a row of ten heavy cast-iron columns, linked laterally by flat-arched, cast-iron girders. Closed to passengers 15 March 1886, when Glasgow City & District Railway opened.

58 Warehouse, 105–69 Bell St, built 1882–3 for the Glasgow & South Western Railway (£100,000). A massive six storey, 4 by 31 bay rustic ashlar fronted building with heavy rusticated ground floor. The interior has massive cast-iron columns, 12 inches in diameter by 18 feet high, supporting heavy cast-iron beams, which carry concrete arches. An early example, in Glasgow, of the use of mass concrete.

59 Warehouse, 175–203 Bell St, built probably *c* 1880 for the Glasgow & South Western Railway. A neat two storey, 6 bay ashlar fronted brick building, with round-headed openings. The interior has flat concrete arches between wrought-iron beams, carried on cast-iron columns. Perhaps the earliest use of mass concrete in a Glasgow building.

60 Power Loom Factory, 299–311 Bell St, founded 1861 by J. & J. McIntyre, dress goods and silk manufacturers. A row of three buildings, constructed in 1861 (easternmost) five storey, 6 by 2 bay, *c* 1866 (centre) three storey, 5 bay, and 1893 (westernmost) three storey, 4 bay, *John Gordon*, architect (£1800). All were brick, the centre block latterly cement-rendered. Demolished *c* 1969.

61 Workshop & Stables, 15–17 Nicholas St, built 1893 for George Eadie, builder, *A. Petrie*, architect (£6000). A two storey, 11 bay red and white brick range, with some cast-iron window frames.

62 Stable & Warehouse, 205 High St, built 1893 for George Eadie, builder. A two storey and attic, 8 bay ashlar fronted building, with dormer windows.

63 Warehouse, College Lane and Shuttle St, built in the late 19th century. A six storey and attic, 12 bay red brick block. The narrow 5 bay sandstone frontage to Shuttle St has five storey pilasters.

64 Warehouse, 182 Albion St, built some time between 1821 and 1828. A three storey, 8 by 3 bay brick and rubble building, with small square windows. Demolished 1971.

65 St Catherine's Leather Works, 12–20 Ingram St, built 1910 for McBride & Logie, leather merchants, *J. W. & J. Laird*, architects (£12,460). A five storey and basement, 7 bay red sandstone ashlar fronted building, with arched recesses embracing the first, second and third floor windows in the three central bays.

66 Warehouse, 131–41 Albion St, built 1906 for Fraser Ross & Co. Ltd, clothing manufacturers. A six storey, 3 by 5 bay red sandstone ashlar fronted brick building.

67 Clothing Factory, 12 Montrose St, built 1898 for Stewart & Macdonald, wholesale warehousemen. A seven storey and basement, 21 by 5 bay red sandstone fronted building, with cast-iron columns and wooden beams in interior.

68 Warehouse, 18 Montrose St, built 1876 for Benjamin Simons, fruit broker (£6000). A six storey and attic, 20 bay sandstone building in Renaissance style. The fifth floor windows are round-headed. Internally there are cast-iron columns and wooden beams.

69 Leather Warehouse, 27–9 Montrose St, built in the late 18th or early 19th century and extended at the rear in 1864 for J. & W. Stiell, leather merchants. A three storey, 3 bay ashlar fronted rubble building, with an arched cart entrance. The extension is five storeys high by 9 bays long, of red brick.

70 Cold Store, 223–33 George St, built as a warehouse 1872–3 for Benjamin Simons, fruit broker (£2000), and converted to a cold store *c* 1900 for the Scottish Cold Storage & Ice Co. A five storey, 7 bay Italian Renaissance building, with wooden floors on cast-iron columns. There was a row of pilasters along the top floor and a heavy cornice. Demolished 1971.

71 Warehouses, 7–19 Montrose St, 7–25 and 49–57 Cochrane St, built in the late 18th century. Two ranges of severely plain four storey ashlar warehouses, some with basements, with octagonal or rectangular courts at the rear. In the courts at 19 and 55 Cochrane St wall cranes survive. These are good examples of a type which also occurs in John St, Ingram St and Candleriggs.

72 Printing Works, 65 Buchanan St and 60–70 Mitchell St, built from 1865 for George Outram & Sons, printers and publishers of the *Glasgow Herald*. The French Renaissance block in Buchanan St is a five storey and attic, 5 bay structure, with pilasters through second and third floors built 1879–80, *J. Sellars*, architect. In Mitchell St is a six storey, 11 bay red sandstone building with a ten storey tower, built 1893–5. An early work by *C. R. Mackintosh*, of *Honeyman & Keppie*, incorporating an unusual system for spraying the windows with water in the event of fire. Between these blocks in the lane are a block added in 1897 (£3250) and another of five storeys and basement, built in 1909 by *J. Beaumont & Son*, architects, Manchester (£10,000).

73 Printing Works, 102–14 Union St, founded 1854 for printing the *North British Daily Mail*. The present building dates from 1898, and was designed by *George Bell* (II) of *Clarke & Bell*, architect (£7500), who also designed a reconstruction after a fire (£2500). A six storey, 3 bay French Renaissance block, of red sandstone ashlar, running through to Union Place.

74 Central Station, Union St, Gordon St and Hope St, built for the Caledonian Railway. The first part was completed in June 1879, and opened 1 August 1879. The station was extended to give 13 platforms in 1899–1905 to designs by *J. Miller*, architect, and *Donald Mathieson*, engineer. The steelwork was executed by the Motherwell Bridge & Engineering Co. The roof is carried partly on flat roof trusses (older part) and partly on elliptical arched girders supported by riveted steel columns and on the Hope St side by a masonry wall pierced with six large arched windows, and surmounted by a corbelled cornice and balustrade. The station hotel, a five and six storey and attic building in French Renaissance style with a massive corner tower, was designed by *R. R. Anderson*, Edinburgh, and completed in 1883. A 16 bay extension in Hope St was built 1905–7, *J. Miller*, architect. The massive seven storey by 12 bay office block in Union St was added in 1901 by *J. Miller*, architect (£40,000).

Of the original internal fittings of the station, little survives, though the splendid train indicator is probably the best in Britain. Below the main station is the underground Low Level Station, opened in August 1896. Closed on 5 October 1964, though the track is now lifted, the platforms and stairs still survive.

75 Printing Works, 65–7 Hope St and Cadogan St, built 1899 for J. M. Smith Ltd, proprietors of the *Glasgow Evening News*, R. *Thomson*, architect (£16,000). A seven storey and attic, 2 bay ornate French Renaissance building, with red sandstone ashlar frontage. SDD category C. The more modern four storey building to the south has plate glass windows displaying the printing presses. In Cadogan St is a five storey, 9 bay block.

76 Warehouses & Offices, 10 Cadogan St and 29 Wellington St, built 1869 for Thomas B. Campbell & Sons, metal merchants. A neat three storey, 11 by 7 bay ashlar building with rusticated ground floor, part of which has been modernised. At the rear, in Wellington Lane, is a four storey, 4 bay plain ashlar addition of 1891, A. *Myles*, architect.

77 Workshop, 69–73 Robertson Lane, built *c* 1874 for John Finlayson & Walter Neilson, japanners. A four storey, 4 bay ashlar fronted brick building.

78 Workshop, 75–81 Robertson Lane, built *c* 1876 for Hannan & Buchanan, pressure gauge makers. A four storey, 6 bay ashlar fronted brick building with a hoist.

79 Warehouse, Robertson Lane, probably built before 1840. A three storey and basement, 11 bay rubble building. An unusual feature is the alternation of large and small windows on each floor.

80 Workshop & Warehouse, 45–59 Robertson St, built 1869–70 for James Gilchrist, engineer and ironmonger. A two storey, 9 bay ashlar fronted building with pairs of round-headed windows at first floor level.

81 Warehouse, 26–30 Robertson Lane, built *c* 1881 for the Central Storage Co. A five storey and basement, 11 bay red and white brick building.

82 Warehouse, 17 Robertson St, built 1899 for Robert Balloch & Co., tea merchants, to designs by J. A. *Campbell*, architect (£5700). A single storey addition at the rear was designed in 1900 by the same architect (£1000). A four storey and attic, 2 by 3 bay red brick building, with windows from first to third floors in arched recesses. The ground floor windows are round-headed.

83 Warehouse, 54–64 Broomielaw and 5 Oswald St, built 1878 for J. & P. Hutchison, shipowners. A four storey and attic, 6 bay ashlar fronted rubble building, with pedimented dormers, each with three round-headed windows.

84 Bonded Warehouse, 11 Oswald St, probably built *c* 1844 for P. Robertson & Co., bonded warehousemen. A four storey and attic ashlar building, 3 by 11 bay, with a circular window in gable end, which faces the street. The gable end is decorated with four low-relief pilasters.

85 Warehouses & Offices, 37–41 Midland St and 28–38 Oswald St, built 1869 for John Stewart & Co., iron merchants. A three storey, 8 by 10 bay sandstone ashlar block, with rusticated ground floor and arched doorways. The interior has cast-iron columns supporting wooden beams.

86 Custom House, 198 Clyde St, built 1840, G. L. *Taylor*, London, architect. An attractive two storey and attic, 9 bay classical revival building. The projecting central portion has six pilasters at first floor level, and there is a fine sculpture of the royal arms at roof level. SDD category B. The end bays, with Palladian windows at first floor level, are a later addition.

87 St Enoch Underground Station, built 1895 for The Glasgow District Subway Co., J. *Miller*, architect. A neat two storey, 3 by 3 bay red sandstone building in

Jacobean style, with corner turrets, on an island site. Originally the headquarters of the Subway Co. SDD category B.

88 St Enoch Station, built 1870–9 for the City of Glasgow Union Railway. The station proper was designed by *John Fowler* and *James F. Blair*, engineers, and the hotel and office block by *Thomas Willson*, Hampstead, and *M. S. Gibson*, architects. The first station, at Dunlop St, was opened on 12 December 1870, and was only temporary in nature. The first station on the present site was opened 1 May 1876, and the development completed by the opening of the hotel on 3 July 1879. The overall five centred arch roof of the station, constructed by Messrs A. Handyside of Derby, has a span of 205 feet and a length of 525 feet, and is of wrought-iron, covering six platforms. Between 1898 and 1902 the station was extended, the viaduct from Eglinton St widened, including the bridge over the Clyde (G138), and a second arched roof added, 198 feet wide and 525 feet long. Awnings were constructed to cover the projecting ends of the new platforms. The extension was designed by *William Melville*, engineer to the Glasgow & South Western Railway, which had taken over the station from the CGUR. In the triangle to the east of the station is the engine shed, built between 1882 and 1885, with a 30 bay frontage to King St. The undercroft of the engine shed has been used for many years as a bonded store. The station itself is SDD category B.

89 Warehouses, Fox St, built *c* 1857–9. 79–80 is a three storey, 6 bay cement-washed building with a hoist, and a wall crane at ground floor level. 60–70 is an 8 bay, four storey ashlar fronted building with a hoist. 59 and 69–75 are four storey and basement, 5 bay blocks; originally both had central hoists, but that on 69–75 has been bricked up.

90 Printing Works, 96 Maxwell St and 70 Howard St, built from 1868 for McCorquodale & Co., general printers. The main block in Howard St is a four storey and attic, 15 bay structure, with a mansard roof, linked by a curved portion to a rather similar 11 bay block, with pairs of round-headed windows at third floor level. The small two storey and attic building on the corner with Fox St, 12 by 6 bay, was probably built in 1868 and rebuilt in 1870, *D. Thomson*, architect.

91 Leather Warehouse, 114 Howard St, rebuilt 1903 after a fire for Schrader, Mitchell & Weir, *A. Balfour*, architect (£4500). A six storey, attic and basement building with 3 wide bays, each of three windows. The red sandstone ashlar frontage has pilasters through the second and third floors, carrying arches framing the fourth floor windows, which are separated from the sixth floor by a heavy cornice.

92 Glass Warehouse, 118 Howard St, built 1903 for William Cotterill, *Beattie & Morton*, architects (£4800). A five storey and attic, 5 bay red sandstone ashlar building with *art nouveau* features. SDD category B.

93 Hat & Cap Factory, 16–22 Fox St, built *c* 1899 for Allan & Orr, hat and cap manufacturers. A six storey, 6 bay ashlar fronted building.

94 Leather Warehouse, 12–14 Fox St, built 1868–9 for Schrader & Mitchell, hide, leather and bark merchants. A six storey, 6 bay ashlar fronted building.

95 Warehouse, 54 Clyde St, built 1914 for Symington & Co., cork manufacturers, *Clifford & Lunan*, architects (£5645). A five storey brick and reinforced-concrete block, with an ashlar frontage to Clyde St, with 3 wide bays. The building runs through to Fox St, on which it has a 6 bay frontage.

96 Custom House Quay, Clyde St, built 1852–7 for the Clyde Navigation Trust. A stone-faced quay with wooden fenders. There were single storey brick warehouses on both sides of the suspension bridge, and until recently there were four travelling cranes, all of which have now been dismantled. Latterly used for sand and gravel traffic, and as a car and bus park, though the RNVR ship *Carrick* is berthed at the east end. Now developed as a promenade.

97 Warehouse, 69–79 Dunlop St, 152–66 Howard St and 50 Ropework Lane, built 1901–2 for Alexander, Fergusson & Co., paint and lead manufacturers, *Burnet & Boston*, architects (£35,000). A six storey and attic, 8 by 8 by 8 bay snecked rubble, red sandstone building, with a mansard roof.

98 Warehouse, 95 Dunlop St, 144–58 Clyde St and Ropework Lane, built 1896–9 for the Great Clyde Street (Glasgow) Heritable Co. (£17,000). A five storey and attic, 3 by 11 by 8 bay snecked rubble, red sandstone building, with a mansard roof. Between this building and the previous one is a four bay block similar in style.

99 Wine Store, 27 Goosedubs, built 1877 for John Baillie, wine merchant. A four storey, 7 bay ashlar fronted rubble building with a two storey extension at the rear, built in 1890 for Peter McIntosh & Sons, tanners, *D. Thomson*, architect (£600).

100 Ice Factory & Cold Store, Osborne St and Old Wynd, built 1901–2 for William Milne, *Alexander Adam,* architect (£30,000). The main block is a four storey, 19 bay terra-cotta brick structure with a flat roof, while there is a matching single storey 13 bay block in Osborne St, with twin crow-stepped gables.

101 Electricity Substation, Osborne St and Old Wynd, built 1912 for Glasgow Corporation Electricity Department (£3080). A neat single storey, 4 by 6 bay terra-cotta brick building, with arched openings separated by pilasters.

102 Leather Warehouse, 47 Old Wynd, built 1899 for J. Thomson & Co., hide and leather factors, *J. Short*, architect (£7000). A five storey, 4 bay red brick building, with low relief arches embracing the first to third floor windows, which are in pairs.

103 Warehouse, 9 New Wynd, built *c* 1859 for Robert Hillcoat, spirit dealer. A plain four storey, 7 bay rubble building with rustic quoins.

104 Warehouse, 6–26 King St, 64–70 Parnie St, built 1899 for the City Improvement Trust, *McKissack & Son*, architects (£32,500). A five storey and attic, 5 by 14 bay red sandstone fronted brick building in elaborate Renaissance style.

105 Warehouse, 34–60 King St, 73–85 Parnie St and 50–68 Osborne St, built 1902 for the City Improvement Trust, *McKissack & Son*, architects (£31,000). A five storey block on a U plan with 9 bays each to Parnie St and Osborne St and 12 bays to King St. Much plainer than G104, with corner oriels and cupolas.

106 Workshops, 46 Parnie St, built 1896 for the City Improvement Trust, *A. B. Macdonald*, architect. A two storey, 3 by 6 bay brick building with crow-stepped gables.

107 Clothing Factory, 62–4 Miller St, built *c* 1877 for T. Macnee & Co., manufacturers. A four storey and basement, 14 bay ashlar fronted building, arcaded through the second and third storeys. There is a heavy cornice with consoles. SDD category B.

108 Warehouse, 108–10 Brunswick St, built 1883 for Simons, Jacobs & Co., fruit merchants (£22,000). A five storey and attic Renaissance building, with 3 wide bays. The front is sandstone, the side and rear walls brick. The part extending through to Candleriggs was destroyed by fire in 1912, and rebuilt to designs by *Thomson & Sandilands*, architects.

109 Warehouse, 1–5 Brunswick Lane, built 1896 for Robert Simpson's Trustees, *Burnet & Boston*, architects (£2800). A narrow four storey, 1 by 10 bay red brick building at right angles to Brunswick Lane.

110 Store, 26–8 Blackfriars St, built 1899 for Thomas Russell, fruit broker (£3500). A three storey and attic, 9 bay red sandstone ashlar fronted building, with decorative low-relief arches, and roundels at attic level.

111 Covent Garden Market, 25–7 Blackfriars St, built 1904 for Thomas Russell, fruit broker, *Brand & Lithgow*, architects (£2800). A two storey, 6 bay red brick building, with panelled side and end, round-headed windows and a large roof ventilator.

112 Workshops & Maintenance Depot, 24–32 Walls St and Blackfriars St, built 1881–1903 for Glasgow Corporation Gas Department. The southern block in Walls St, a two storey and attic, 13 bay structure, was built in 1881, the corner block, with 7 bays to Walls St and 5 to Blackfriars St, was added in 1888 (£2000), and the L plan group completed by a three storey and attic, 10 bay building in Blackfriars St, built 1903, *G. Sinclair*, architect (£6600). All the buildings are ashlar, with rusticated ground floors, and segmentally-arched cart entries.

113 Glasgow Cross Station, Trongate, built for the opening of the Glasgow Central Railway in August 1896, and rebuilt *c* 1923. The original surface building was octagonal, with rounded corners and a dome, *J. J. Burnet*, architect, while the replacement is much plainer, with two round-headed doorways facing High St. The railway was underground at this point with waiting rooms on an island platform, ventilated through an opening to the west of the station building, surrounded at street level by an iron grille with a C.R. monogram alternating with a lion rampant on its panels. Closed 5 October 1964.

114 Cleansing Department Depot, 142–4 Bell St, for Glasgow Corporation Cleansing Department, built 1896–8, *A. W. Wheatley*, engineer to the department, and opened 31 May 1898 (£13,500). A four storey red sandstone block, 9 by 13 bay, with decora-tive low-relief arches. There is a central courtyard, and the interior has floors on riveted girders supported by massive cast-iron columns.

115 Steam Power Coffee Roasting & Grinding Works, 150–66 Bell St, built 1871 for David Minto. A three storey, 10 bay ashlar fronted block with segmentally arched doorway.

116 Railway Stables, 174 Bell St, built *c* 1900 for the Glasgow & South Western Railway. An L plan terra-cotta brick building with a 17 bay frontage to the street. At the rear, ramps and balconies give access to the stalls, which are ventilated by brick stacks. The top floor windows are framed by semicircular arches springing from corbelled supports.

117 Workshop & Store, 18 Watson St, built 1891 for Alexander Rowat & Co., wire workers, *J. S. Smith*, architect (£1200). A group of two and three storey brick buildings.

118 Warehouse, Molendinar St, Spoutmouth and 69–99 Gallowgate, built 1873–4 for William Anderson, spirit merchant (£28,000). A spectacular triangular series of four storey blocks, with a 33 bay curved frontage to Gallowgate, a 20 bay angled frontage to Spoutmouth, both ashlar, and a 23 bay red and white brick frontage to Molendinar St. Partly destroyed by fire in 1970, and since demolished.

119 Saracen Tool Works, 272 Bell St and 13 East Campbell St, founded on this site *c* 1856 by Alexander Mathieson & Son, edge tool makers. A four storey red brick building with white glazed brick string courses, on an L plan, 7 by 11 bay, built 1896, *Honeyman & Keppie*, architects.

120 Store, 45 McFarlane St, built *c* 1876 for Peter Paterson, fish merchant, and extended in 1911 for Bell & Co., hide, skin and tallow brokers (£500). A small group of one and two storey red and white brick buildings round a courtyard.

121 Clay Pipe Factory, 26–42 Bain St, 71–91 Moncur St and 15 Gibson St, built 1876–7 for W. White & Son, clay pipe makers, *M. Forsyth*, architect. Whites had been in Gibson St since 1824. An ornate group of two and four storey French Renaissance red and white brick buildings (originally intended to be stone), with 15 bays to Gibson St (this part built 1867), 9 and 11 bays to Moncur St and 7, 5 and 7 bays to Bain St. In the centre of the Bain St frontage is a round headed doorway, with a plaque above 'W 1877 W'. In the middle of the block is a tall circular-section chimney.

122 Rumford Works (Ironmongery), 233 London Rd and Stevenson St, built 1892 and 1905 for Charles Lindsay, manufacturing ironmonger. The block facing London Rd is four storey, 7 bay, of red sandstone with round-headed windows on the second floor, and was designed in 1905 by *G. S. Hill*, architect (£2500). At the rear, in Stevenson St, is a three storey, 8 bay red and white brick structure, with brick pilasters through the ground and first floors, designed in 1892 by *J. M. Monro*, architect.

123 Workshop, 153 Greendyke St, built *c* 1894 for Alexander Marshall, plane, saw and edge tool maker. A three storey, 6 by 2 bay red and white brick building, behind a tenement.

124 Camp Coffee Works, 77–81 Charlotte St and 115 Greendyke St, built 1891–1908 for R. Paterson, coffee essence manufacturer. The three storey, 8 bay ashlar fronted block in Charlotte St, with a balustrade at roof level, was built in 1898 to designs by *Gavin Paterson* (£1400). In Greendyke St, the three storey, 5 bay block with circular windows was built in 1893 and the three storey, 5 by 5 bay building with round-headed windows on the second floor was added in 1908, by *A. Skirving* and *W. Baillie*, respectively.

125 Preserve Works, 57–9 Charlotte St, built as a villa *c* 1780 and reconstructed in 1888 for Walker & Son, *D. V. Wyllie*, architect (£500). The original building was two storeys high, 5 bays wide with an ashlar front, a pediment and rustic quoins. At some time before 1888 an extra bay was added on each side, D. V. Wyllie's addition being a third storey.

126 Glasgow Stamp & Brand Works, 153 London Rd, built *c* 1846 as a workshop for Park & Stewart, joiners. A two storey, 4 bay ashlar fronted rubble building, with rustic quoins.

127 St Catherine's Leather Works, 14 Moir Lane, built *c* 1880 for Thomas McBride, currier and leather merchant. A four storey attic and basement, 11 bay red and white brick building.

128 Cast-iron Girder carrying London Rd over course of Molendinar Burn (now culverted) dated 1826, of arch form with relieving holes and 'keystone'.

129 Bedding Factory, 3–5 Charlotte Lane South, built 1887 for John & James Walton, bedding and leather belting manufacturers, *H. D. Walton*, architect (£1350). Plain three storey, 7 bay red and white brick building.

130 Tobacco Factory, 36 St Andrews Square, reconstructed from *c* 1875 for Stephen Mitchell & Co. Two three storey blocks, one 6 bay, the other 3 bay, forming the south-east corner of the square, then a four storey and attic, 5 bay building, probably added in 1884 (£2100), and a four storey and attic, 5 bay structure. At the rear, on the other side of Dyers Lane, is a six storey attic and basement, 8 bay red brick block, partly finished with white glazed tiles, and linked at three levels with the St Andrews Square blocks. This part was designed in 1898 by *Steel & Balfour*, architects (£9000).

131 Hide, Wool & Tallow Auction Market, 33–43 Greendyke St, built 1890 for Robert Ramsay & Co., brokers, *J. Keppie* of *Honeyman & Keppie*, architect (£12,000). Replaced a smaller building of

1885 that was destroyed by fire. A fine four storey, 7 bay red sandstone ashlar fronted brick building, with three and four storey additions at the rear, built in 1891 (£1500). SDD category C.

132 Leather Warehouse, 48 St Andrews Square, built 1876–7 for John Inglis & Co., leather factors (£5000). A five storey and basement, 5 by 5 by 9 bay building with ashlar front and side, and red and white brick back. A central hoist at the rear has now been bricked up. The goods entrance at the front has a bull's head carved on the keystone, and above the office entrance is the inscription 'Tannery Buildings'.

133 Stable, 2 Mart St, built 1910 for James McKelroy's trustee, *Watson & Salmond*, architects (£440). A one storey and attic ashlar fronted building with 4 bays to the street.

134 King's Bridge, Ballater St, built 1932–3. A three span reinforced-concrete girder bridge with granite cutwaters and parapets.

135 St Andrew's Suspension Bridge, built 1853–5, *Neil Robson*, engineer (£6348) to enable workers from Bridgeton and Calton to reach factories in Hutchesontown. The pylons consist of heavy entablatures supported by pairs of Corinthian columns, all of cast-iron. Flat link chains support a light lattice girder span. An attractive and little known structure.

136 Weir, the fourth on the Clyde at or near this point, marking the upper tidal limit on the river. The Act for the construction of this weir was obtained in 1894, and it was opened 28 December 1901, *Sir Benjamin Baker*, engineer. There are three movable sluices, each 80 feet wide. The steelwork of the weir was reconstructed in the 1940s (completed 13 May 1949), though the masonry is original.

137 Albert Bridge, built 1870–1 to replace a bridge of 1829–33 (£48,900). A three span cast-iron arch bridge, with stone piers. There are eight ribs per span, with the Glasgow Arms in the spandrels of the outer ribs. The contractors were Hanna, Donald & Wilson, Paisley.

138 Union Railway Bridge, rebuilt 1898–1902 to serve the extended St Enoch Station (G88). The original bridge was constructed 1864–7 for the City of Glasgow Union Railway, the contractors being Brassey & Co. The reconstructed bridge is a five arch structure with steel arches on pairs of stone piers. There are single lattice girder spans at each end leading to the brick arch approaches. The piers are extended upwards to imitate crenellated turrets, and there is a cast-iron Gothic parapet.

139 Victoria Bridge, built 1851–4, *James Walker*, engineer (£46,206). The contractor was William Scott of Glasgow. A five arched sandstone bridge encased in Kingstown (Dublin) granite. The centre span is 80 feet, the adjacent arches 76 feet and the outer spans 60 feet. The roadway is 58 feet wide. SDD category B.

140 Portland Street Suspension Bridge, built 1851 by the Heritors of Gorbals, and reconstructed 1871. The Classical pylons were designed by *A. Kirkland*, architect, and the metalwork by *George Martin*, engineer. The light lattice girder deck is suspended from flat link chains, and the clear span is 414 feet. The bridge retains its gas lampholders, now electrified. SDD category A.

141 Glasgow Bridge, built 1894–9, *Blyth & Westland*, engineers (£129,500), replacing an earlier bridge designed by *Thomas Telford*, engineer. A seven arched masonry bridge, with granite facing, part of which came from the old bridge. Each pier has three transverse arches, and the width of the bridge is 80 feet.

142 Central Station Bridges, built 1876–8 and 1899–1905 for the Caledonian Railway. The first bridge, designed by *Blyth & Cunningham*, engineers, and built by William Arrol & Co., was about 700 feet long.

The approach spans, over Clyde Place and Broomielaw, were of plate and lattice girder construction, respectively 60 and 90 feet long, while the main spans, 164, 184 and 152 feet long, were wrought-iron lattice girders with their top edges linked by light arched lattice girders. The girders were carried on twin masonry piers linked by cast-iron arches. At each end of the bridge were cast-iron plaques with the Caledonian lion rampant encircled by a garter, with the date 1878. This bridge was demolished 1966–7, only the granite piers and cast-iron arches remaining. The present bridge was built 1899–1905 and is of much more substantial steel construction, on granite piers, each of which is founded on five steel caissons. It also was built by Arrol & Co.

143 King George V Bridge, built 1924–8, *T. M. Somers* and *Considéré Constructions Ltd*, engineers (£249,877). The memorial stone was laid on 12 July 1927. A three span, reinforced-concrete continuous beam bridge, faced with Dalbeattie granite. The outer spans are 110½ feet and the central span 146 feet long, with a 50-foot carriageway.

144 Warehouse, 30 Clyde Place, built 1906 for D. Wight & Co., tea merchants, *Monro & Son*, architects (£6800). A four storey and attic, 5 bay, red sandstone ashlar fronted building in Renaissance style.

145 Tradeston Grain Mills, 6–10 Commerce St, established *c* 1846 by William Muir, and badly damaged by an explosion on 9 July 1872. The present building was constructed in 1873–4 (£12,000). A fine six storey, 9 bay ashlar fronted rubble building, with two windows per bay, now converted to a cold store.

146 Bridge St Station (1), built 1840–1 for the Glasgow & Paisley Joint Railway, *J. Collie*, architect, and opened 6 April 1841, replacing a temporary wooden structure opened, with the railway, on 14 July 1839. A two storey building with 5 central bays and two projecting end pavilions, each with the remains of an arched entrance. There was originally a central tetrastyle Doric portico, removed *c* 1950, and the building was much deeper than at present. The four storey building to the north was an hotel associated with the station.

147 Stables, 21–5 Carlton Court, built *c* 1895 for the Clyde Shipping Co. Ltd. A three storey and attic, 9 bay ashlar fronted brick building with a central hoist. At the rear is an offset well with wooden horse ramps giving access to the upper floors, and hoists above the granary.

148 Store, 12 Carlton Court, built 1888 for Wm Rankine & Sons, cork cutters. A three storey, 2 by 12 bay red brick building.

149 Warehouse & Offices, 63 Carlton Place and 3 South Portland St, built 1908 for Finnie & Co., wholesale ironmongers, *H. Campbell*, architect (£7920). A five storey and basement, 9 by 3 bay red sandstone warehouse. The top two floors were damaged by fire in 1969.

150 Shoe Factory, 26–36 Oxford St, built *c* 1865 for E. & S. Scott, wholesale and retail shoe manufacturers, and extended in 1874 (£1500). A rectangular four storey and attic, 6 by 10 bay building with a mansard roof (added in 1890–1, *T. Dykes*, architect). In the front of the building there are two groups of three arched windows extending through the second and third floors.

151 Loch Katrine (or Adelphi) Distillery, 4 Inverkip St, founded *c* 1825 by C. & D. Gray. A group of red and white brick buildings, the largest of which was a seven storey, 4 by 5 bay silo block. Facing the street were five storey, 5 by 7 bay, five storey, 7 bay and four storey, 4 bay blocks. The complex was dominated by a large circular-section chimney with a flared top. Demolished 1968–70.

152 Warehouses, 13–31 Inverkip St, built 1882–1902 for C. & D. Gray, distillers. Two adjacent five storey and attic red brick buildings with mansard roofs, one 12 bays (1882, £12,000), the other 5 bays long (1902, £7500). Both buildings extended through to St Ninian's St. Demolished 1971.

153 Caledonia Wire Works, 30 Thistle St, built c 1884 for Robert McDonald. A plain two storey, 8 by 2 bay red brick building, now harled.

154 Clutha Iron Works, 35 Florence St, built 1860 for P. & W. McLellan, and altered to a tube works for David Richmond in 1874 (£1500). A three storey, 12 bay brick building, painted grey, with round-headed windows having cast-iron frames. Demolished c 1965.

155 Engineering Works, 41 Florence St, built c 1860 for William Whitesmith, veneer saw and power-loom manufacturer, and reconstructed as a school in 1874. A three storey, 10 by 4 bay building with round headed windows, pedimented doorways, and roof ventilators, which were presumably added during conversion. Demolished 1968.

156 Sawmill, 241 Ballater St, built 1875 for Frost & Woyka, timber merchants (£1000). A plain four storey, 10 bay red brick building, with central cart entry. Demolished 1965.

157 Albyn Cotton Mills, 47–71 Waddell St, built c 1845 for McBride & Co., cotton spinners and power-loom cloth manufacturers. The oldest part is a five storey, 6 by 15 bay rubble and red brick block, with three rows of columns. The Ballater St frontage, of brick, has pilasters through the first to fourth floors, with capitals and cornice of white brick. In Waddell St is a four storey and attic, 11 bay brick block, with altered frontage, probably added in 1868.

158 Bakery, 12 McNeil St, Adelphi St, Moffat St and Ballater St, built 1886–1916 for the United Co-operative Baking Society, *Bruce & Hay*, architects. The oldest part is

the Flemish block on the corner of McNeil St and Ballater St (1886, £4500), extended along McNeil St in 1889 (£7000) and 1891 (£9500), and along Ballater St in 1895–6 (£28,000). The main part of the Moffat St frontage was added in 1900 (£17,000) and the ornate Renaissance front to Adelphi St was completed in 1908. The whole is executed in red and white brick, with extensive use of moulded bricks, and red sandstone carved panels.

159 Govanhaugh Factory, 563 Ballater St, built 1911 for Andrew Gray & Co., solder manufacturers, *J. A. Laird*, architect. A neat two storey, 1 bay terra-cotta brick fronted building, with Flemish gable.

160 Bonded Warehouse, 546 Ballater St, built 1897–1900 for C. & D. Gray and A. & J. Walker, distillers, *Burnet & Boston*, architects (£44,000). A very large six storey and attic red brick building and U plan with mansard roof, built in three parts. Facing Ballater St is a five storey, 8 bay red brick building, the only surviving part of the Adelphi Dyeworks, built c 1878.

161 Glasgow Paper Mills, 44 McNeil St, founded c 1858 by Stewart & Brown, papermakers, and extensively reconstructed 1867–8. The only surviving part is a two storey, 3 bay red and white brick building, probably added in 1862.

162 Engineering Works, 132 McNeil St, founded c 1875 by D. Cockburn & Son, boilermakers, and altered 1904–7 to a biscuit factory for W. & J. McLintock. The two storey, 3 bay McNeil St frontage makes bold use of red and white brick, and was built in 1892, *John Hamilton*, architect. The four storey red brick block between the streets was added in 1907 (£4500) and the two storey buildings at 265 Moffat St altered in the same year (£780), both to designs by *J. Nisbet*, architect.

163 Workshop & Stables, 148–62 Moffat St, built 1897 for the United Co-operative Baking Society, *Bruce & Hay*, architects (£32,500, not completed). Two long parallel ranges of buildings, one two storey and the other four storey, of red and white brick, with a single storey link block. The ground floor facades are of red sandstone with arched openings.

164 New Adelphi Mill, 50 Commercial Rd and Rutherglen Rd, founded *c* 1886 by William Wiseman, cleaning waste manufacturer. The corner block is a two storey, 3 by 5 bay red brick building, and in Commercial Rd is a two storey, 17 bay block.

165 Weaving Factory, 189–203 Rutherglen Rd and 76 Commercial Rd, founded *c* 1822 by Alexander Brown & Co. At 203 Rutherglen Rd is a four storey, 10 bay red brick building, with central elliptically-arched cart entry, now blocked up, while at the rear is a cut down fireproof building, of jack-arch construction. At 189 Rutherglen Rd is a five storey, 5 by 9 bay red brick building extended by 8 bays and one storey in the interwar years.

166 Quilt Factory, 210 Ballater St, built 1889–90 for Thomas Nicol, *Richard Murray*, engineer (£2500). A four storey and attic, 11 bay red brick building, with weaving sheds at the rear. The ground floor windows are round-headed.

167 Cooperage, 13–27 Camden St, built 1894–6 for T. Lindsay, cooper (£700). A two storey and attic, 11 bay red brick building, with a small two storey, 4 bay office block.

168 Grocery Warehouse, 111 Thistle St, built 1912 for Alexander Massey & Sons, *J. Lindsay*, architect (£2120) and extended in 1914 (£1650). A four storey, 3 by 13 bay terra-cotta brick building, with a Renaissance frontage to Cleland St.

169 Furniture Factory, 29–41 Surrey St, founded *c* 1862 by James Brown, cabinet-maker. A four storey red brick building behind a tenement, built 1868, was extended to the south in 1878 by a four storey and attic, 8 bay red and white brick building.

170 Warehouse, 172–8 Gorbals St, built *c* 1907 for S. R. McCall, warehouseman. A two storey, 4 bay red brick building, with two ornamental cast-iron heads between the outer pairs of first floor windows. Addition at rear was built in 1913 for G. C. Trainer, metal merchant, *A. Adam*, architect (£507).

171 Gorbals Grain Mills, 87–97 Surrey St, established *c* 1884 by Andrew Motherwell, grain merchant. A four storey and attic red and white brick building, in two portions, one 4 bay, cast-iron and wood framed, with a high water tower, built 1890 (£3500). The other part has 5 bays, and has steel beams on cast-iron columns (1895–6, £9000). There are two fine round-headed doorways, and decorative use is made of white bricks and moulded bricks. The stables at the rear, two storeys high, were added in 1891 (£1000). All these structures were designed by *John Hamilton*, architect, while the two storey retail shop and office block at the corner of Cumberland St and Gorbals St was added in 1910 to designs by *Arthur Hamilton*, architect (£1080). Demolished 1970.

172 Victoria Foundry (Brass), Gorbals Lane, built 1876 for Adam Clark, brass-founder and gasolier manufacturer (£4000). A five storey, 4 bay red and white brick building with a chimney at the rear.

173 Workshop, 9–13 Gorbals Lane, built in the late 19th century. A three storey, 11 bay red and white brick building.

174 Aerated Water Factory, 23–7 Oxford St, built 1885 for Barclay Bros, bottlers (£3000). A four storey, 5 bay ashlar fronted brick building, with the ground floor extended to the rear. As well as the factory, and stables, the building contained six three-roomed houses.

175 Brass Works, 26–30 Buchan St, built 1889–90 for John Wilson & Son, brass and bellfounders, *Bruce & Hay*, architects (£12,000). A four storey, 8 bay ashlar fronted building, with a red brick extension and square-section chimney at the rear.

176 Warehouse, 45–65 Oxford St, built 1882 for James Wilson, iron tube manufacturer (£6500). A three storey, 2 by 14 bay, ashlar fronted building. Each bay has three windows separated by narrow mullions.

177 Warehouse, 47 Bridge St, built 1902–3 for the Kinning Park Co-operative Society, *Bruce & Hay*, architects (£18,300). A six storey and attic, five bay ashlar fronted brick building in French Renaissance style, the end bays having oriel windows. At the rear, in Coburg St, is a four storey and basement, nine bay red sandstone ashlar fronted warehouse added in 1909, *Bruce & Hay*, architects (£8800).

178 Bridge Street Station (2), 36–54 Bridge St, built 1890 for the Caledonian Railway, *James Miller*, architect. A three and four storey and attic, 18 bay sandstone block, in early French Renaissance style. SDD category B. Only the main block survives; the station was closed when Central Station was extended in 1899–1906.

179 Centre Street Grain Mills, 103 Centre St, founded *c* 1872 by William Primrose, flour merchant. The Centre St frontage is four storeys and attic high, 4 bays wide, of red brick and concrete, while the mill at the rear is seven storeys and attic high, by 5 bays long, *Bruce & Hay*, architects, 1892 (£1700). The mill was rebuilt in 1912 to designs by *D. A. Home Morton*, engineer (£1140).

180 Warehouse & Workshop, 115 Centre St, built *c* 1889 for Currie & Co., lithographers and printers. A three storey, 5 bay ashlar building, with three large windows per bay, separated by mullions. There is a large arched cart entrance with a pediment.

181 Factory, 19 Dunmore Lane, probably built *c* 1881 for W. & J. McLintock, biscuit makers, manufacturing confectioners and jam makers. A five storey, 5 bay red and white brick building with a circular-section brick chimney.

182 Bonded Warehouse, 95 Nicholson St, built 1905 for Robert Brown, warehouseman, *R. Ewan*, architect (£12,000). A six storey and basement, 9 bay red brick flat roofed building, with Renaissance details on an otherwise plain facade. The single storey block at the north end was added by the same architect in 1913 (£240).

183 Warehouse, 133 Norfolk St, built *c* 1896 for the Kinning Park Co-operative Society. A three storey and attic red brick block on a U plan, with a 6 bay ashlar front to Norfolk St. The building has a heavy cornice with urns at each end and a mansard roof. There are pilasters at each end.

184 Warehouses, 90–2 Commerce St, built 1878 for William Gillespie, lath splitter (£2000). A plain ashlar fronted four storey, 8 bay building, with red brick body.

185 Tradeston Tube Works, 70–2 Wallace St, built 1899–1900 for the Scottish Tube Co., *J. M. Monro*, architect (£3000). A single storey, 5 bay red brick workshop with a large arched doorway. The glazed fanlight has a fine wrought-iron grille to protect it. Adjacent to the west is a three storey, 3 bay office block in similar style.

186 Workshop, 96 Commerce St, rebuilt 1901 after a fire, for William Shaw & Son, building contractors, *George Bell* (II), architect (£1700). A plain three storey and attic, 3 by 8 bay block with outside stairway, a small yard and a two storey block facing Commerce St.

187 Warehouse, 98 Commerce St, built 1900 for C. S. Whitelaw, coopers, vat-builders, stave, hoop and cask merchants, *A. Skirving*, architect (£10,000). A four storey and attic, 13 by 10 bay red sandstone block with a massive corbelled oriel window on the corner, and a mansard roof.

188 Thistle Rubber Works, 110 Commerce St, built *c* 1886 for Campbell,

Achnach & Co. A three storey and attic, 9 bay red brick building, with mansard roof. The windows on the ground floor, and one doorway, are round-headed. The four storey additions at the rear, in reinforced concrete, were designed by *C. H. Robinson*, architect, in 1910 (£4890).

189 Cook Street Cotton Mill, 18 Cook St, built *c* 1844 for Robert Gilkison Jun., power-loom cloth manufacturer. A six storey, 7 by 4 bay building on a corner, with the street walls of rubble and the side walls of red brick. The interior has two rows of cast-iron columns supporting wooden beams and floors. Adjacent to the west is a two storey engine house.

190 Wrights' Workshop, Kilbarchan St, off 85 Bedford St, rebuilt 1904 for James Herbertson & Sons, *Monro & Son*, architects (£650). A three storey, 7 bay harled brick building, with an asbestos roof.

191 Cumberland Street Station, opened as Eglinton Street Station in 1900 by the Glasgow & South Western Railway. A high level, four platform through station, with a central island platform, on the former City of Glasgow Union Railway. Entrance was by subway from Cumberland St and Eglinton St. The station was supported on a viaduct, partly of brick and partly of iron, and that part of the frontage which could be seen from Eglinton St was disguised as an office building. The Cumberland St entrance block is massive in scale, on a triangular plan, with large circular windows at first floor level, and a cut-off corner with an arched entrance flanked by Doric columns and surmounted by a pediment. The platform buildings were demolished *c* 1969, though the station was closed some years earlier.

192 Laundry, 263 Eglinton St, built *c* 1877 for Andrew C. Swan, shirt front and collar dresser. A plain two storey red brick building, 4 bays deep.

193 Contractor's Depot, 41 Cavendish St, built *c* 1860 for Alex. Ritchie, contractor. A two storey, 2 by 4 bay red brick office block, with stables at the rear.

194 Curled Hair Factory, 37–9 Cavendish St, founded *c* 1855 by Gourlie & Linn, upholstery manufacturers. A group of two storey buildings on a U plan. A foundry was added in 1863 and extended in 1871–2 (£1500).

195 Grain & Hay Store, 240 Pollokshaws Rd, built 1908 for Andrew Motherwell, *J. Chalmers*, architect (£1270). A plain two storey, 7 bay red brick building.

196 St Andrews Works, 245 Pollokshaws Rd, built 1899–1900 for Glasgow Corporation Electricity Department, *A. Myles*, architect (£60,000). A large rectangular single storey building, 15 bays long, in terra-cotta brick, with ornamental plaques, urns, and a pediment. At the north end is a neat two storey sandstone office block, and at the south end a two storey, 1 by 18 bay addition, with round-headed windows, now used as a substation.

Section H
Finnieston, Anderston, Kingston, Tradeston and Kinning Park

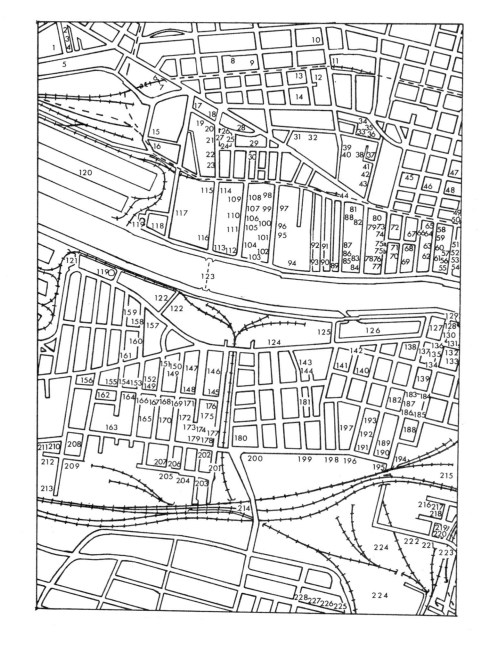

1 Kelvinhaugh Boiler Works, 90 Kelvin-haugh St, built 1880–1 for J. & G. Thomson (£7500) and subsequently extended. The oldest parts were a two storey office block and a massive 2 bay workshop, both red and white brick with round-headed openings. The extension was of corrugated-iron clad steel. Demolished 1968.

2 Stables & Workshops, 66 Lymburn St, built 1882 for John Finlay & Co., iron-mongers (£2000) and altered to a grain mill in 1914 for R. Murray & Sons, *A. D. Hislop*, architect (£180). A three storey and attic, 12 bay red and white brick building, with ornamental string courses.

3 Garage, 52 Lymburn St, built *c* 1902 for R. Hamilton, carting contractor. A small 2 bay, single storey building, with one segmental arched doorway and two round-headed windows. There are cut-down remains of a third bay to the south.

4 Kelvinhaugh Tram Depot, 40–4 Kel-vinhaugh St, built 1893 (£10,000) for Glasgow Corporation Tramways Depart-ment and extended back along Lymburn St in 1895 (140 stalls, £3300), *W. Clark*, engineer. A two storey, 3 by 8 bay red and white brick building, with three entrances in Kelvinhaugh St, each with a steel girder lintel and a small pediment at roof level. Each of the 9 bays in Lymburn St has two round-headed windows at ground floor level and a single segmentally arched window at first floor level, all with white brick voussoirs.

5 Kelvinhaugh Sawmills, 107 Kelvin-haugh St, built *c* 1892 for John Scott, timber merchant. A large timber yard, with three storey stores and two storey mill buildings. The larger of the stores has a brick frontage to the street and concrete floors. A water tower was added in 1903 to designs by *George Bell* (II).

6 Finnieston Station, 1059 Argyle St, built for the opening of the Glasgow City & District Railway in 1886. The offices were built in 1884 (£700). A one storey, 9 bay ashlar building, with rustic quoins, which contained the booking office, sub-sequently extended by the addition of a second storey. Of the station in cutting below, closed in 1916, only traces of platforms remain.

7 Cabinet Works, 1061 Argyle St, built *c* 1877 for John Laird, cabinetmaker. A three storey and attic, 11 bay red and white brick building, with a circular-section brick chimney at the east end.

8 Garage, 119–25 Berkeley St, built 1906 for the Western Motor Co., *A. K. Robert-son*, Edinburgh, architect (£10,000), and added to in 1911 (£880). A two storey brick-fronted building, with 3 wide bays.

9 Stables & Workshops, 97–113 Berkeley St, Elderslie St and Kent Rd, built 1870–3 for John Wylie, later Wylie & Lochhead, *J. Sellars*, architect. The oldest part is the Kent Rd block, while the Kent Rd and Elderslie St block was added in 1872–3 (£9000). A rectangular block of two storey and basement buildings, 19 by 20 by 17 bay, with corner three storey pavilion. The roof trusses are of wrought-iron, of unusual design. SDD category B.

10 Charing Cross Horse Bazaar, 16–22 Berkeley St, built *c* 1868 for William Forbes, livery stable keeper and carriage hirer. A one storey and basement, 10 bay ashlar building with later showrooms to the west. The large entrance, which gives access to the basement, has an ornamented lintel.

11 Charing Cross Station, 154–6 North St, built *c* 1886 for the Glasgow City & District Railway. The booking office, at street level, was a single storey, 7 bay ashlar fronted rubble building (demolished 1969), with wooden stairways to the platforms in cutting. There are glazed awnings over the platforms, linked across the cutting by lattice girders. Until recently there were small wooden waiting rooms set into the cutting wall, but these were demolished to make way for the new stairways and offices, at Elmbank Crescent.

12 Biscuit Factory, 4 Dorset St, built *c* 1876, and rebuilt after a fire in 1881 (£2500) for John Walker, baker. A two storey and attic, 13 bay red and white brick building, with a short stretch of ashlar frontage to Dorset St.

13 Cabinet Works, 53 Kent Rd, built from 1879 for Wylie & Lochhead, *J. Sellars*, architect (£17,000). The oldest part has four storeys, attic and basement in French Renaissance style with 3 wide bays to Cleveland St and 19 to Kent Rd. The top floor windows are semicircular. The interior has brick arches on cast-iron columns. The specially designed cast-iron railings are noteworthy. SDD category B. A six storey, 12 bay red sandstone ashlar building, with a flat roof, in Cleveland St was added in 1900, *Sir William Arrol & Co.*, engineers (£16,000). In Dorset St there are two reinforced concrete blocks, one four storeys high, used as a drying shed, *Sir William Arrol & Co.* (£750), and the other six storeys high, with 6 bays to Dorset St and 8 to Beltane St.

14 Coach Works, 412–24 St Vincent St, built *c* 1870 for John Robertson, coach-builder. The St Vincent St part consisted of showrooms, now shops, while at the rear are a two storey, 11 bay rubble building with an external stairway and, on the other side of a narrow alley, adjacent three storey, 10 bay and two storey, 6 bay red and white brick blocks.

15 Brass Foundry, 131 Minerva St, built 1869 for J. & W. Young, ships' plumbers and brassfounders. A two storey and attic, 2 by 16 bay red and white brick building (now partly harled) with round-headed windows with fine cast-iron frames. There are smaller outhouses at the rear.

16 Stobcross Station, built *c* 1896 for the Glasgow Central Railway. An underground station, situated at the junction of the Glasgow Central and Lanarkshire & Dumbartonshire railways. The surface building is a single storey Renaissance structure of red sandstone, 2 by 4 bay, with a rounded corner. The windows are round-headed. Closed 5 October 1964.

17 Engineering Works, 31 Finnieston St and Houldsworth St, built from 1897 for David Carlaw & Sons. The oldest part, a plain three storey, 7 by 10 bay block facing Finnieston St, was designed by *Robert Brown* in 1897 (£5500), a five storey, 5 bay red brick building with a flat roof added in 1905, *Burnet, Boston & Carruthers*, architects (£6610), and a third block, five storey, 4 bay, was constructed of reinforced-concrete in 1913, *The Indented Bar & Concrete Engineering Co.*, engineers (£3585). At the rear is a circular-section chimney.

18 Turning Works, 22 Elliot St, built 1872 for J. Turnbull, wood turner (£700). A neat two storey and attic, 12 by 4 bay red and white brick building, with round-headed openings and a rounded corner. Similar in style to H20.

19 Lancefield Boiler Works, 127 Houldsworth St, built 1865–6 for William Mitchell, boilermaker, and extended 1871–2 for Hugh Wallace. The only recognisable surviving part is a wide single bay workshop with a two storey frontage, having round-headed windows, altered in 1914 for Robert Young & Co., chemical manufacturers, R. J. Walker, architect (£250).

20 Glasgow Saw & File Works, 24 Elliot St, built 1870 for William Cook & Sons, edge tool makers. A two storey and attic corner block, 7 by 12 bay, with round-headed openings. Striking use is made of white brick. Similar to H18.

21 Anderston Brass Foundry, 32 Elliot St, built 1870–1 for Steven & Struthers, added to in 1875 (£700) and 1883, and reconstructed as a paint and colour works in 1914 for Smith & Rodger. The street frontage is partly two and partly three storey, of red and white brick, with a doorway, having a large semicircular fanlight.

22 Cranstonhill Foundry (Iron), 58 Elliot St, built c 1854 for James Aitken & Co., engineers, millwrights and founders. A well-proportioned high single storey engineering shop with four tall, narrow, round-headed windows on each side of a large arched central doorway. The window frames, and the frame of the glazed fanlight, are of cast-iron. At the southern end is a two storey, 3 bay office block.

23 Anderston Galvanising Works, 80 Elliot St, built c 1865 for Dugald Buchanan, metal refiner. A block of single storey engineering shops with a small two storey office at the front. Demolished in 1966.

24 Cranstonhill Tool Works, 53–9 Elliot St, built 1872 for Dron & Lawson, machinists (£3000). The main block, facing Cranston St, is a three storey and attic, 20 by 4 bay red and white brick building, with a 2 bay high single storey engineering shop behind.

25 Cranstonhill Engine Works, 58–60 Port St, built c 1858 for Alexander Chaplin & Co., engineers, iron house and roof builders, and extended in 1860. Two bays of single storey workshops with a 3 bay, two storey office block, both red and white brick.

26 Vulcan Smith Works, 63 Houldsworth St, founded 1871 by P. & R. Fleming, manufacturing ironmongers. The main four storey, 4 by 9 bay red and white brick block was probably built in 1877 for J. & A. McFarlane, mangle manufacturers (£1000). The two storey block to the east was added in 1899 for John Reid & Son, printers, paper bag and box makers (£600).

27 Victoria Bolt & Rivet Works, 37 Elliot St, built 1874 for John Bilsland & Co. (£2000) and extended 1890 by the addition of a four storey block in Houldsworth St, *Burnet & Boston*, architects (£2500). All the buildings have now been cut down to one storey in height.

28 Paper Staining & Cardboard Works, 20–38 Houldsworth St, built from 1873 for George Stark & Sons, paper stainers, cardboard and pasteboard manufacturers. A four storey, 8 bay red and white brick building, with the remains of a similar structure to the west. The 1873 part cost £2500.

29 Cranstonhill Bakery, 38–42 Cranston St, built 1877–8 for B. M. & J. Stevenson, grain and commission merchants (£10,000 and £3500), architects probably *Salmon & Son*. The main block was five storeys high, constructed in two parts, one 8 bay (bakery) the other 6 bay (stores) similar in style. A spectacular red and white brick building in Italian palace style. The bakery part was partly jack-arched; the store had cast-iron columns and wooden beams. A two storey extension at the rear, in Houldsworth St, was added in 1898 (£500) and a five storey, 3 bay reinforced concrete and brick block built to the west of the main block in 1912, *Salmon, Son & Gillespie*, architects (£5670). Demolished 1969.

30 Warehouse, 45 Cranston St, built 1874 for George McPhail, bag and mat merchant. A four storey, 11 by 10 bay red and white brick building, with white brick string courses. Demolished 1965.

31 Shirt Factory, 249–51 William St, built from 1889 for Arthur & Co., wholesale drapers, *J. Ritchie*, architect (£6000), replacing a building of 1866. A fine range of sandstone fronted red brick buildings in French Renaissance style, four storeys and attic, 29 by 7 bay, with mansard roof. Demolished 1963–4.

32 Sausage Factory, 143–7 William St, built 1889 for William Annacker, *J. M. Monro*, architect (£4000) and extended at the rear in 1898 to designs by the same architect (£3800). An attractive three storey attic and basement, 9 bay red sandstone fronted brick building in French Renaissance style, with a central decorated gable. The second floor windows were round-headed. Demolished 1965.

33 Box Factory, 52 William St, built 1911

for John Allan, *Burnet & Boston*, architects (£3570). A two storey and attic, 9 by 4 bay red brick building, with large windows.

34 Coach Works, 337–9 St Vincent St, founded *c* 1853 by J. Buchanan & Co., coachbuilders and harness makers. Two storey, 5 bay and three storey, 6 bay blocks, with showrooms in the ground floor of a four storey tenement.

35 Merino Spinning Mill, 335 St Vincent St, built *c* 1835 for C. S. Cochran & Co., worsted and woollen spinners. A five storey and attic, 16 bay rubble building with margins round the windows. On the south side was an external spiral staircase. The wooden floors were supported on timber beams carried on a central row of cast-iron columns and two side rows of timber pillars. Demolished 1967.

36 Grain Store, 40 William St, built 1860 for George Wilson Clark, grain merchant. A five storey and basement, 11 bay rubble building, with wooden beams and floors on cast-iron columns. Demolished 1967.

37 Grocery Warehouse, 75 Bishop St, built *c* 1913 for Cooper & Co. A four storey, 8 by 11 bay, terra-cotta brick fronted, reinforced-concrete building. Demolished 1966.

38 Bishop Garden Cotton Mill, Bishop Court, built 1826 for James Johnston, power-loom cloth manufacturer. A four storey and attic, 23 bay rubble building, with cast-iron window frames. There were cast-iron columns on the ground floor, apparently a later addition, and wooden pillars above, with timber joists and flooring throughout. At the rear was a small single storey engine house, with a circular-section brick chimney. Demolished 1966.

39 Coach Works, 58 North St, founded *c* 1854 by J. Henderson & Co., and altered in 1902, *Burnet, Boston & Carruthers*, architects. A three storey ashlar-fronted office and showroom block on the street, with three storey, 14 bay and two storey,

6 bay red brick workshops extending back to Bishop Court. Demolished 1966.

40 Tram Depot, 52–6 North St, built 1884 for the Glasgow Tramway & Omnibus Co. (£8000) to replace a smaller structure dating from 1875. The roof was renewed in 1911 by *William Bain & Co.*, engineers, Coatbridge (£990). Apparently a four storey, 29 bay red and white brick building, the ground floor had two rows of windows. Originally there were 244 stalls in the building. Demolished 1966.

41 Bishop Street Engineering Works, 57–61 Bishop St, built 1865 for Walker, Brown & Co., engineers. A handsome three storey, 14 by 3 bay red and white brick building, with round-headed windows. The ground floor was tall, and was extended to the rear by more modern single storey brick sheds with steel roof trusses. Demolished 1966.

42 Bishop Street Foundry, 47 Bishop St, founded *c* 1860 by D. McPherson & Co., ironfounders. A high single storey red and white brick building, with a large arched doorway flanked by single round-headed windows. Demolished 1966.

43 Warehouse, 11–25 Bishop St, built 1894 for T. Hodge, wholesale and retail warehouseman, *Bruce & Hay*, architects (£4000). A four storey, 5 bay French Renaissance sandstone fronted brick building. At the rear were single storey sheds and a seven storey flat-roofed red brick block. Demolished 1968.

44 Anderston Cross Station, 4–14 Stobcross St, built *c* 1896 for the Glasgow Central Railway, *J. J. Burnet*, architect. An island platform station, partly in cutting, partly in tunnel, with waiting rooms on the platform, and booking offices and station houses in a two storey, 8 bay sandstone surface building with a curved, Renaissance frontage. Closed in 1959. The buildings were demolished in 1967, but the tunnel and platform have been retained. SDD category C.

45 Electricity Generating Station, 133 Waterloo St, opened 25 February 1893 by Glasgow Corporation Electricity Department, *W. Foulis*, engineer (£86,332 including machinery), and subsequently extended. A tall single storey sandstone-fronted building, with a smaller two storey block (the original) to the west. Demolished 1966.

46 Printing Works, 58 Cadogan St and 24 Douglas St, built 1899 for Aird & Coghill, printers and publishers, *H. E. Clifford*, architect (£28,200). A six storey and basement, 7 by 5 bay red sandstone French Renaissance building, with round-headed windows at ground floor level, and a semi-octagonal corner surmounted by a dome. Above the door is a sculptured vignette of a hand printer.

47 Stores and Offices, 64 Waterloo St, built 1898 for Wright & Greig Ltd, distillers, *J. Chalmers*, architect (£11,500). A most unusual four storey and basement, 5 by 3 bay red sandstone French Renaissance building. The building remains unfinished, but is remarkable for its rich and bizarre details.

48 Warehouse, 36 Cadogan St and Blythswood St, built 1898 for Robert Brown Ltd, whisky merchants, *R. Ewan*, architect (£13,800). A four storey and attic, 6 by 7 bay red sandstone building with corner towers. The elaborate Renaissance main office entrance is flanked by granite columns, and the goods entrance has a fine ornamental wrought-iron gate.

49 'McGeoch's Building' (Ironmongery Warehouse), 28 West Campbell St, built 1905 for William McGeoch & Co., wholesale ironmongers, *J. J. Burnet*, architect (£15,000). A fine six storey and basement red sandstone building in French Renaissance style, with 6 bays to Cadogan St and 7 bays to West Campbell St. Effective use was made of sculpture. SDD category A. Demolished 1970.

50 Warehouse, 14 West Campbell St, probably built *c* 1840. A four storey, 7 by 3 bay ashlar fronted rubble building, with a hoist in Holm St. The West Campbell St frontage has been modernised.

51 Warehouse, 19 Robertson Lane, built *c* 1870 for Miller & Pyle, coppersmiths. A four storey, 7 bay red and white brick building.

52 Warehouse, 3 Robertson Lane, built *c* 1893 for Miller & Lang, stationers. A three storey, 6 bay rubble building.

53 Grain Store, 64 York St, built *c* 1877 for Sclanders Bros & Co., extended by two storeys for John Hopkins & Co., in 1895, *M. S. Gibson*, architect (£9000) and reconstructed after a fire in 1901, *Inglis & Gibson*, architects (£26,000). A six storey, 6 bay sandstone building, with pilasters through the ground and first floors.

54 Warehouse, 11 Robertson Lane, built in the late 19th century. A curious narrow-fronted three storey red brick warehouse, with 3 bays to the lane, and a hoist operated from street level.

55 Warehouse, 3 James Watt Lane, built *c* 1850. A plain two storey, 6 bay rubble building.

56 Bonded Store, 6 James Watt Lane, built *c* 1901 for the Central Bonding Co. A five storey and basement, 7 bay red and white brick building with a hoist.

57 Queen's Tea Store, 23 York St, built 1843 for William Connal, storekeeper, *J. Stephen*, architect. The building at the rear was constructed 1839–40, and reconstructed after a fire in 1897, *A. Gardner*, architect (£3500). The front building has four storeys, attic and basement and is 17 bays long. Effective use is made of rustication and coursed masonry and there is a heavy cornice supported by brackets above the second floor. The central doorway is of very unusual design. The interior is of fireproof jack-arch construction.

58 Warehouse, 82 James Watt St, built 1864 for J. Kennedy, grain store keeper. An L plan four storey and attic, 8 by 12 bay ashlar block on the corner of Argyll St and James Watt St. The end 6 bays in James Watt St are plain, the others have mouldings round the windows and decorated chimney heads.

59 Warehouse, 68–72 James Watt St, built 1847–8 for William Connal & Co., storekeepers. A fine classical warehouse, five storeys high and 9 bays long, with a central pilastered portico. The frieze has been used as an attic storey. The fifth storey was added in 1881 for James C. Alston (£3500). The interior is of 'fireproof' jack-arch construction. SDD category B.

60 Public Store, 44–54 James Watt St, built 1861 for Thomas Mann as grain and general free stores. A splendid four storey, 13 bay classical building. The ground floor is of coursed masonry and there are end pilastered porticos. The frieze has been used as an attic storey, and the building has been carefully lined in with H58. SDD category B.

61 Warehouse, 22 James Watt St, built 1876–7 for J. William Latta, builder (£12,000), later converted to a model lodging house. A four storey and attic, 7 by 6 bay Renaissance building with mansard roof.

62 Warehouse, 17–25 James Watt St, built c 1861 for T. Mann, storekeeper. A neat three storey and basement, 10 bay ashlar fronted building, with arched windows on the ground floor. Destroyed by fire on 18 November 1968 with the loss of 22 lives.

63 Grain Store, 41–5 James Watt St, built 1854 for Alexander Harvie as a grain store, and enlarged in 1910–11, R. *Thomson*, architect (£18,826). A six storey, 21 bay sandstone fronted brick building, with a flat roof, incorporating part of the older building's frontage (two storeys, 14 bays, with the centre 4 bays extended up a further floor and terminating in a pediment). The interior is of reinforced concrete, and the reconstructed block runs through to Brown St. SDD category C.

64 Grain Store, 65–73 James Watt St, built c 1848 for Harvie & McGavin. A fine classical revival building on a U plan, with two hoists at the rear. The street frontage is five storeys and basement, 13 bays long, with a central pilastered portico, occupying four storeys. The interior has wooden beams and floors on cast-iron columns. SDD category C.

65 Store, 75–9 James Watt St, built 1874 for J. & M. Brown & Hugh Taylor, merchants (£1500). A three storey, 7 bay ashlar fronted building, with central ornamental arched doorway.

66 Harbour Paint Works, 54 Brown St, built 1891 for J. & J. Dickson, oil merchants, paint and colour manufacturers, *D. V. Wyllie*, architect (£1400). An attractive two storey, 6 bay ashlar fronted block with Greek details.

67 Stores, 49–51 and 53 Brown St. Number 53, a two storey and attic, 8 bay red brick building, was probably built c 1877 for David Hutcheson & Co., steamboat proprietors, while 49–51, a three storey, 5 bay red and white brick structure, was built in 1897 for Gibson & Mathie, paint and varnish makers, *A. Petrie*, architect (£1800). Both buildings were demolished in 1968.

68 Warehouse, 40 Crimea St, built 1896–7 for John McQueen, *Brand & Lithgow*, architects (£900). A plain three storey, 4 bay red sandstone ashlar fronted building.

69 Warehouse, 16 Carrick St, built 1877 for James Taylor, ironmonger (£5600). A neat four storey, 6 bay ashlar fronted brick building, with pilasters separating the bays on each floor, and a heavy cornice supported by consoles.

70 Workshop, 35 Carrick St, built c 1890 for Andrew Burns, engineer and machinery maker. A two storey, 3 bay sandstone fronted brick building with three gables to the street. There are arched recesses in the front of the building to receive the open doors, and circular windows at first floor level.

71 Contractors' Depot, 20 Crimea St, built *c* 1910 for Brown & Kerr, cartage contractors. A three storey, 3 by 4 bay red and white brick building with a high ground floor.

72 Warehouse, 87–91 McAlpine St, built 1899 for R. B. Miller, *N. C. Duff*, architect (£5700). A five storey and attic, 5 bay terra-cotta brick fronted red brick building, in French Renaissance style. The interior had cast-iron columns supporting wooden beams and floors. Demolished 1966.

73 Warehouse, 87–91 McAlpine St, built 1899 for R. B. Miller to designs by *N. C. Duff*, architect (£10,500). A similar building to H72, but extending farther back.

74 Waterloo Saw Mill, 73–83 McAlpine St, built 1895–6 for George Miller (£2000) and extended by the addition of a storey in 1898 (£5000) for R. B. Miller, both *N. C. Duff*, architect. An L plan four storey, 9 bay red brick building, with French Renaissance detail in red sandstone on the top floor.

75a River Engine Works, 63–71 McAlpine St, built *c* 1879 for Ruthven & Glen, engineers. A three storey and attic, 6 bay red and white brick building with Greek key pattern frieze.

75b Brass Foundry, 57–9 McAlpine St, built *c* 1866 for Wallace & Connell, brass-founders, coppersmiths and hydraulic engineers. A single storey, 5 bay red and white brick building with round-headed windows, with further single storey workshops at the rear, and a circular-section chimney. Above the north end of the front block is a two storey water tower with corbelled top.

76 Store, 37–55 McAlpine St, built 1905 for W. Johnstone, *A. Gardner*, architect (£12,500). A fine five storey, 7 bay red brick building with terra-cotta brick frontage. The building is boldly styled, with round-headed openings on the

ground floor and three low-relief arches running from the first to the third floors. The top floor windows are circular, and there is a heavy cornice.

77 Globe Tube Works, 33–5 McAlpine St, built *c* 1859 for McLaren, Wright & Co., manufacturers of patent wrought-iron tubes for gas, water and steam. The street frontage is two storeys and attic high, 4 bays wide, with a crow-stepped gablet over the central cart entrance. The gable ends are also crow-stepped.

78 Sugar Refinery, 59 Washington St, built *c* 1852 for Hoyle, Martin & Co., sugar refiners. A massive seven storey and attic, 3 bay rubble building, with a large arched doorway. To the south was a square-section brick chimney. Demolished *c* 1966.

79 Cooperage & Store, 41–5 Washington St, built 1872–3 for John Stewart & Son, coopers and vat builders (£800) and extended 1877 for Robert Brown (£3000). Adjacent one storey and attic, 8 bay, and two storey, 6 bay buildings, with crow-stepped gablets, in snecked rubble. The later, two storey, part has an oriel window and a round-headed doorway.

80 Anderston Grain Mill, 27 Washington St, built as a cotton store before 1845 and added to in 1865 for Harvie & McGavin. The main block is a four storey rubble building, 6 by 4 bays, to which a fifth storey has been added in brick. The 1865 addition is five storeys high, 6 by 3 bays, of red and white brick, with a low relief arch enclosing each bay.

81 Anderston Ropework, 19 Stobcross St, founded *c* 1849 by R. & J. Jarvie. A neat three storey, 4 by 3 bay rubble building, with round-headed windows at first floor level on the north wall. Demolished 1967–8.

82 Bonded Warehouse, 30–42 Washington St, built in two parts. The northern 6 bays were built in 1897–8 for W. P. Lowrie & Co., *A. Gardner*, architect (£22,300) and the rest was added in 1906 for Buchanan & Co. to a similar design by *H. E. Clifford*, architect (£49,970). The second part was built on the site of the old Saracen Foundry. A five storey and basement, 13 bay red sandstone fronted terra-cotta brick building, with a central oriel window bay running from the first to the third floor, framed in an arch, and flanked on each side by six low relief arches. The fourth floor windows are circular (*cf* H76). There is an adjacent four storey, 3 bay office block in similar style.

83 Crown Flour Mills, 66–8 Washington St, built 1862 for John Ure & Son, and subsequently extended. At the rear of the site is a four storey, 5 bay rubble building, presumably the original, while the oldest of the buildings in Washington St is a five storey, 5 bay ashlar building, with rusticated ground floor. At roof level is a small pediment with a sculpted wheatsheaf in the tympanum.

84 Washington Grain Mills, 90 Washington St, built *c* 1849, and extended in 1874 and 1875 (£3000) and later, for J. & R. Snodgrass. Takes in 82–6 Washington St, built as a warehouse for W. & D. Cross in 1865, a five storey, 4 bay Italian Renaissance building. The oldest surviving part of the mills proper is a four storey, 4 bay rubble building at the rear of the site, while the front buildings include a six storey, 7 bay Italian Renaissance block, dated 1874 (£5000) cut down from a 10 bay structure. The more modern parts include a tower block built in 1897, *R. Ewan*, architect (£1500).

85 Oil Works & Store, 105–13 Clydeferry St, founded *c* 1844 by Jamieson & Co. The building latterly standing was a plain three storey and attic, 11 bay ashlar fronted brick building, possibly dating from the 1870s. Demolished 1967.

86 Store, 93–5 Clydeferry St, built 1900 for James W. Grainger. A four storey and attic, 7 bay French Renaissance red brick building, with ornamental gable above the central doorway. Demolished 1967.

87 Store, 85 Clydeferry St, built 1875 for J. Alexander. A two storey, 7 bay red brick building, with round-headed windows, a central segmental-arched doorway, and a pediment. Demolished 1967.

88 Store, 59–63 Clydeferry St, built 1898 for J. C. Robertson & Co., *J. Short*, architect (£3600). A two storey and attic, 8 bay red brick building with central stair bay and semicircular ventilators.

89 Engineering Works & Stables, 96–100 Clydeferry St, founded *c* 1840 by John Barr. The oldest recently surviving part was built in 1880, and was a two storey, 8 bay red brick structure (£2500). The other part was a three storey stable block with 2 wide bays, of red brick with white brick string courses, built 1907 for James Anderson & Son, *L. B. Buik*, architect (50 stalls, £3500).

90 Anderston Cotton Work, 93 Cheapside St, built *c* 1804–6 for Henry Houldsworth, and extended southwards between 1854 and 1864. In use as a bonded warehouse 1878–1964, when part of the older portion collapsed. A six storey and attic red brick building with five storey pilasters between the bays. The older part (14 bays) had two rows of cast-iron columns supporting cast-iron beams and brick arches. There were unusual cast-iron roof trusses, originally supported by pairs of columns; when the roof was raised, these were replaced by a central row of columns with cantilevered beams. The more modern part (13 bays) had three rows of cast-iron columns, of large diameter at ground floor level, diminishing upwards. The roof trusses in this portion were of the normal timber type. SDD category B. Demolished 1969.

91 Cheapside Flour Mills, 79 Cheapside St, built 1860 for A. & W. Glen, millers, of Haughhead, Paisley, and since *c* 1895 used as a store. A five storey, 10 bay square-dressed rubble building with a small drying kiln at the north end. At the south end, detached, is a neat two storey ashlar office block built in 1868. In Piccadilly St, at the rear, is a five storey and attic, 7 bay red and white brick building, with a three storey engine house adjoining to the south added in 1887 to designs by *J. MacClelland*, architect (£200).

92 Anderston Foundry, 100 Cheapside St, founded 1823 by Henry Houldsworth & Co. The only surviving fragment is a three storey, 14 bay cement-rendered brick building, probably a reconstruction of 1899 as fitting shop, store and showrooms (£1920).

93 Cold Store, 124–36 Cheapside St. The first (northernmost) part, three storeys high, 10 bays wide, was built in 1888 for John Bell & Sons, *J. B. Wilson*, architect (£9000), who also designed the middle portion, three storeys, 10 bays, built for Eastmans in 1893 (£4500). The Anderston Quay block was built in 1911 for Eastmans, *J. B. Wilson & Son*, architects, and is a five storey, 6 by 2 bay building with rusticated ground floor (£8350). All buildings are in Renaissance style, mainly of red and white glazed brick.

94 Diesel Engine Works, 53 Anderston Quay. The oldest part of this complex, in the centre of the frontage, was built in 1888 for the London & Glasgow Engineering & Iron Shipbuilding Co., *A. Myles*, architect (£2500), and was a three storey, 10 bay office block with 3 bays of workshops. A high single storey, 4 by 12 bay block of erecting shops, steel framed with brick outside walls and roof lighting was built in two parts in 1909 (£6000) and 1910 (£6260) to designs by *Sir William Arrol & Co.* The block on the corner of Hydepark St was added in the 1930s. Demolished 1968–9.

95 Iron Store, 107–9 Hydepark St, built *c* 1884 for Thomas Stewart & Co., iron, steel, metal and machinery merchants. An altered two storey, 4 bay red and white brick block. Demolished 1969.

96 Cooperage, 53–69 Hydepark St, built 1898 for W. P. Lowrie & Co. Ltd (£3000). A 4 bay, single storey brick building, with gable ends to the street, much altered. At the rear is a circular-section brick chimney.

97 Hydepark Bakery, 45 Hydepark St, built from 1881 for Bilsland Bros, *Bruce & Hay*, architects. The first part consists of a three storey, 13 bay ashlar fronted block on the street with two large round-headed doorways, and at the rear a five storey, 18 bay, red and white brick bakehouse, with 38 ovens. The front buildings included a 38 stall stable (total £15,000). A large five storey, 8 by 11 bay bakehouse was added in 1912 also to designs by *Bruce & Hay* (£13,700), while in the same year a three storey stable, with 63 stalls, was built to designs by *Burnet & Boston* (£8900). The last-named has been replaced by a modern structure, but the others are all intact.

98 Hydepark Joinery Works, 58 Hydepark St, built in the late 19th century for Reid, Macfarlane & Co. Ltd, makers of boiler lagging composition. A three storey and attic L plan red and white brick block, 5 by 7 bay, with a three storey and attic 11 bay red brick building at the rear.

99 Part of Lancefield Cotton Work, Hydepark St, probably built *c* 1840. A five storey, 13 bay rubble block with three hoists, demolished in 1966, and a range of 6 bays of single storey red brick weaving sheds.

100 Engineering Works, 104–10 Hydepark St, dating from the late 19th and early 20th centuries. A group of one and two storey red brick buildings, the largest of which had its gable end to the street, with four round-headed windows. There was a tall circular-section chimney. Demolished 1968–9.

101 Windlass Engine Works, 130 Hydepark St, built *c* 1863 for Neilson Bros, engineers and toolmakers. A one storey, 12 bay ashlar building with large round-headed openings, most of which are bricked up.

102 Hydepark Foundry, 136–8 Hydepark St, founded *c* 1836 by Mitchell & Neilson. The only surviving parts of the original foundry are the two storey office block and massive gateposts.

103 Rope Works, 68 Anderston Quay, probably built 1856–7 for R. S. Newall & Co., wire rope makers. A two storey, 9 bay Italian Renaissance building, with a heavy cornice, arched central entrance, and rusticated ground floor openings. Demolished 1969.

104 Engine Works, 181 Lancefield St, built *c* 1914 for Harland & Wolff, marine engineers. A fine steel framed, brick clad, single storey building, 13 by 7 bay, with large segmentally-arched windows. Demolished 1968–9.

105 Sawmill, 111 Lancefield St, built from 1907 for W. P. Lowrie & Co. Ltd (vat building department). A two storey red brick with gable end to the street (1911, £1560), forming, with single storey buildings, a rectangular block round a courtyard. There is a four storey tower, and a neat circular-section chimney (1908, £180).

106 Warehouse, 97–107 Lancefield St, built 1905 for Liptons Ltd, grocers, *A. B. Dansken*, architect. A plain four storey, 10 bay red sandstone ashlar fronted building.

107 Lancefield Cotton Work, 87 Lancefield St, built *c* 1826 for the Lancefield Spinning Co. The original part is a five storey, attic and basement square-dressed rubble building, 5 by 23 bay. This has been extended to the north by a five storey, 13 bay ashlar block, probably built 1877 for Thomas Brown, storekeeper (£7000). In the angle formed by these adjoining buildings are two detached five storey red brick warehouses, one of which was probably erected in 1890 (£2000).

108 Havelock Copper Works, 69–71 Lancefield St, founded *c* 1879 by Samuel Smillie, condenser manufacturer, and rebuilt in 1884 (£2000). A rectangular block of single storey brick workshops, with office block facing the street, and a small circular-section chimney.

109 Store & Workshop, 76 Lancefield St, built 1910 for Reid, Macfarlane & Co. Ltd, boiler lagging makers, to designs by *W. M. Mackay*, Craighall Ironworks (£1560). A single storey, 4 bay red and white brick building, with an integral square-section chimney.

110 Lancefield Galvanising Works, 88–92 Lancefield St, built 1886 for McHutcheon & Finlayson, galvanisers (£1600) and extended in 1896 (£2100). A single storey building with two large elliptically arched doorways. The roof has recently been replaced.

111 Lancefield Brass Foundry, 110 Lancefield St, built 1887 for J. Miller Reid, brassfounder and coppersmith (£2500) and extended in 1906, *Charles Henry*, engineer (£1480). An L plan single storey red and white brick building, with round-headed windows and prominent ventilators.

112 Boiler Works, 172 Lancefield St, built from 1864 for the London & Glasgow Engineering & Iron Shipbuilding Co. The original works, a 3 bay building with large arched entrances in the gables, was built in 1864, and the adjoining single bay block, with two arched entrances with circular glazed fanlights, was added in 1865. A 9 bay, high single storey steel framed red brick workshop was built in 1907, *Sir William Arrol & Co.*, engineers. The original office block was a two storey, 6 by 7 bay structure, with a rounded corner, built 1882 (£2500), and an extension was built in 1913, three storeys high, with 4 wide bays, each three windows wide, with round-headed windows on the ground and first floors. The 1913 addition was designed by *Hutton & Taylor*, architects (£4480).

113 Engineering Works, 153–239 Elliot St, built from 1867 for David Rowan, marine engineer and boilermaker. The corner block at Lancefield Quay, a two storey, 9 by 15 bay red and white brick building, was built as stores and drawing office in 1894, *J. U. Macauslan*, engineer (£2000), while the high single storey, 4 bay building to the north was added in 1896–7 (£5000) and has a large ornamental doorway. Next to the north is a single storey, 13 bay red and white brick block added in 1898–9 (£16,000), and a two storey office block with oriel windows, built 1912 to designs by *Walter Bridges & Co.* (London) (£2375). Next again is an 8 bay block of steel framed sheds, built 1905, *Sir William Arrol & Co.*, engineers (£11,500).

114 Engineering Works, 117 Elliot St, built 1890 for D. & W. Henderson & Co., engineers and shipbuilders (£1700). Two wide bays of single storey red and white brick engineering shops, with prominent louvred roof ventilators.

115 Scotia Engine Works, 132 Elliot St, built from 1865–6 for Muir & Caldwell, engineers. The oldest part is an L plan single storey ashlar fronted brick building, with rustic quoins and base, segmental-arched doors and windows, and large roof ventilators, on the corner with Stobcross St. Adjacent to the south is a three storey, 13 bay red and white brick building with round-headed openings, added in 1868–9. The rest of the rectangular complex was completed by additions in 1872 (£1000) and 1882 (£5000). The 1865–6 block has wooden roof trusses, reinforced with iron straps.

116 Rope Store, 204 Elliot St, rebuilt *c* 1869 for John Black & Co., rope and sailmakers. A four storey and attic, 8 by 7 bay ashlar fronted rubble and brick building with cast-iron columns supporting timber beams and floors. The top two storeys were added in 1869, when the building was reconstructed after a fire, and are of red and white brick.

117 Offices, 169 Finnieston St, of Clyde Bank Engine Works, founded *c* 1847 by J. & G. Thomson. A neat three storey, 11 by 3 bay ashlar building with moulded doors and windows.

118 Offices, 4 Finnieston Quay, built 1863 for Robert Curle, marine engineer. A three storey, 7 by 2 bay red brick building, with sandstone dressings. The north wall is the only surviving part of an engineering shop built at the same time, which was 15 bays long.

119 Harbour Tunnel, Tunnel St to Plantation Place, authorised in 1889, and built 1890–6. Two vehicular tunnels, now closed, and a pedestrian tunnel still open. Vehicles were lowered on hydraulic lifts to tunnel level, and the circular brick buildings housing the lifts, with iron framed domed roofs, still stand. The whole of one side of each building is open, with the brickwork above supported on plate girders carried on five cast-iron Corinthian columns. Adjacent to the terminal buildings are three storey red and white brick towers which housed the hydraulic accumulators, while on the south side are the single storey tunnel workshops.

120 Queens Dock, originally known as Stobcross Dock, planned in 1846; construction was re-authorised in 1870, and started in August 1872. The dock was opened in August 1877 when the Anchor liner, *Victoria*, entered the tidal basin, though the last copestone was not laid until 20 March 1880. The dock has two basins, an area of 33½ acres, and has single storey brick warehouses lining the quays. At the entrance there was, until the 1950s, a hydraulic swing bridge by *Sir Wm Armstrong & Co.* and hydraulic pumping station for both bridge and cranes (K12). The dock closed on 31 December 1969.

121 Hydraulic Pumping Station, Prince's Dock, built 1894 for the Clyde Navigation Trust, to designs by *Burnet, Son & Campbell*. The pump-house itself is a high single storey 6 bay red brick building, with a plain frontage to the dock, and a decorated front to Mavisbank Rd. At the north end is a splendid accumulator tower, with elaborate corbelling, in the style of an Italian campanile. At the south end is the stump of an octagonal chimney in the form of a 'Tower of the Winds', with sculptured panels forming the frieze. SDD category B. (See K25.)

122 Clyde Galvanising Works, Marine St, built from 1875 for Smith & McLean, galvanisers. A large complex of buildings, mostly corrugated iron clad steel framed structures, with a two storey, 7 bay office block built in 1875, *A. L. Miller*, architect. Part of the works was rebuilt in 1914 (£4312).

123 Finnieston Ferry. Originally authorised in 1878, the first ferry was to the west of the present one, at the bottom of Tunnel St. When a new bridge at Finnieston was planned, the ferry terminals were moved to the bottom of Elliot St and Marine St. The high-level vehicular ferry introduced in 1890 was withdrawn on 22 January 1966, though the terminal facilities still exist. The passenger ferry still operates from recessed stairways.

124 Parkholm Biscuit Bakery, 354 Paisley Rd, founded *c* 1857 by Robert Wylie & Co., biscuit manufacturers. The oldest part is the three storey, 9 bay ashlar fronted brick block facing Paisley Rd. This has unusual segmentally-arched windows at first floor level. At the rear is a flat-roofed three storey and basement block built 1902, *Burnet, Boston & Carruthers*, architects (£3800).

125 Riverside Mills, Shearer St, built as general stores *c* 1870 and converted to mills in 1910 for the Riverside Milling Co. The main processing building was a five storey, 4 by 10 bay rubble building, extended in brick to seven storeys, and there was a four storey and attic, 24 bay mansard roofed warehouse block. The destruction by fire of this warehouse in 1968 forced the mills to close, and both these buildings have now been demolished. The surviving reinforced-concrete grain silos, seven storeys high, 2 by 6 bay, were

built in 1914, *Home Morton, Ker & Gibson,* engineers (£9830). Until closure, the mills were driven by an inverted vertical triple-expansion Corliss-valve engine, built in 1932 by Marsdens of Heckmondwyke, the last large steam engine to operate in the city.

126 Kingston Dock, recommended by Thomas Telford in 1806, the dock was not opened until 10 October 1867. This was Glasgow's first enclosed dock, with a water surface of 5½ acres, wharfage of 830 yards, and cost £127,740. The original wooden quays were destroyed by fire in 1914 and replaced in concrete during the First World War. On three sides of the dock were single storey brick warehouses, rebuilt from 1913 (£11,073), and there were two travelling cranes at the east end. Across the entrance was a wrought-iron lattice girder swing bridge built in 1867 (scrapped 1967), consisting of three parallel girders mounted on a turntable, and driven by a twin cylinder high pressure non-condensing horizontal engine mounted, with the launch-type boiler, below the deck. The engine, now in store at the Transport Museum, has separate inlet and exhaust piston valves, a speciality of the makers, John Yule & Co. of Hutchesontown. The dock is now filled in.

127 Kingston Grain Mills, 21–3 West St, founded 1856 by John Lamb, miller and grain merchant. The original mill was six storeys high, with ten pairs of stones driven by a compound engine by Coats & Young, Belfast. The rest of the machinery was built by Norman & Clinkskill. The present building, a fine four storey and basement, 9 bay polychrome brick building in Italian Renaissance style, with sandstone entablature, cornice and balustrade, was built 1875–6 for Stevenson & Coats, grain millers (£4000). At the rear is a 4 by 5 bay extension, built 1878 (£3000).

128 Workshops, Stable & Van Shed, 3–7 Tradeston St, built 1874 for J. & W. Bishop, ship-chandlers (£800). A plain two storey and attic, 8 bay ashlar fronted brick building.

129 Warehouse, 35 Clyde Place and Centre St, built 1878 for Duncan McGregor, nautical instrument maker. A four storey and attic, 8 by 15 bay ashlar fronted brick building, with mansard roof. Above the first floor windows are low relief panels.

130 Engineering Works, 13–23 Tradeston St and 46 Centre St, built 1858–60 for Randolph, Elder & Co., *W. Spence*, architect. An L plan block, with the Centre St end four storeys high, 5 bays wide with windows in pairs. The wooden beams and floors were supported by cast-iron columns and wrought-iron suspension rods depending from the roof trusses. The Tradeston St block, which had massive rock-faced masonry Egyptian frontages to Tradeston St and Kingston St, was of one storey, with two wide and high arched doorways. This block had heavy built-up wooden beams for the former travelling crane supported on brick piers and cast-iron columns. Between the four storey and Tradeston St portions was the extraordinary single storey part, where the built up beams supported side galleries and the roof as well as the crane. SDD category A. Demolished 1970.

131 Warehouse, 56–64 Kingston St, built 1878 for William M. Hayman, contractor (£8000). A fine five storey, 16 bay ashlar fronted brick building with hoists at the rear.

132 Confectionery Works, 71–3 Kingston St, built *c* 1884 for R. Montgomery, confectioner. A three storey attic and basement, 5 bay Renaissance ashlar fronted building.

133 Grain Store, 104 Centre St, built 1895–6 for William Primrose & Sons, grain millers, *Bruce & Hay*, architects (£2700). A seven storey and attic red brick building, with a 5 bay red sandstone ashlar frontage surmounted by a wheatsheaf.

134 Brass Foundry, 136 Nelson St, built 1865 for Robert Livingstone, brassfounder. A plain three storey, 8 bay red and white brick block.

135 Grain Mill, 60 Tradeston St, built *c* 1875 for J. Buchanan, grain miller. A plain four storey and attic, 6 bay, ashlar fronted brick block with a three storey extension to the rear, added 1888–9 (£1000).

136 Grain Stores, 46–8 Tradeston St, built 1889 for James McCash, grain merchant, *Niven & Haddin*, engineers (£1200). A plain three storey, 8 bay ashlar fronted brick building.

137 Grain Store, 69–73 West St, built 1887 for J. Buchanan, grain miller, *A. Watt*, architect (£1000). A five storey, 7 bay red and white brick building, with a four storey, 7 bay wing to the rear, forming an L.

138 Contractors' Depot, 38 West St, built 1895 for Wordie & Co., haulage contractors, *W. Tennant*, architect (£10,000). A fine three storey, 12 by 15 bay terra-cotta brick fronted red brick building, with a series of low relief arches at ground floor, and corbelling at roof level. Plain three storey blocks form, with the decorated portion, almost a complete rectangle of buildings round a central courtyard. As designed, there were 151 stalls and 12 loose boxes.

139 Warehouse, 76 Tradeston St, built 1878 for James & George Roy (£4000). A four storey and attic, 6 bay ashlar fronted brick building with a long wing extending to the rear, with two pairs of hoists. The bays were separated by pilasters running through the first, second and third floors, and there was a heavy cornice. Destroyed by fire in March 1966.

140 Warehouse, 250 Wallace St, built 1871–2 for the Glasgow Storage Co. Ltd, *W. Spence*, architect (£44,000). A well-proportioned five storey attic and basement sandstone building on a U plan, with a central pilastered portico and pilastered corner pavilions, a rock-faced basement and rusticated ground floor. The upper portions are rubble with ashlar dressings. The frontage is 20 bays long, with side wings 12 bays long, with hoists on the inside.

141 Store, 280 Wallace St, founded on this site by John Drysdale, hair and lime merchant in 1875, and extended in 1882 (£1000) and 1889 for Currie & Co. A 3 bay, two storey red and white brick building, with 1 bay decorated to resemble a lime kiln.

142 Warehouses & Factories, Wallace St, Morrison St, Paisley Rd, Paterson St, Laidlaw St and Carnoustie St, built for the Scottish Co-operative Wholesale Society from 1872. The first part of this large complex to be built was a five storey, 5 by 7 bay block in Laidlaw St between Morrison St and Paisley Rd (£5000) and four storey extensions covering the rest of this triangle were completed in 1876. The most impressive part is the head office, in Morrison St between Carnoustie St and Dalintober St, a four storey, attic and basement, 18 by 23 bay building with a central tower in elaborate French Renaissance style, built 1893, *Bruce & Hay*, architects (£110,000). Apart from these buildings, more than £90,000 was spent on buildings, most elaborate French Renaissance, in this area, *Bruce & Hay* and *James Davidson*, architects.

143 Dock Engine & Boiler Works, 27 Weir St, built 1864 for W. King & Co., engineers, boilermakers and steamship builders. Additions were made in 1878 (£500), 1891 (£1000) and 1894 (£300), the last named to designs by *J. Lindsay*, architect. A block of buildings on a U plan, partly three storey, partly one high storey of the same overall height, of red and white brick. In the single storey parts the roof trusses were wooden, with a gantry crane supported on cast-iron columns. The office blocks, facing the street, were both three storeys high, one 4, the other 5 bays wide. Demolished 1969.

144 Wire weaving factory, 51–5 Weir St, built 1891 (£2000) and 1899 (£1350) for George Christie Ltd, wireworkers, R. A. *Wightman*, architect. The older block is two storeys high, 5 bays wide, with a crow-stepped gable, while the newer is four storeys high, 5 bays wide, both red and white brick. The first floor windows of both are round-headed, with a key-pattern string course below. There is a circular-section brick chimney at the rear.

145 Kingston Bakery, 90 Seaward St, built c 1870 for the United Co-operative Baking Society Ltd. A much altered group of one and two storey red brick buildings.

146 Rivet Works, 31 Admiral St, built c 1888 for Edward Crosher, bolt, nut and rivet manufacturer. A rectangular block of two storey buildings, round a courtyard, with a 14 bay red and white brick frontage to the street.

147 Confectionery Works, 26 Admiral St, founded c 1866 by Robert Wotherspoon & Co., manufacturing confectioners. A very large four storey block, in two portions, each 11 bays long, extending through to Stanley St. The main facade to Admiral St is 5 bays wide, of red and white brick, with an oriel, while the body of the building is of red brick.

148 Standard Oil Works, 54 Admiral St, built c 1898 for Percy & Halden, oil refiners, and extended in 1911 (£5000). The main block is two storeys and attic high, L shaped, 6 by 10 bay, in red and white brick with string courses, extended to the north by a two storey, 8 bay building. In the angle is a three storey building, with 2 wide bays, built 1907 (£4200). All the buildings were probably designed by *Bruce & Hay*, architects.

149 Portman Street Engine Works, 61 Middlesex St, Milnpark St and Portman St, built from 1874 for William Thomson & Co., engineers. The main group consists of an L-plan two storey, 12 by 15 bay block on the corner of Milnpark St and Middlesex St, a single storey block on the corner of Milnpark St and Portman St, and a three storey, 11 bay range in Portman St, with back buildings. There is a detached three storey, 11 bay building in Stanley St, with a small yard in front.

150 Contractors' Depot, 18 Stanley St, built 1908 for A. & J. McLellan, cartage contractors, *Bruce & Hay*, architects (£1295). A four storey, 7 by 6 bay red brick building with round-headed windows on the first, second and third floors of the frontage. To the south is an older two storey building.

151 Warehouse, 9 Portman St, built c 1902 for J. Findlay & Co., merchants. A three storey, 5 bay red brick block, with decorative courses of white glazed brick.

152 Factory, 43 Middlesex St, built c 1882 for Andrew Gillespie, bakers' engineer. A neat three storey and attic, 4 bay, red and white brick building with gable end to street, capped by a ball finial.

153 Parkholm Iron Foundry, 36 Middlesex St and Milnpark St, built c 1873 for Robertson & Thomson, ironfounders. An L plan block of single storey red and white brick buildings, much altered, with round-headed windows.

154 Contractors' Depot, 96 Milnpark St and Sussex St, built c 1895 for James Bow & Son, cartage contractors. A striking three storey and attic, 2 by 4 bay terracotta and white brick building, with low relief arches framing the ground and second floor windows.

155 Warehouse, 28–30 Sussex St and Milnpark St, built 1914–15 for A. & J. McLellan, cartage contractors, *Bruce & Hay* and *Burnet & Boston*, architects. A plain four storey, 6 by 7 bay red brick building with a flat roof. There are single courses of angled bricks dividing the floors.

156 Grain & Hay Store, 16–18 Lambhill St and Milnpark St, built c 1894 for Andrew Wylie, grain and hay merchant. A two storey, 5 bay ashlar building, with two large cart entrances in Lambhill St.

157 Mavisbank Flour Mills, 1–3 Mair St, built as a warehouse in 1873 for John Tod & Co., *W. Spence*, architect, and altered to a flour mill in 1885 for Ramsay Bros. A four storey, 8 bay building extended for 5 bays to five storeys, with a further single storey added to form a tower. A wing extends to the rear, forming an L with the main block. The interior has wooden floors and beams on cast-iron columns.

158 Plantation Starch Works, 14 Mair St, built from 1868 for Browns & Co., starch and cornflour manufacturers, and extended in 1874, 1878 and 1885. The main part was a five storey, 13 bay ashlar fronted brick building, with a pediment at the south end. Adjacent to this was a four storey, 8 bay block, and in Craigiehall St a four storey, 4 bay block with pilasters, the addition of 1885. Destroyed by fire on 9 October 1967.

159 Boat Shed, 23–9 Eaglesham St, built 1909 for D. White & Co., to designs by *Bruce & Hay*, architects. A plain two storey, 3 bay block with large doorways on both floors.

160 Office & Stores, 38 Mair St, built 1907 for R. B. Lindsay, patent steam packing manufacturer, *Whyte & Galloway*, architects. The office block is two storeys high, 6 by 1 bay, with a terra-cotta brick frontage, and there are stores behind.

161 Carpenter & Joiner's Workshop, Eaglesham St, built 1874 for David Guthrie & Co. A two storey, 8 bay terracotta brick back building with cast-iron window frames, with two wide brick bays of stores behind.

162 Stables, 31 Lambhill St and Milnpark St, built 1901 and 1911 for Biggar & Co., and John McPhail, contractors, the second part *W. Ross*, architect. A small group of plain single storey buildings, with two gable ends to the street.

163 Kinning Park Iron Works, 570 Scotland St, built from 1875 for Charles McNeil, Jun., blacksmith. An extensive group of single storey brick and corrugated iron engineering shops. The apparently two storey, 26 bay frontage in fact conceals a single storey and the first floor 'windows' are in fact ventilators.

164 SCWS Works, 105 Milnpark St, Sussex St and Middlesex St, built 1905 as a hamcuring and sausage factory. The main part is a four storey and basement, 4 by 13 bay red brick building with a row of pilasters extending from the second floor to above the roof line. At the rear are later buildings.

165 Waterproof Factory, 89 Middlesex St, built 1913 for the scws (£1400). A two storey red and white brick block, with a zig-zag string course – a motif repeated on the two small buildings on the street front. A small circular-section chimney is lettered scws.

166 Kinning Park Colour Works, 73 Milnpark St and Middlesex St, built c 1895 for Hird, Hastie & Co. Ltd, paint and colour manufacturers. A group of one and two storey buildings, the oldest of which appear to be a single storey, 4 by 12 bay red and white brick building, with round headed windows, on the corner with Middlesex St, and an ornate two storey red and white brick office block, with two fine ornamental doorways, probably designed by *Bruce & Hay*.

167 Kingston Engine Works, 71 Milnpark St and Portman St, founded c 1866 by Smith Bros, engineers and ironfounders, and probably rebuilt c 1873. A handsome three storey, 4 by 19 bay red and white brick building, with round-headed windows, and a large elliptical-arched doorway, now partly blocked up. Most of the window frames are of cast-iron. On the west side is a small three storey, 4 by 4 bay red and white brick office block.

168 Engine Works, 67 Portman St and Milnpark St, built c 1872 for Kemp & Hume, engineers. A plain two storey and attic, 5 by 10 bay red brick building with a high ground floor. At the rear is a group of outhouses round a courtyard.

169 Kinning Park Bakery, 70 Stanley St and Milnpark St, built c 1883 for the Kinning Park Baking Co. Ltd. A single storey L plan block and a two storey, 5 bay building, both harled, forming three sides of a rectangular courtyard.

170 Parkhouse Colour Works, 97 Portman St, built c 1895 for William Brown, Sons & Co., colour, paint and varnish manufacturers and drysalters. A rectangular group of two storey buildings round a central courtyard, which has now been roofed in. The street frontage is of red brick, 21 bays long. There is a small circular-section chimney.

171 Paragon Foundry, 27 Milnpark St, built c 1865 for Duncan & Smith, ironfounders, and extensively altered by subsequent occupiers. The only recognisable fragment is the office block, a three storey, 4 by 5 bay building with later mansard roof and stair tower, but with original D-shaped staircase at the rear.

172 Biscuit Factory, 115 Stanley St, founded 1861 by Gray, Dunn & Co. The block on the corner of Milnpark St was burned down in 1875, and the present building, a four storey, 3 by 9 bay building, was probably built 1875–6 to designs by *John Baird* (II). The fourth storey is a recent addition. The next building to the south is three storeys high, 13 bays long, of red and white brick, then there is a modern brick and concrete block, and two identical four storey red and white brick buildings, each 5 bays wide, with arched openings at ground floor level, designed by *Stark & Rowntree*, architects, in 1893, and built in 1893 and 1897. These two blocks have had a fifth storey added, with a band of decorative chequer brickwork at the join. At the rear are 8 bays of single storey workshops.

173 Kinning Park Foundry, 120 Admiral St, founded c 1860 by George Bennie & Co., ironfounders. A group of one and two storey workshops, with ventilators, and a one and two storey office block built 1911 for the Glasgow Patents Co. Ltd, *Bruce & Hay*, architects (£500).

174 Kinning Park Smelting Works, 121 Admiral St, built from *c* 1901 for R. & W. Mackinlay, metal refiners. The scanty remains of one storey workshops round a yard. May incorporate parts of the Kinning Park Foundry.

175 Horse Tram Depot, 105–15 Admiral St, built *c* 1893 for Glasgow Corporation Tramways Department, *W. Clark*, engineer. A neat two storey red and white brick block, with 6 bay frontages to both Admiral St and Seaward St. Each bay has a pediment surmounted by a chimney and, on the Admiral St side, a large doorway. There are 9 bays of roof between the streets. Immediately to the north in Admiral St are the two wide bays of Admiral Street Substation, 97, 99 Admiral St, added in 1901, which has round-headed windows and large steel-lintelled doors.

176 Kinning Park Sewage Pumping Station, 100 Seaward St and Milnpark St, built 1909–10 for Glasgow Corporation, *D. & A. Home Morton*, engineers, in connection with Shieldhall Sewage Works (£12,300). The station was opened on 4 April 1910, and the total cost was £95,000. A high single storey, 1 by 5 bay terracotta brick building lit by semicircular windows at 'first floor' level, by round-headed windows at ground floor level, and by roof lights. Originally designed for steam pumping engines, there is an adjacent boiler house with 2 wide bays. The lift of the pumps, now electrically operated, is about 45 feet.

177 Contractor's Depot, 140 Seaward St, built *c* 1898 for James Gault, cartage contractor. A plain single storey harled brick building, 2 bays deep.

178 Aerated Water Factory, 146–66 Seaward St, built 1914–16 for the SCWS, *William Mercer*, architect (£15,097). A four storey and basement, 18 bay red and white brick block, with end pediments and a central ogival feature.

179 Chemical Works, 436 Scotland St, built *c* 1880 for J. Martin, sheep-dip manufacturer. A neat two storey, 4 bay brick building, with a small chimney at the rear.

180 Sailmaking Works, 145–7 Shields Rd, built 1888 for John McFarlane & Co. A four storey, 4 bay, red sandstone ashlar fronted tenement building, the bottom two floors of which are workshops, the upper two being residential.

181 Cement Store, 109 Weir St, built 1893 for Currie & Co., lime and cement merchants, *John Gordon*, architect (£1500). A single storey red and white brick building, with 3 wide bays. The outer walls were raised to the height of the roof ridges, and in each 'gable' was a large circular louvred ventilator. Demolished 1967.

182 Brass Foundry, 122 West St, probably built *c* 1870. A three storey, 8 bay rubble and red brick building, with an adjacent two storey, 2 bay structure, both behind a tenement block. Demolished 1967.

183 Victoria Grain Mills, 159 West St and Wallace St, founded 1879 by Hamilton & Manson, grain millers. The four storey and attic, 2 bay red brick building with the Flemish gable in West St was built in 1888 (£1500), the similar three storey and attic, 4 bay block in Wallace St was added in 1894–5 (£5000), and the four storey and attic, 4 by 3 bay corner block, with its striking castellated tower, was added in 1896 (£3700). *W. F. McGibbon*, architect, designed all these buildings.

184 Glasgow Copper Works, 86 Tradeston St and Wallace St, built 1876 for Miller & Pyle, coppersmiths. A one and two storey, 7 by 10 bay red and white brick building, with a large arched doorway and white brick string courses. The roof is supported on timber trusses, and the floors are wooden, supported on cast-iron columns. The appearance of the building has recently been modernised, the exterior harled, and new windows inserted.

185 Paint Warehouses, 106 Tradeston St and Cook St, built 1888–1900 for Blacklock, McArthur & Co. The older block is four storeys high, 9 bays wide, with an ashlar front surmounted by a pediment with a stag's head on it in low relief – the firm's trademark – *H. & D. Barclay,* architects (£5000). The 1900 addition was designed by *W. F. McGibbon,* architect, in 1896, and is four storeys high, 4 by 8 bay, terra-cotta brick in Venetian Gothic style, with a neat tower.

186 Tradeston Paint Mills, 54 Cook St and West St, built from 1866 for H. McBean & Co., oil merchants. A fine three storey and attic, 4 by 10 bay ashlar block, dated 1866, the top storey being a later addition. The two storey portion in Cook St was added in 1907 (£3300), and has a crow-stepped gablet.

187 Dyeworks & Paint Factory, 161–73 West St. Two two storey buildings, each 5 bays wide, one with a mansard roof, built 1896 for Blacklock & McArthur, *W. F. McGibbon,* architect (£2240). The other was probably built 1880 for James Mills, dyer, and has a basement (£2000).

188 Eglinton Engine Works, 120 Tradeston St, Cook St and West St, built from *c* 1855 for A. & W. Smith & Co., general engineers, and subsequently greatly extended. The 1855 block is three storeys high, 4 by 17 bay, ashlar, with margins round the windows. It has a large arched doorway, now bricked up, while some of the windows have cast-iron frames. The interior has wooden floors on cast-iron columns. The later additions include 3 wide bays of workshops, with wooden roof trusses, and a four storey, 9 bay red and white brick block of stores and workshops.

189 West Street Chemical Works, 182 West St, founded 1841 by Richard Smith, chemist. A heterogeneous collection of brick, wood and steel sheds, with a two storey, 3 bay office block, formerly a villa.

190 Scotland Street Engine Works, 2 Scotland St, West St and Paterson St, founded *c* 1841 by P. & W. McOnie, engineers. The oldest parts of the complex are the ashlar buildings on the corners, both originally two storey, and extended to three storey. The ashlar centre block, three storeys high, 16 bays wide, and the red and white brick Paterson St frontage, three storeys, 27 bay, are later additions. The Paterson St block was probably added in 1878 for W. & A. McOnie (£4000).

191 Engineering Works, 8–18 Scotland St, Laidlaw St and Paterson St, built 1870–1 for James Howden, engineer. A two storey, 4 by 7 bay block with a high ground floor, a lower two storey, 15 bay block and a two storey, 4 by 6 bay block, with ashlar frontages to Scotland St and Laidlaw St, and a red and white brick frontage to Paterson St.

192 Co-operative Workshops & Warehouses, 119–31 Laidlaw St and 100–28 Paterson St, built 1898–1913 (£34,460) for the SCWS, mostly to designs by *James Davidson,* architect. The Laidlaw frontage consists of a four storey, 9 bay and a three storey and attic, 4 bay block, both in red brick, with low relief arches through the ground and first floors, semi-circular windows in the first floor, and circular windows alternating with pairs of orthodox windows at second floor level. The Paterson St frontage is much less interesting, consisting of two plain four storey red and white brick buildings, one 10 bays, the other 26 bays long, and a tall four storey, 4 bay building with a large arched entrance.

193 Clyde Rivet Works, 113 Laidlaw St, built 1872–3 for the Clyde Rivet Works Co., managing partner John H. Ziegler (£500), and extended in 1898 for W. & R. B. Macowat, *Burnet & Boston,* architects (£1500). A 4 bay, single storey building, with crow-stepped gables to the street, and prominent roof ventilators. There is a small office block, and single storey sheds at the rear, with wooden roof trusses on cast-iron columns.

194 West Street Underground Station, 299 West St, built *c* 1895 for the Glasgow District Subway Co., *John Gordon*, architect. A small single storey terra-cotta brick building with an ornamental gablet over the entrance, surmounted by a ball finial. This structure houses the booking office and the head of the stairway to the underground island platform.

195 Scotland Street Engine Works, 1–3 Scotland St, founded *c* 1851 by W. & A. McOnie, engineers. The latterly existing buildings probably dated from 1857–8, though extensions were made in 1882 (£6500), 1893 (£9000), 1902 (£2500) and 1911 (£1580). A high single storey, 5 by 14 bay ashlar block with three rows of windows. To the west was a two storey, 3 bay office block and a single storey, 4 bay block, with large arched doorways. Demolished 1969.

196 Engineering Works, 45 Scotland St, founded 1860 by J. B. Mirrlees & William Tait, engineers, and extended in 1872–3 (£3500), 1873 (£2500), and 1876 (£4000). Two office blocks, one three storeys high, 3 bays wide, with round-headed openings on the ground and first floors, the other 8 bays wide, plain, with 7 bays of red brick and iron workshops behind, presenting a three storey frontage to the Glasgow & Paisley railway. Demolished 1968.

197 Engineering Works, 98 Laidlaw St and Kinning St, founded 1883 by Watson, Laidlaw & Co., subsequently greatly extended. Facing Laidlaw St were a four storey, 10 bay block, built 1913, *Sir William Arrol & Co.*, engineers (£14,920), a three storey, 14 bay building, built 1883 (£2000) and a three storey, 20 bay building, built 1883 (£6000). Running through to Kinning St were tall workshop buildings, added to in 1910 (£2600, £2670, £1000). Demolished 1968–9.

198 Engineering Works, 195 Scotland St, built from 1897 for James Howden & Co., engineers, *Nisbet Sinclair*, engineer, *Bryden & Robertson* and *Dykes & Robertson*, architects (£18,310). The original offices were single storey, the later block two storey and attic, 8 bay, mansard-roofed, with steel-framed workshops at the rear. Greatly extended since 1914.

199 Subway Power Station, 175 Scotland St, built *c* 1895 for the Glasgow District Subway Co., *John Gordon*, architect. Two wide, high single storey buildings with red brick walls and steel roof trusses. The gable ends face the street, and that of the larger bay has an arched doorway, with moulded brickwork above.

200 Garage & Workshops, 327–35 Scotland St, built from 1914 for the South West Motor Carriage Works, to designs by *J. Galt*, architect (£460). A range of 5 wide bays of single storey buildings, roof lit.

201 Bonded Warehouse, 401 Scotland St and Seaward St, built 1903 for Slater, Rodger & Co., bonded warehousemen, whisky blenders and exporters, and subsequently extended, *John Gordon*, architect. A six storey terra-cotta brick warehouse, with a 3 bay red sandstone frontage to Scotland St, with a central oriel window. The original part has 16 bays to Seaward St, and the extension 10 bays, with a fire wall between.

202 Lancefield Soap Works, 425 Scotland St and Keyden St, built *c* 1877 for Robert Burns & Co., soap makers. A plain two storey, 3 by 10 bay red and white brick building. The adjacent building, a wide single storey structure with gable end to Scotland St, has so far escaped identification.

203 Vermont Works, 13 Vermont St, built *c* 1869 for the Dowie Patent Metal Co., bush and bell founders. A plain, low 3 bay, single storey structure with the stump of a circular-section chimney at the south-west corner.

204 Strathclyde Paint & Varnish Works, 41 Vermont St, built *c* 1893 for Ferguson, Hamilton & Morrison. A three storey, 8 bay red and white brick building, with a two storey extension to the rear. Recently most of the ground floor windows and one of the two doors have been blocked up, and harling applied to the whole building.

205 Workshops, and Iron & Steel Stores, 47 Vermont St, built from *c* 1913 for P. & W. MacLellan & Co. Ltd, structural engineers and steel stockholders. Two groups of 3 long bays of corrugated-iron clad steel framed buildings, at right angles to the street. The eastern group has now been demolished.

206 Stables & Garage, 181 Stanley St and Vermont St, built *c* 1899 for the Kinning Park Co-operative Society, probably *Bruce & Hay*, architects. A two storey, 6 bay block and a four storey, 5 by 2 bay building. In both buildings, especially in the latter, bold and effective use is made of white bricks, some moulded, for decoration. A notable feature is the row of broken arches along the ground floors of both buildings.

207 Confectionery Works, 184 Stanley St and Vermont St, built *c* 1890 for Hay Bros, manufacturing confectioners. A three storey, 8 by 24 bay red and white brick building on an L plan, with a corner turret. The Stanley St frontage has two arched doorways with circular windows above, and round-headed windows on the ground floor. At the rear are three storey, two storey and single storey extensions.

208 St Crispin Works, 57 Cornwall St, built 1895 for Melvin Bros, wholesale and export boot and shoe manufacturers and leather merchants. A three storey and attic, 6 bay red sandstone ashlar fronted building, with a chimney at the rear, added for the Glasgow Syrup Refinery in 1903, *Miller & Black*, architects.

209 Warehouse, 39 Durham St and Cornwall St, built 1907–8 for J. & P. Coats Ltd, thread manufacturers. Five large bays of plain single storey red brick buildings, with circular ventilators in the gable ends, which face Durham St. There is a circular-section brick chimney at the north-east corner.

210 Aerated Water Factory, 60–4 Durham St and 15, 17 MacLellan St, built 1897 for John Mackay & Co., to designs by *P. Caldwell*, Paisley, architect. The MacLellan St frontage is in Tudor style, two storey, 3 bay, with a large elliptically arched doorway, while the Durham St frontage is one and two storeys high, 8 bays wide, red brick, with ornate Renaissance doorways with broken pediments.

211 Clutha Bakery, 21–3 MacLellan St, built 1881 (£3000) and extended in 1888 for George Milne & Co., rusk manufacturers, *R. A. Wightman*, architect. A two storey, 8 bay red and white brick building, with twin gables to the street, and a two storey, 7 bay red brick building, with roof ventilators.

212 Plantation Bakery, 63–73 Durham St, built 1881–2 for J. & B. Stevenson, bakers (£18,000) and extended in 1903 and 1914 (£6060), *Salmon & Son* and *J. G. Gillespie*, architects. A five storey, 8 bay flat roofed red brick building, with two windows per bay. At the west end is a neat single storey arched entrance surmounted by a wreathed head, the date 1882 and topped by a ball finial. On the frontage of the main block is a low-relief panel depicting breadmaking.

213 Vulcan Tube Works, 126 Cornwall St, built *c* 1872 for Cruikshanks, Low & Co., malleable iron tube manufacturers. The office and warehouse block, the oldest part of the complex, is a two storey, 16 bay ashlar fronted rubble building.

214 Shields Road Station, 326 Shields Rd, opened 10 October 1863 and extended in 1885 for opening of Canal line. A junction station with platforms on the Paisley Canal (G & SWR) and Glasgow & Paisley Joint lines. The booking offices

were at street level, with stairways to the platforms below, those for the G & P Joint being of wood, 10 bays long. The station was closed in 1965 and demolished in 1967; the Canal line station was burned in 1966.

215 Canal Warehouse, 106–14 Salkeld St, built *c* 1810 for the proprietors of the Glasgow, Paisley & Ardrossan Canal, *David Henry*, engineer, Paisley. A five storey, 8 bay Palladian building with three low-relief arches and two hoists.

216 Glass Works, 51–65 Mauchline St, built *c* 1900 for Love & Co. Ltd, mirror manufacturers. A single storey brick building, with 12 bay frontage, with low relief arches.

217 Warehouse, 39 Mauchline St, probably built *c* 1887 for Caulfield & Co., glass and china merchants. A three storey, 4 by 5 bay brick building, with three round-headed entrances on ground floor in Mauchline St, now partly bricked up, flanked by tall round-headed windows.

218 Falfield Mills, 8–38 Falfield St and 16 Stromness St, built from *c* 1840 for G. L. Walker & Co., power-loom cotton manufacturers. The main block is a four storey and attic, 18 bay red brick building, partly cut down, while at right angles in Stromness St is a three storey, 9 bay ashlar fronted brick building, probably built in 1861.

219 Port Eglinton Cabinet Works, 9–11 Ritchie St, built 1874 (£900) and extended 1875 (£800) for A. Thomson & Son. A three storey, 13 bay red and white brick block with a 4 bay ashlar frontage to Stromness St.

220 Motor Car Works, 44 Kilbirnie St, built 1913 for William Park, bodybuilder, *R. Henderson*, architect (£3000). An interesting three storey, 6 by 9 bay reinforced concrete building, with large rectangular steel-framed windows.

221 Cabinet Works, 53 Kilbirnie St, built 1894 for A. Thomson & Son, *J. Chalmers*, architect (£2000). A four storey, 9 by 6 bay red and white brick block, the top storey of which has been added in a different style.

222 Refuse Disposal Works, 55 Kilbirnie St, built from 1882 for Glasgow Corporation Cleansing Department, *A. W. Wheatley*, engineer. The first stage cost £25,000. A large group of red and white brick buildings, the most spectacular of which is a two storey stable, muster hall and store block, 16 bays wide, originally with 68 stalls, with a Greek key pattern string course, built 1898–9 (£7500). The main destructor building has 3 wide bays, one of which spans two railway sidings. The complex is dominated by a very tall brick chimney. A pleasing feature of the entrance is a neat octagonal weighbridge house.

223 Eglinton Street Station, 450 Eglinton St, built 1879 for the Caledonian Railway, and extended *c* 1905. The main line station had a central island and two single-sided platforms in a cutting, with access by two footbridges. There were attractive wood and iron waiting rooms on the platforms and a sandstone booking office at street level. To the west of the main station and at a higher level was the suburban section, with a one-sided platform and an island. Closed 1 February 1965, and demolished *c* 1970.

224 Tradeston Gasworks, 95 Kilbirnie St, built originally 1835–9 for Glasgow Gas Light Co. (£20,000), and rebuilt 1869–74, 1924 and 1946–55. The works were closed officially on 31 March 1970. The General Terminus & Glasgow Harbour Railway intersects the works. To the north is the retort house, of red brick, four storeys high, and coke store, reinforced concrete, five storeys high. There is a set of four condensers with cross water tubes, scrubbers, and four sets of steam driven exhausters, two with engines by R. Laidlaw & Son (1887–9). On the south side are the purifier houses, with Belfast roofs, the main coal store and three of the four gasholders. The largest, number one, was built by Barrowfield Ironworks in 1922, and rebuilt in 1928. Numbers two and three are similar in style, the latter being built in 1886 by Clayton. Number four, built by Barrowfield in 1897, is behind the offices on the north side, and was used for water gas storage. A large brick and steel coal store in Gourock St was added in 1913 (£12,160).

225 Aerated Water Works, 164 Maxwell Rd and St Andrews Rd, built 1898 for G. & P. Barrie, *J. Sibbald*, architect, Dundee (£4000). A single storey brick factory, with an L plan 9 by 11 bay, two storey office block.

226 Sawmill, 176 Maxwell Rd, reconstructed 1908–9 for A. Bowie & Co., *McKissack & Son*, architects. The front buildings have recently been demolished, but at the rear are two plain red brick blocks.

227 Timber Yard, 194 Maxwell Rd, built *c* 1914 for John Fairley, timber merchant. A two storey, 2 by 2 bay terra-cotta brick office block, with timber shed at the rear.

228 Lillybank Sawmills, 198 Maxwell Rd, built *c* 1880 for Allan & Baxter, wrights. A two storey, 2 by 2 bay brick office block with round-headed windows. There is a two storey brick shed at the rear, built in 1904, *W. R. Watson*, architect.

Section I
Pollokshields, Govanhill and Polmadie

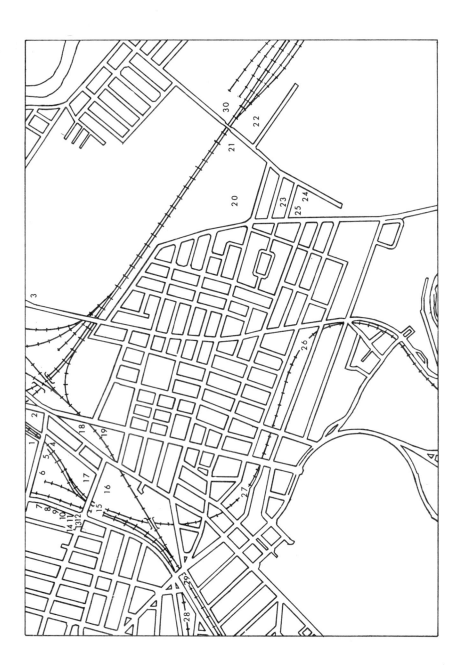

1 Etna Foundry, Milan St and Lilybank Rd, founded on this site *c* 1854 by David Ritchie & Co., ironfounders. The main surviving part is a three storey, 22 bay red brick building, from 1912 a Glasgow Corporation Gas Department, now Scottish Gas Board, store and workshop. This structure was probably built in 1874 (£6500). In Lilybank St is a neat sandstone gateway with an elliptical arch, now bricked up, and at the rear, cut down remains of other buildings. Between 1875 and 1901 £8000 was spent on additions.

2 Bakery, 654 Eglinton St, built *c* 1896 for D. & S. McNaught, bakers. A block of one and two storey buildings on an L plan, behind a tenement.

3 Govan Ironworks, 525 Crown St, founded 1839 by William Dixon of Calder. This, the last blast furnace plant to operate within the city boundary, was demolished in the early 1960s. The handsome two storey red and white brick offices, with round-headed windows, and a contemporary 2 by 4 bay engine house in similar style, both built in 1888 (£1500) lasted as a site office for the redevelopment of the area until 1966.

4 Motor Works, 29 Maxwell Rd and Barrland St, built 1907 for the Kennedy Motor Co., *Burnet, Boston & Carruthers*, architects (£4900). A single storey, 18 bay red brick building with a Belfast roof, and an ornamental gable to Maxwell Rd.

5 Caledonian Railway, Engineer's Department, 57 Maxwell Rd, built 1902–3. Two two storey red brick buildings, one 11 bay, the other 6 bay, with ancillary blocks. There is a one storey, 10 bay office block built in 1902 (£1200). A narrow-gauge hand-operated tramway serves the sawmills.

6 Muirhouse Sawmills, 129 Maxwell Rd, built 1886–98 for J. Watt Torrance & Co. (£7100). A group of plain red brick and corrugated-iron buildings.

7 Workshop, 40 Darnley St, built 1906 for William Tennent, builder, *Joseph Boyd*, architect (£550). A plain two storey, 3 by 9 bay red brick building.

8 Printing Works, 50 Darnley St, built 1901 for Miller & Lang, art publishers, and extended at the rear in 1903, *Gordon & Dobson*, architects (£5000 and £3600). A three storey, 5 bay red sandstone fronted brick building, with an ornate *art nouveau* frontage. The Forth St warehouse has two storeys and an attic, and 3 bays and is linked to the front block by a red brick structure. Front block SDD category C.

9 Warehouse, 52–6 Darnley St, built in 1903 (£3250) and extended in 1904 (£2500), for James Brown & Son, printers and publishers, *Gordon, Son & Dobson* and *D. W. Sturrock*, architects. A plain red sandstone ashlar fronted three storey, 4 bay building.

10 Felt Works, 62 Darnley St, built *c* 1885 for the Clyde Felt & Composition Co. A two storey and basement, 7 bay red and white brick building.

11 Timber Sheds & Sawmills, 79 Forth St and Darnley St, built 1892–3 (£1000) for Gilmour & Aitken, mahogany merchants, *W. J. Anderson* (I), architect, and extended in 1902 (£750), *R. A. Bryden*, architect. A group of brick and timber sheds with slatted ends and open sides, extending through to Darnley St.

12 Glasgow Cabinet Works, 86–96 Darnley St, built in 1877 for William Hill, cabinet and chair maker, and upholsterer; and extended in 1905, *Burnet, Boston & Carruthers*, for R. & J. Jackson (£2900). A group of three buildings, the oldest a cream sandstone fronted three storey, 3 bay block, then a three storey, 5 bay red and white brick structure, and the 1905 red brick extension, four storeys high, 3 bays long. All have mansard rooves.

13 Glasgow Laundry & Carpet Beating Works, 100 Albert Drive, founded *c* 1895 by Thomas Donald. A rectangular block of red sandstone buildings in French Renaissance style, with single storey wings having semicircular windows and louvred ventilators, and a two storey and attic corner office block with a cast-iron crown and weather vane.

14 Joinery Works, 89 Forth St, built *c* 1894 for Dick & Benzies, joiners, and extended in 1900 (£1300). The oldest parts are two storey, 5 bay and two storey, 7 bay red brick buildings.

15 Pollokshields East Station, Albert Drive, built *c* 1886 for the Cathcart District Railway. A simple island platform station, with a timber building having glazed awnings. The station is connected with Albert Drive by a lattice girder stairway.

16 Coplawhill Tramway Works & Tram Depot, Albert Drive. The first part was built as a horse tram depot for Glasgow Corporation Tramways Department in 1894, *W. Clark*, engineer. It is a two storey, 9 by 4 bay ashlar fronted red brick building, with stables on the first floor. The main workshops were built 1899–1912 (£69,800). There are 9 wide bays of single storey workshops, with steel roof trusses on red and white brick walls. The main Albert Drive frontage was cream sandstone ashlar with 11 large round-headed doorways, all but two of which were bricked up on conversion to a transport museum. On the other side of Albert Drive was the covered timber yard, with four wide bays, built 1911 (£1260) and now converted to offices.

17 Tramway Permanent Way Depot, Barrland St. A large yard with single storey brick buildings, part built 1911 (£1260), housing rail bending machines. There was a steel derrick crane for handling rails and crossings. Now much altered.

18 Clydesdale Brewery, 44–50 Victoria Rd and Pollokshaws Rd, built 1883 for M. D. Dawson & Co., brewers and maltsters (£3500) and rebuilt and enlarged 1896 for the Tonbur Brewery Co. Ltd, brewers of non-alcoholic beers, R. H. Paterson, Edinburgh, architect (£2000). Facing Pollokshaws Rd was a four storey,

9 bay rubble building, and on Victoria Rd was a two and three storey, attic and basement, 13 bay block. Demolished 1967.

19 Bakery, 78 Victoria Rd, built 1903 for A. F. Reid, baker and confectioner, *J. F. Henderson*, architect (£2500). The front block is a two storey, 8 bay French Renaissance sandstone building, with brick bakehouses behind.

20 Queen's Park Locomotive Works, 321 Aitkenhead Rd, founded as Glasgow Locomotive Works 1864 by Henry Dübs, and extensively rebuilt between 1896 and 1908 (£164,900). A large complex of brick and steel-framed buildings, many of the latter corrugated-iron clad. The last additions of this period (1906–8, £146,000) were designed by *Sir William Arrol & Co. Ltd*, engineers. Most of the works have been demolished since closure in 1963, but the administration block, a two storey and basement, 31 bay red brick building, and some of the shops still remain.

21 Acme Tea Chest Works, 204 Polmadie Rd, built 1896–8 for the Acme Tea Chest Co., *T. L. Watson*, architect (£5900). A nondescript group of one and two storey red brick buildings on a triangular site, with a two storey, 2 by 5 bay office block, and a three storey water tower.

22 Sentinel Works, Jessie St, built 1903–14 for Alley & McLellan, engineers, *A. Leitch* and *Brand & Lithgow*, architects (£31,475), and extended after 1914. The most interesting and important building on the site is a four storey, 3 by 12 bay reinforced-concrete block, designed by *Archibald Leitch* as pattern shop and offices in 1903. This was the first reinforced-concrete building of any size in the city.

23 Polmadie Iron Works, 33 Hamilton St, built *c* 1887 for J. H. Carruthers & Co. Ltd, pump makers, and extended in 1898 (£3500) and 1901 (£400), R. Ewan, architect, 1904 (£3600) and 1914 (£940) Brand & Lithgow, architects. Probably also incorporates parts of James Bennie & Co.'s

Clyde Engine Works, established 1885 and vacated in 1899. An extensive group of single storey engineering shops, with a three storey, 14 bay block facing Hamilton St and a three storey, 4 bay building on Polmadie St.

24 Sentinel Works, 344 Polmadie Rd, built from c 1880 for Alley & McLellan, engineers. Additions were made in 1893 (£2750) *A. Myles*, architect, 1906 and 1911 (£2270) *Brand & Lithgow*, architects. A block of single storey engineering shops, demolished c 1967.

25 Rosehill Works, 491 Aitkenhead Rd, built c 1888 for the Scotch & Irish Oxygen Co. Ltd and subsequently greatly enlarged. A large group of two and three storey buildings, mostly red brick, extending along Hamilton St.

26 Crosshill Station, Cathcart Rd, built c 1886 for the Cathcart District Railway. An island platform station in a narrow cutting, with bullnose masonry retaining walls. The platform is so narrow that originally the main offices were in a sandstone building at street level, a shelter only being provided below. This building was demolished in the late 1950s and a small booking office made out of part of the shelter. A minor alteration was made during electrification, when the trackbed and platform were lowered to give clearance for overhead wires passing under two road bridges. The building is now therefore mounted on concrete blocks. There was, until resignalling, a neat signal cabin on the platform, with a six lever frame.

27 Queen's Park Station, Victoria Rd and Niddrie Rd, built c 1886 for the Cathcart District Railway. An island platform station in a shallow cutting with a grass embankment on the north and a retaining wall on the south. A wooden platform building with glazed awning is provided, having a central booking office. As with Crosshill, there was a signal cabin on the platform. Access from the streets is by lattice girder stairs, the gateposts having formidable spiked iron ball finials.

28 Pollokshields West Station, Terregles Avenue and Fotheringay Rd, built c 1894 for the Cathcart District Railway. An island platform station in a cutting with an unusual two-level station building of wooden construction. The booking hall is at street level, approached by lattice girder footbridges, and an enclosed stairway gives access to the platform, where there are waiting rooms and stores.

29 Strathbungo Station, Nithsdale Rd, opened 1 December 1877 by the Glasgow, Barrhead & Kilmarnock Joint Railway. A two platform station in a shallow cutting, with the booking office on a plate girder overbridge, with stairways to the platforms. The office building has been altered to shops, and the platforms cut back, since the station was closed in 1962.

30 Polmadie Engine Shed, 103 Polmadie Rd, opened c 1879 by the Caledonian Railway, and subsequently rebuilt and extended. A group of single storey red brick buildings incorporating a large repair shop.

Section J
Pollokshaws

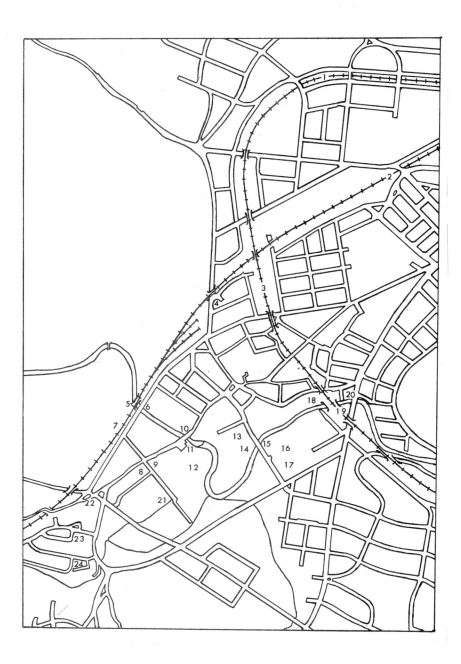

1 Maxwell Park Station, Fotheringay Rd and Terregles Avenue, built *c* 1894 for the Cathcart District Railway. An island platform station in a cutting, with a two storey wooden building. The station is entered from both streets by footbridges at first floor level, and there are waiting rooms on the platform (similar to I28).

2 Crossmyloof Station, Titwood Rd, opened 1 October 1888 by the Glasgow, Barrhead & Kilmarnock Joint Railway. A two platform station, with the booking office in a wooden building on a road overbridge, and wooden waiting rooms on both platforms. There was a large goods and mineral station on the south-east side of the line, and a long, lattice girder footbridge still spans the site.

3 Shawlands Station, Pollokshaws Rd, built *c* 1894 for the Cathcart District Railway. An island platform station, partly on an embankment and partly in cutting, with approach by subway at the south, and by footbridge at the north end. There is a wooden platform building with a glazed awning. On the south side of Pollokshaws Rd are two houses under the railway, which were occupied until the mid 1950s.

4 Electricity Substation, Ellangowan Rd and Haggs Rd, built 1908 for the Glasgow Corporation Electricity Department (£4780). A two storey 3 by 5 bay snecked rubble building, with one bay of the 3 bay frontage projecting. Designed to harmonise with existing residential development.

5 Pollokshaws Viaduct, completed by 5 October 1847 for the Glasgow, Barrhead & Neilston Direct Railway, *Neil Robson*, engineer. A four span masonry viaduct, with segmental arches, two spanning the White Cart, one a relief arch and one over a minor road.

6 Pollokshaws Road Bridge, built 1928, *T. Somers* and *Considére Constructions Ltd*, engineers (£20,415). A two span reinforced-concrete girder bridge with granite balustrades, carrying the A736 over the White Cart Water. The spans are both 34 feet long.

7 Pollokshaws West Station, Pollokshaws Rd, built *c* 1847 for the Glasgow, Barrhead & Neilston Direct Railway. A two platform through station on an embankment. The up platform building is two storeys high, 9 bays long, of brick and sandstone construction, with the street entrance at ground floor level and the platform entrance at first floor level.

8 Avenue Ironworks, Cogan St, founded *c* 1874 by John Dalglish, engineer. The main building is a four storey and attic, 8 bay, red and white brick block, and there are two single storey workshop bays.

9 Auldfield Weaving Mills, 11 Cogan St, founded *c* 1851 by R. Cogan, cotton spinner. The oldest surviving part of the complex is a single storey, 15 bay ashlar block, much altered, facing the street. To the north and west there are two storey additions including an office and warehouse built in 1902 for Lowndes, Macdonald & Co., power-loom cotton manufacturers, *J. B. Wilson*, architect.

10 Shaws Bridge, Shawbridge St, built 1934, replacing a two arch masonry bridge. A two span plate girder bridge with solid granite parapet, spanning the White Cart Water.

11 Bridge Turbine Works, Shawbridge St, reconstructed *c* 1907 for John Macdonald & Co., mechanical engineers. The remains of what was probably an early 19th century grain mill. The base of the wheelhouse, with arched headrace and tailrace, and of part of the body can still be seen. The weir still exists a short distance upstream.

12 Renfield Works (Weaving), 137 Shawbridge St, built from *c* 1891 for David Barbour & Co. A 25 bay block of single storey weaving sheds, with some ancillary two storey buildings.

13 Viking Thread Mills, 34 Riverbank St, built *c* 1914 for George Melville Ltd, sewing cotton manufacturer. A block of one and two storey red brick buildings with a two storey, 9 bay frontage to the street. The office was a converted villa. Engaged in the dyeing and rewinding of thread, the works were closed in 1969.

14 Riverbank Works, 110 Riverford Rd, founded *c* 1893 by Robert Brown, bleacher and finisher. A group of single storey brick buildings, mostly built after 1914.

15 Riverford Road Bridge, Riverford Rd, built 1923, T. *Somers* and *Considére Constructions*, engineers (£19,069). A single span, segmental-arched reinforced-concrete bridge on a skew, over the White Cart Water.

16 Newlandsfield Print & Bleach Works, 109 Riverford Rd, built from *c* 1812. A large group of one and two storey red brick buildings.

17 Newlands Tram Depot, Newlandsfield Rd, built 1909 for Glasgow Corporation Tramways Department, *J. Dalry*, engineer. A long 8 bay, single storey red brick building with roof lighting. The Riverford Rd frontage is finished in red sandstone to harmonise with surrounding residential development.

18 Coustonholm Factory (Cotton Weaving), 8–48 Coustonholm Rd, built *c* 1858 for the Coustonholm Weaving Co. A large block of one and two storey buildings, partly rebuilt recently. The most interesting surviving part is a two storey block on an L plan, having a blank wall to the street and large windows with cast-iron frames facing a small courtyard.

19 Pollokshaws East Station, Kilmarnock Rd, built *c* 1894 for the Cathcart District Railway. An island platform station, similar in most respects to Shawlands and Langside Stations (J3, M63), but unusually the offices are on a masonry arch bridge over the White Cart Water. Approach at both ends is by subway, that at the north end crossing Coustonholm Road on a lattice girder footbridge.

20 Macquisten Bridge, Kilmarnock Rd, built 1832. A segmental masonry arch over the White Cart Water, with rusticated voussoirs and granite balustrades. Widened in 1907.

21 West of Scotland Boiler Works, 64 Cogan St, built 1898–9 for A. & W. Dalglish, boilermakers. A high single storey steel-framed building with brick end walls. Lean-tos were added later on both sides. In the east end is a large round-headed doorway.

22 Tollhouse, 1 Cross St, built *c* 1800. A perfectly circular building with a conical roof and central chimney stack. Now empty, but preserved in a large roundabout. SDD listed category B.

23 Wellmeadow Laundry, 72 Harriet St, built as a bleachworks in the early 19th century, and rebuilt as a laundry 1894–1902 for Donald Macfarlane. The red brick office block, with Flemish gable and twin oriel windows, is dated 1899. At the rear are one and two storey red, and red and white brick buildings, while adjacent to the office is a fragment of masonry building, probably a survival from the bleachworks.

24 Eastwood Engine Works, 11–15 Westwood Rd, built *c* 1889 for Haythorn & Stuart, engineers and brass founders. A two storey, 2 by 18 bay range of cement washed brick building, on an L plan, with a square-section brick chimney at the rear.

Section K
Kelvinhaugh, Govan and Ibrox

1 Fairfield Shipbuilding Yard & Engine Works, 1048 Govan Rd, founded 1863 by Randolph & Elder, engineers and iron shipbuilders. Though the yard has been extensively reconstructed within the past 10 years, the large rectangular engine works, a high single storey brick building, with cast-iron columns in the interior, and pairs of pilasters at intervals along the sides, is substantially unaltered (completed *c* 1874). The main office block, a particularly fine French Renaissance two storey, 39 bay structure with a tower at the rear, was built in 1889 (*J. Keppie of Honeyman & Keppie*, architects, SDD category B). The main office entrance, round headed, with low relief sculpture, is flanked by statues of a shipwright and a mariner, each standing on the prow of a ship. The three storey offices in Elder St were added in 1903.

2 Meadowside Ferry, Wanlock St to Meadowside St. Opened *c* 1900 by the Clyde Navigation Trust. A standard passenger ferry with berths having angled wooden side walls and steps, and small wooden shelters at street level, closed 22 January 1966.

3 Graving Dock, Castlebank St (see L28).

4 Pointhouse Shipbuilding Yard, Ferry Rd (see L36).

5 Govan Ferry, Ferry Rd to Water Row, a very old-established crossing point taken over by Clyde Navigation Trust in 1857; a high level vehicular ferry replaced a chain ferry in 1912. The vehicular ferry was closed in 1965 after the opening of the Whiteinch Tunnel, while the low level passenger ferry, similar to K2, lasted until 22 January 1966.

6 Yorkhill Basin, Pointhouse Rd, built *c* 1908 for the Clyde Navigation Trust, under an Act of 1904. A large rectangular basin with single storey sheds on both sides. The shed on the east side was destroyed by fire in the mid 1960s. The adjoining wharf was authorised in 1868.

7 Brass Foundry, 80 Eastvale Place, built from 1897 for Steven & Struthers, bell and general brassfounders, *A. Myles*, architect for the first part (£12,000), and two additions (1905, £2000 and 1903, £670) were designed by *F. Southorn*. A row of high single storey workshops, with round-headed doorways. There are two three storey office blocks, one of which has a cast-iron crown. Effective use is made of white brick for decoration.

8 Kelvinhaugh Refuse Disposal Works, Gilbert St, built 1889–90 for Glasgow Corporation Cleansing Department (£15,000). The works is dominated by a very large iron-bound chimney. The main block is three storeys high, 6 by 8 bay, and there is a large two storey stable block with wooden galleries giving access to the first floor – originally had 50 stalls. There are three storey blocks of tenements at the entrance, built to house the workers, *John Carrick*, architect.

9 Kelvinhaugh Cotton Mills, Sandyford St, built *c* 1848 for Black & Wingate, cotton spinners and weavers. A three storey, 12 bay building, now harled. The cast-iron window frames are original. Five bays of weaving sheds adjoin, added in 1874–7 (£1700). The roof was altered after a serious fire on 3 December 1881, when damage was estimated at £50,000. At that time there were 30,000 spindles.

10 Clyde Cooperage, 50 Eastvale Place, built 1889 for the Clyde Cooperage Co., *J. S. Kent*, architect (£4000). A plain two storey, 12 bay red brick building with a central segmental-arched doorway and a single storey extension at the rear.

11 Kelvinhaugh Engine Works, 130 Kelvinhaugh St, founded 1874 by Hutson & Corbett, engineers and boilermakers. The front building is two storeys high, 11 bays long, of red brick, with roof lighting and windows at first floor level only. There is an associated three storey, 2 bay office block, and extensions at the rear. Between 1874 and 1900 four additions were made (£7650), and after a fire in 1909 the engine shop was restored at cost of £1500.

12 Hydraulic Pumping Station, Queen's Dock, built 1877–8 for the Clyde Navigation Trust, *J. Carrick*, architect. A single storey, 2 by 3 bay building, with pedimented gables and round-headed windows. Adjacent to the north is a similar flat-roofed building and a four storey accumulator tower with a clock, built in the style of an Italian campanile. The station powered cranes and a swing bridge (see H120).

13 Kelvinhaugh Ferry, Pointhouse Rd to Highland Lane, opened *c* 1900 by the Clyde Navigation Trust. A standard passenger ferry (see K2).

14 Govan Graving Docks, Stag St, built 1869–98 for the Clyde Navigation Trust. The first, nearest the river, was constructed between 1869 and 1875, and is 551 feet long, 72 feet wide, with a depth of 22 feet 10 inches of water at high tide. The second was opened on 13 October 1886 and is 575 feet long and 67 feet wide, of the same depth as number one. The largest, number three, is 880 feet long, 83 feet wide and 26 feet 6 inches deep. When opened on 27 April 1898 it could take the largest vessels afloat. Number one had until 1970 a fine steam travelling crane, the last of its type in the harbour.

15 Shipbuilding Yard, Clydebrae St, Govan Rd and Water Row, built from 1912 for Harland & Wolff, shipbuilders, incorporating three smaller yards, in the centre Middleton Yard, founded 1842 by Smith & Rodger, purchased 1864 by the London & Glasgow Engineering & Iron Shipbuilding Co., to the west a yard founded *c* 1839 by MacArthur & Alexander, purchased in 1841 by Robert Napier, and to the east the New Yard, built by Robert Napier in 1850 to replace the 'Old Yard'. The yard had seven building berths with steel mitre gates, a fitting out basin at the east end, and large single storey workshops on Govan Rd and in Water

Row. The Water Row block, irregularly shaped, with 24 bays to the river, was built in 1914–15 to designs by *Sir William Arrol & Co.*, engineers (£85,647), and like the other had steel columns and roof trusses, with terra-cotta brick faced outside walls. In Clydebrae St is a high single storey red brick building, 7 by 5 bay, with tall round-headed windows and attractive roof ventilators. Immediately to the east are a two storey, 5 bay block (1889–90) and a three storey, 8 bay building (1885) both built as offices for the L & GE & IS, and both with round-headed windows on the ground floor. Most of the yard was dismantled in 1965, but the Water Row and Clydebrae St buildings still survive.

16 Stables, 2 Water Row, built 1907 for William Robin, spirit merchant. An irregular group of one, two and three storey red brick buildings.

17 Warehouse, 2 Pearce Lane, built 1904 for J. Armstrong, grain and potato merchant, *R. A. Wightman*, architect. A three storey and attic, 5 bay red brick building with gable end to the street.

18 Govan Pier, built *c* 1885 for the Clyde Navigation Trust. A timber pier with single storey wooden waiting rooms and a flashing light.

19 Govan Sawmills, 60 Robert St, founded 1868 by Hamilton Marr & Co., wrights and builders. A two storey brick and timber workshop and a substantial two storey, 5 bay brick office block with a courtyard.

20 Govan Railway Station, 737 Govan Rd, built *c* 1868 for the Glasgow & Paisley Joint Railway. The station was closed to regular passenger trains on 9 May 1921, but was used for excursion traffic for some time after. The large single storey stone goods shed was demolished in 1967–8, while the small triangular office block in Govan Rd (built 1889), with its neat clock tower, has been converted to a shop. A tramway carried traffic along Govan Rd to the Fairfield Shipbuilding Yard (K1), and across the road to Harland & Wolff's Yard.

21 Subway Workshops, 18 Broomloan Rd, built *c* 1896 for Glasgow District Subway Co. An irregularly shaped, single storey red brick building, 2 bays wide, with a raised central portion over the pit communicating with the subway tunnels. An overhead gantry crane is used for lifting cars for overhaul.

22 Govan Press Buildings, 577 Govan Rd, built 1888–9 for John Cossar, printer and publisher, *F. Stirrat*, architect. The building facing Govan Rd is a four storey, 5 bay Renaissance block, with pilasters from first to top of second floor and busts in panels above first floor windows. At the rear are two storey and attic red brick workshops.

23 Stables, Vicarfield Place, built 1906 for Robert Lyle, *L. B. Buik*, architect. A two storey and attic, 2 by 12 bay red brick building with external ramp, roofed in corrugated iron, for the horses to climb to the first floor.

24 Steam Crane, Princes Dock, built 1894 for the Clyde Navigation Trust by *Cowans, Sheldon & Co.* of Carlisle (£16,000) and rebuilt in 1920. A massive fixed crane on a stone base, with a maximum capacity of 95 tons (reduced from 130 tons). The jib consisted of two large tubular girders with bracing ties to an A frame of riveted plates into which the cab was built. Coal bunkers were situated at each corner of the square base. Demolished 1970.

25 Prince's Dock, Govan Rd, originally known as Cessnock Dock, and built 1893–7 for the Clyde Navigation Trust. The formal opening was performed by the Duchess of York on 10 September 1895. There are three basins, with a total water area of 35 acres, 3737 yards of quay, and an entrance 155 feet wide. The depth at opening was 20–28 feet at low water, 31–39 feet at high water. Originally the cranes and capstans were hydraulically

operated, and the power station still stands (H121). A second accumulator tower, three storeys high, was added at the south-west corner of the dock in 1911–12. Alone among the Glasgow docks, all the warehouses are two storeys in height, with upper floors supported on heavy riveted plate girders, though as usual the walls are of brick. The doors on the road side have segmental arched heads. The dock cost about £1,250,000.

26 Govan Tram Depot, 29–35 Brand St and Harvie St, built 1913–14 for Glasgow Corporation Tramways Department, *J. Ferguson*, engineer (£22,888). The brick car shed has 5 wide bays opening on to a forecourt, each 8 bays long, with steel roof-trusses on cast-iron columns. The administration block in Harvie St is a two storey, 4 by 14 bay red sandstone building.

27 Whitefield Works, 167 Whitefield Rd, built 1878 for Anderson & Lyall, engineers and boilermakers. The main block consisted of two three storey red and white brick offices, one 4, the other 2 bays long, with round-headed windows on the ground and first floors, and a large corrugated-iron clad erecting shop at the rear. To the north is a two storey, 16 bay plain red sandstone fronted brick building. The larger block was demolished in 1969.

28 Engine & Boiler Works, 24 Fairley St and Carmichael St, built 1901 for James Anderson, *D. W. Sturrock*, architect, and converted to a bakery for Montgomerie & Co. in 1908, *Thomas Young*, engineer. A long range of two and three storey buildings, the main part being two storeys high, 12 bays long, with pairs of segmental-arched windows.

29 Timber Sheds, 51 Woodville St, built *c* 1907 for Hagert & Co., timber measurers and carting contractors. Two wide bays, of timber construction, with Belfast roofs and slatted sides.

30 Stables & Stores, 9 Fairley St, built 1897 for A. Hailstones, fish curer. A two storey, 2 by 13 bay red and white brick building, with the proprietor's name in white glazed brick on the gable end.

31 Ibrox Ironworks, 15 Fairley St, built 1891 (£500) and extended in 1904 for J. M. Adam & Co., pneumatic engineers. A 3 bay, single storey brick building with raised central bay, gable ends to the street.

32 Hammer Shaft Factory, 17 Fairley St, built 1892 (£1250), and extended in 1901, for Robert Burley & Sons, makers of hammer shafts and tool handles. A two storey, 30 bay red brick block, with five crow-stepped gables to the street.

33 Bakery, 145 Copland Rd, built 1903 for R. A. Peacock & Son, bakers, *Burnet, Boston & Carruthers*, architects. A three storey, 8 bay red brick block facing Copland Road, with more modern extensions at the rear.

34 Glasgow Candle Works, 164 Copland Rd, built *c* 1897 for Shearer & Harvey, candle makers. A small single storey red and white brick building with gable end to the street.

35 Workshop, 156 Copland Rd, built 1896 for N. McKinnon & Sons, *Bruce & Hay*, architects. A single storey brick shed with gable end to the street.

36 Bakery, 150 Copland Rd and Mafeking Place, built 1904 for J. Marshall, bread manufacturer, *T. Melvin & Sons*, engineers. A plain two storey, 7 by 2 bay brick building.

37 Brush Factory, 140 Copland Rd, built 1897 for William Morier, wholesale and export brushmaker, *J. Chalmers*, architect. An interesting three storey and attic Renaissance building with a mansard roof and a four storey corner tower.

38 Copper Works, 143 Woodville St, built from 1903 for Blair, Campbell & McLean, coppersmiths and engineers. The office block is an interesting three storey, 7 bay brick structure with dormer windows having curved pediments, and a Flemish

gable at the west end. *A. Hamilton*, of *John Hamilton & Son*, architect. The workshops at the side and rear are of corrugated-iron clad steel.

39 Park Saw Mills, 159 Woodville St, built 1902 for Lawson & Co., sawmillers, *Brand & Lithgow*, architects. Constructed on the site of the Clyde Match Works (1877), the present buildings are three storey and attic, 4 by 18 bay, with smaller ancillary structures. There is a square-section chimney.

40 Phoenix Copper Works, Woodville St, built 1897 for D. Brown & Co., *R. A. Wightman*, architect. The surviving three parts are steel-framed corrugated-iron clad sheds, large and one small. One of the large sheds has a brick front with a large arched doorway, now bricked in, and a circular window.

41 British Hair Works, 199 Woodville St, built *c* 1881 for the British Hair Co. Ltd, manufacturers of curled hair and importers and purifiers of bed feathers. A nondescript group of one and two storey buildings round a small yard.

42 Broomloan Foundry, 207 Woodville St, built *c* 1886 for Hugh Lawson & Sons, ironfounders. A high single storey brick building with gable end to the street, pierced by a circular ventilator.

43 Albion Works, 186 Woodville St, built 1880 for G. & A. Harvey, engineers and machine tool makers. A U shaped block of single storey red brick engineering shops, with roof lighting, and a two storey, 7 bay plain office block.

44 St Mungo Works, 183–7 Broomloan Rd, built 1901–13 for the St Mungo Manufacturing Co., india rubber, gutta percha and golf ball manufacturers, *J. S. Kent* and *Denny & Blain*, architects. Facing the street are a two storey, 6 bay and a two storey, 5 bay block, both red brick, with one and two storey buildings at the rear.

45 Broomloan Factory, 197 Broomloan Rd, built c 1877 for John Wylie & Co., power-loom cloth manufacturers. A two storey, 14 bay brick building, now harled, with single storey weaving sheds at the rear.

46 Govan Tube Works, 328 Broomloan Rd, founded c 1873 by the Govan Tube Co. The present single storey buildings, which have a 9 bay frontage to the street, were built in 1901, for David Richmond & Co., *E. A. Sutherland*, architect.

47 Tarpaulin Works, 312 Broomloan Rd, built 1883 for James McIlwraith, and rebuilt in 1910, *Robert Brown*, architect. A three storey, 3 by 17 bay red and white brick building, with a 6 bay extension along a lane. One and two storey buildings at the rear were built in 1883, *A. B. Dansken*, architect. The best feature of the main block is an impressive rusticated doorway. The works was badly damaged by fire in 1968.

48 Ladywell Wire Works, 306 Broomloan Rd, built 1907–8 for George Christie Ltd, wire drawers and wire cloth manufacturers, *R. A. Wightman*, architect. A two storey and attic, 32 bay red brick building with a slate roof. There are three round-headed gables facing the street, each above a round-headed doorway. The extensions at the rear were built in 1912, *Miller & Black*, architects.

49 Govan Ropeworks, 272 Helen St, built from 1890 for the Govan Rope & Sail Co. Ltd, *W. Burns Stewart,* architect. A group of one and two storey brick buildings, with a panelled frontage to the street. At the rear was a long ropewalk extending under Edmiston Drive. The works was closed in 1967 and finally demolished in 1969.

50 Moorepark Boiler Works, 161 Helen St, founded c 1884 by Lindsay Burnet & Co., engineers, boilermakers and steel plate flangers. Six large bays of engineering shops, part built 1905, with two storey offices. Incorporated in the complex is the former Govan Electricity Generating Station, built 1899–c 1911, *W. Arnot*, engineer.

51 Clyde Foundry, 184 Helen St, built c 1922 for Harland & Wolff, shipbuilders and marine engineers. A very large steel-framed building, clad with reinforced glass. Demolished 1967.

52 St Helens Engine Works, 150 Helen St, founded c 1893 by Hall-Brown, Buttery & Co., marine, electrical and general engineers. A three storey and attic, 4 by 18 bay office block, with a mansard roof and 5 bays of heavy engineering workshops, steel-framed, with brick gables. Extends through to Harmony Row. Part of the three storey block was built 1895–8, *Honeyman & Keppie*, architects.

53 Cranstonhill Engine Works, 89 Helen St, built c 1891 for Alexander Chaplin & Co., crane manufacturers. The street frontage consists of a two storey, 8 bay office block, with round-headed openings, a gatehouse, and a two storey, 12 bay building with round-headed openings on ground floor only. Both blocks are of red and white brick. At the rear are single storey engineering shops.

54 Glasgow Railway Engineering Works, 87 Helen St, built c 1891 for D. Drummond & Sons, railway engineers. The street frontage consists of a one storey, 7 bay building with round-headed windows, a two storey office block, added in 1907, and a single storey plain building, while further buildings extend to the railway at the rear.

55 Aerated Water Works, 100 Helen St, built c 1900 for McDiarmid & Co., aerated water manufacturers. A small single storey, 2 bay structure, of white-washed brick.

56 Caledonian Steel Foundry, 94 Helen St, built 1893 for the Caledonian Steel Castings Co., *W. Ingram*, architect. A high single storey brick engineering shop, with a single storey, 5 bay office block incorporated in the lower part of the street frontage.

57 Colonial Ironworks, 78 Helen St, built *c* 1882 for Aitken, McNeil & Co., engineers. A large block of buildings extending through to Harmony Row. The erecting shop is a high single storey steel-framed building, probably built in 1893, with 6 bays to Harmony Row. The office block is a plain two storey, 3 bay red and white brick structure in Helen St.

58 Govan Steel Works, 73 Helen St, built 1881–2 for the Govan Forge & Steel Co. (£5500). The street frontage consists of a single storey building with gable end to the street, and another at right angles to the first.

59 Stables & Depot, 6 Wick St, built 1900 for A. & J. McLellan, carting contractors, R. A. *Wightman*, architect. A two storey L plan red and white brick building with a 6 bay frontage to the street. At the rear a third storey was added in 1910 by the same architect.

60 Govan Weaving Factory, 50 Helen St, built *c* 1886 for the Govan Weaving Co., power-loom cloth manufacturers. A range of typical single storey weaving sheds, later altered to a foundry by raising part of the roof and inserting ventilators. Demolished 1967.

61 Govan Tube Works, 63 Helen St, founded 1871 and rebuilt and extended in 1880–8 for the Govan Tube Co. A large single storey, 3 bay workshop with gables to the street, and a two storey, 23 bay office block, both harled.

62 Govan Crane, Chain & Testing Works, 106–8 Harmony Row, built *c* 1908 for D. Watson & Co., crane & chain makers. A high single storey brick fronted corrugated-iron clad building with large sliding doors. Demolished 1968.

63 Engineering Works, 119–25 Golspie St, built 1908 for the Thermotank Ventilating Co. Three bay engineering workshops, with two storey, 3 by 4 bay offices, both red and white brick. The 2 bay steel framed sheds in Nethan St were added in 1913 (£1000), *W. Baillie*, architect.

64 Workshops, 154–6 Elder St, built 1912–13 for J. & D. Reid, coachbuilders and cartwrights (£2490). A single storey red brick building with gable end to the street.

65 Elder Park Works, 46 Uist St, built 1903 for C. Wishart Hall & Co., oil refiners, rosin distillers and manufacturers of printing inks. A group of plain one and two storey sheds, without windows to the street, and a neat cylindrical brick chimney stalk.

66 City of Glasgow Pickle & Sauce Works, 77 Craigton Rd, built 1892 for Rowat & Co., *A. Myles*, architect (£1250). A 2 bay north-light building at right angles to the street, with a small single storey, 6 bay office block.

67 Bakery, 62 Craigton Rd, built from 1911 for Galbraith's Stores Ltd. The oldest part, at the southern end, consists of a two storey, 5 bay block, and a three storey, 10 bay building with end pediments. Both are of red and white brick. To the north and west are large post-1914 additions.

Section L
Partick and Hyndland

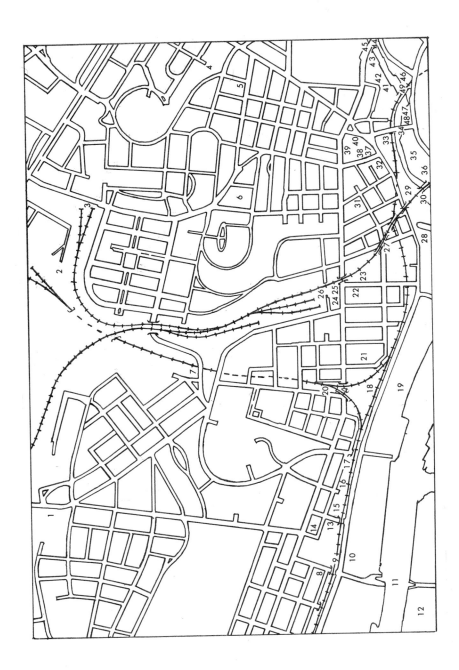

1 Great Western Steam Laundry, 459 Crow Rd, built 1883 for the Great Western Steam Laundry Co., *J. R. Mackenzie*, Aberdeen, architect. Stables were added in 1884 by the same architect. A one storey, 19 bay ashlar fronted rubble building, with pediments over the end 3 bays and a central louvred tower with a wind vane. The large chimney is a modern replacement.

2 Kelvinside Electric Power Station, Hughenden Lane, built 1892 for the Kelvinside Electricity Co., *Anderson & Munro*, engineers (£2500). A high single storey building with an arched doorway, later extended by the addition of a second, larger, bay. Originally equipped with Willans central valve engines.

3 Hyndland Station, 66 Hyndland Rd, built *c* 1886 for the Glasgow City & District Railway, probably *J. Carsewell*, engineer. The offices, at street level, are Italian Renaissance in style, two storeys high, 9 bays long, with a pediment over the central 3 bays. These were linked to a terminal island platform at a lower level, with a substantial glazed awning. The station was closed in 1960 and the awning demolished in 1966. The name has been transferred to a new through station.

4 Stables, 51 Ruthven Lane, built *c* 1870 for J. B. Price & Co., and converted to a garage in 1905. A two storey, 6 bay block, with a 2 bay extension to the west. Until recently there were stalls on the first floor.

5 Western Telephone Exchange, 24 Highburgh Rd, built 1907 for the Post Office, *L. Stokes*, London, and *C. Menzies*, architects. A three storey, 9 by 10 bay, red and cream sandstone block, with oriel windows.

6 Workshop, 14 North Gardner St, built 1905 for William Fulton, joiner. A two storey, 4 bay plain red brick building, with outside wooden stairway.

7 Crow Road Station, 270 Clarence Drive, built *c* 1896 for the Lanarkshire & Dumbartonshire Railway. An island plat-form station, with glazed awning and waiting rooms on the platform, which was in a cutting. There was a neat brick and red sandstone, single storey office block at street level, with a mosaic name panel. Closed on 5 October 1964 and demolished, all but the platform, in 1967.

8 The Royal Laundry, 2–4 Curle St, built 1899 for G. Laing, *Wyllie & Blake*, architects. A plain two storey, 6 by 8 bay red brick building.

9 Whiteinch (Riverside) Station, built *c* 1896 for the Lanarkshire & Dumbarton-shire Railway. An island platform station, with a steel and timber station building having a glazed awning supported on lattice girders. The station was on an embankment, and was approached by a subway. Closed on 5 October 1964, it was demolished in 1968.

10 Sawmill, 237 South St, built 1905 for the Scottish Wood Haskinizing Co., *J. Cairns*, architect. A group of single storey red brick buildings round two sides of a large yard, containing two derrick cranes.

11 Whiteinch Ferry, Ferryden St to Holmfauld Rd. A high-level vehicular ferry was introduced here in 1900, and withdrawn in 1963. The southern terminal has been obliterated, but the northern has been decked over.

12 Linthouse Shipbuilding Yard, Holm-fauld Rd, founded 1869 by Alexander Stephen & Sons, and subsequently greatly extended. An engine works was added in 1872 and substantial additions made in 1905, 1908 and 1914. The three storey, 3 by 7 bay office block was built in 1914 (£14,438). A large complex of mainly single storey red brick, corrugated-iron and corrugated-asbestos clad steel buildings.

13 Whiteinch Galvanising Works, Harmsworth St, built 1898 for the White-inch Galvanising Co. A pair of 12 bay, high, single storey workshops, with large louvred roof ventilators, and a two storey, 5 bay office block with round-headed openings on the ground floor. There is a circular-section brick chimney, and a large yard.

14 Victoria Park Laundry, 52–62 Byron St, built 1901 for the Victoria Park Hygienic Laundry Ltd. A two storey, 8 bay block, originally red and white brick, now harled, added 1901–2. Adjacent to the west is a two storey, 5 by 2 bay building, extensively rebuilt from a single storey 8 by 6 bay structure.

15 Bellfield Sawmills, 45 Byron St, built from 1899 for A. McDougall. A group of plain red brick one, two and three storey buildings, with a two storey, 3 bay office block. First part *G. Simpson*, architect, part added 1903 was designed by *P. C. Bonner*, architect.

16 The West End Sanitary Steam Laundry, 27 Byron St, built 1898–9 for A. B. Boyd & Co., and reconstructed as a two storey building in 1907, *J. G. Morton*, architect. A two storey, 13 bay red and white brick block with the windows in recesses. Demolished 1971.

17 Glenavon Engineering Works, Byron St, built 1899 for James Ritchie, laundry engineer. A one storey, 12 bay block, with the easternmost bay of two storeys, having 7 bays to Sawmill Rd, and a two storey, 7 bay building with a large arched entry, both red and white brick, with wooden roof trusses. Demolished 1971.

18 Partick West Station, built *c* 1896 for the Lanarkshire & Dumbartonshire Railway. Situated at the junction of lines to Dumbarton and Maryhill, this station had two platforms on each line, with a semi-circular-fronted office building in the angle. There was access to Meadow Rd and Dumbarton Rd by subway. Closed 5 October 1964 and demolished 1968.

19 Meadowside Granary, Castlebank St. The first part of this very large granary was built 1911–13 for the Clyde Navigation Trust, *William Alston*, engineer (£130,000). The capacity of the first part is 31,000 tons, and it is 13 storeys high, 6 by 13 bays. The adjacent quay was built under an Act of 1907.

20 Confectionery Works, 18–20 Thornwood Avenue, built 1907 for J. S. Birrell, *J. B. Wilson*, architect. A plain two storey, 11 bay red brick building.

21 Partick Electricity Generating Station, 15 Meadow Rd, built 1905 for the Partick Electric Co., *John Bryce*, burgh surveyor, engineer. Part of a larger complex incorporating a refuse destructor. There are two large single storey buildings and a smaller single storey, 10 bay red brick building facing the street, with crow-stepped gables.

22 Stable & Store, 22 Hayburn St, built *c* 1904 for Hugh Miller, grain merchant. Two ranges of two storey buildings, one 4 bays, the other 5 bays long, with a small yard. Situated behind a tenement.

23 Partick Tram Depot, 21 Hayburn St, built 1894 for Glasgow Corporation Tramways Department and extended in 1895. A single storey, 10 bay building on an irregular plan, with a two storey, 3 by 13 bay office block, added in 1901, *W. Clark*, engineer. The depot was closed in 1962, and has since been replaced by a new bus garage, though the offices still survive.

24 Greenbank Leather Works, 450 Dumbarton Rd, founded in 1895 by W. Thomlinson. At first a building was shared with John Thomlinson (see L25), but in 1908 a six storey, 3 by 4 bay, flat roofed block was constructed, *J. Sim*, architect.

25 Stanley Works, 436 Dumbarton Rd, founded in 1895 by John Thomlinson, printer. Additions were made in 1896, 1904 and 1908. The 1896 block was three storeys high, 4 by 4 bay, and has subsequently had a storey added, *H. & D. Barclay*, architects. The 1904 addition was a two storey, 4 bay sandstone block, and in 1908 a six storey, 5 by 4 bay block was built, both to designs by *J. Sim*, architect.

26 Partickhill Station, originally Partick Station, Dumbarton Rd and Norval St, built 1887 for the North British Railway. The passenger station was completely rebuilt in 1958, the only original parts being the stairways linking the high level platforms with Dumbarton Rd. To the west of the passenger station was a large goods and mineral station, with a fine single storey, 3 by 10 bay goods shed, now used as a store. To the north is another goods shed, built for the Lanarkshire & Dumbartonshire Railway *c* 1896.

27 Viaduct, Merkland St, built *c* 1873 for the North British Railway. A four span lattice girder skew bridge supported on five cast-iron Tuscan columns.

28 Meadowside Shipbuilding Yard, 85 Castlebank St, founded *c* 1845 by Tod & MacGregor. The oldest recently surviving part was the drydock, built 1857–8 (£120,000), which was 474 feet long, 61 feet wide and 18 feet deep. It was demolished in 1969 and filled in. The slipways may still be seen, though building ceased in 1935. The office block, built in 1885 for D. & W. Henderson (*Bruce & Hay*, architects) is a two storey, 14 bay red brick and sandstone structure in French Renaissance style, with a central tower.

29 Partick Foundry, 83 Castlebank St, built *c* 1864 for Kelt & Duncan, ironfounders, and subsequently rebuilt and extended. The oldest part was a high single storey structure, with stone walls extended in brick, and steel roof trusses. There were two cupolas and a drying stove. The pattern-making and finishing shops were in a two storey, 3 by 5 bay, red brick building, since reconstructed as offices. The other building was demolished in 1965.

30 Viaduct, Ferry Rd, built *c* 1873 for the North British Railway, carrying the line over Ferry Rd, Pointhouse Shipbuilding Yard, the River Kelvin and the Lanarkshire & Dumbartonshire Railway's branch

to the Pointhouse Yard. There are 8 plate girder spans and a longer lattice girder span over the river. Until *c* 1964 an iron footbridge was cantilevered from the south side of the viaduct.

31 Upholstery Works, 12 Purdon St, built *c* 1901 for John Reid, cabinetmaker, upholsterer and bedding manufacturer. A plain, but well-proportioned four storey and attic, 9 bay red brick building, behind a tenement which had office and showrooms on the ground floor.

32 Kelvin Works, 32 Keith St, founded *c* 1876 by P. & R. Fleming & Co., manufacturing ironmongers, and rebuilt 1897–8. The present single storey red and white brick building in Keith St has been cut down from a two storey and attic structure, while there are single storey brick and corrugated-iron sheds at the rear.

33 Kelvin Hall Station, originally Partick Central Station, Benalder St, built *c* 1896 for the Lanarkshire & Dumbartonshire Railway. An island platform station with booking office at street level and stairs down to the platform. Closed 5 October 1965, the platform buildings were demolished in 1968.

34 Old Partick Bridge, Benalder St, built 1896 for the Lanarkshire & Dumbartonshire Railway to replace the 16th century, four arched Partick Bridge. A single lattice girder span over the River Kelvin and four plate girder spans over the railway, both with cast-iron parapets.

35 Pointhouse Boiler Works, 58 Ferry Rd, built 1873–8 for A. & J. Inglis (£4000). Two bays of high, single storey engineering shops, with blocked-up arched doorways. The timber roof trusses and gantry cranes were supported on heavy cast-iron columns. There was a two storey office block adjoining the shops on the south side. Demolished in 1964.

36 Part of Pointhouse Shipbuilding Yard, 230 Ferry Rd, founded 1862 by A. & J. Inglis. Much the most interesting building on this site was a wrought- and cast-iron-framed timber building, the first part of which was built in 1864–5. There were also several one and two storey brick buildings, some dating back to 1862–6. A slip dock was added in 1865–7, 850 feet long by 57 feet wide with a carriage 150 feet long, powered by a 30 horsepower steam engine. It was designed by *A. G. Thomson*, civil engineer and architect. There were until *c* 1965 shear legs 96 feet high with a travel of 25 feet of riveted wrought-iron construction, with separate steam engines for hoisting and movement. The wooden building was burned to the ground on 25 August 1965, and the other buildings have since been demolished.

37 Wine Store & Stable, 39–45 Keith St, built 1910 for William McColl, spirit dealer, *J. Nisbet*, architect. A two storey, 4 by 6 bay red brick building.

38 Workshops, 37 Keith St, built *c* 1899 for James Sellar & Co., masons, builders, granolithic step makers and pavement layers, incorporating parts of the Partick Gas Works. There is a 5 bay street frontage, with round-headed arches, and behind it sheds and lockups have been built as lean-tos on to the walls of a large brick building, possibly the retort-house of the gas works.

39 Partick Engine Works, 181 Dumbarton Rd, built 1880–1 for William Smith & Sons, engineers, boilermakers, sugar mill manufacturers and weighing machine makers. Two large single bay engineering shops with circular windows high up in the sides. One was converted to a dance-hall, and is now a bingo hall. The other was a spirit store, the roof being removed and the front wall cut down in 1969. The two storey office and gatehouse were added in 1893–4 for W. & T. Avery, weighing machine makers, *J. U. Mac-Auslan*, architect.

40 Electricity Substation, 10 Benalder St, built 1910 for Glasgow Corporation Tramways Department, *John Ferguson*, engineer. A neat two storey red brick building with a Flemish gable, and 5 projecting ventilation shafts along the west side. There is a small yard enclosed by a high brick wall, and a short length of tram track may still be seen.

41 Scotstoun Flour Mills, Scotstounmill Rd, occupied from *c* 1847 by John White and his successors. The present buildings have been constructed since 1877, the oldest being a four storey block, 3 by 3 bay, *A. B. Dansken*, architect. The spectacular five storey, 2 by 10 bay building with tower, which faces the River Kelvin, was built in 1898, *W. F. McGibbon*, architect, and the five storey block and tower facing Thurso St was added in 1909, *J. W. & J. Laird*, architects. Most of the last-named building has recently been hidden by an addition.

42 Horse Tram Depot, Thurso St, built *c* 1883 for the Glasgow Tramway & Omnibus Co., *A. Petrie*, architect. Originally a three storey and attic, 5 by 8 bay, red and white brick building, with car sheds on ground floor, stables on first floor and grain stores above. The top two floors have been removed and the surviving part, with three round-headed doorways, incorporated in a large grain store.

43 Partick Sewage Pumping Station, 35 Dumbarton Rd, opened in 1904 by Glasgow Corporation. An ornate Renaissance red sandstone building with a large single storey engine house which contained three inverted vertical, triple-expansion pumping engines with plunger pumps. At the rear is a lower single storey boiler house with a water tank in the roof and a fine octagonal chimney stalk, and 4 bays of stables. The steam pumps were replaced by electric *c* 1960. The main sewer crosses the Kelvin on a roofed lattice-girder bridge, which also carried a steam main to the Kelvin Hall.

44 Partick Bridge, built 1877–8 for the Glasgow & Yoker Turnpike Trust to carry a double line of tramway over the

River Kelvin. A cast-iron skew-arched bridge with 9 ribs. The spandrels of the outermost girders are filled with Gothic tracery and display the arms of Glasgow (at the east end) and Partick (at the west end).

45 Bridge, Kelvingrove Park, built 1800 to carry the Glasgow to Yoker road over the Kelvin. A masonry bridge with three segmental arches over the river and a smaller one over the lade of Bunhouse (now Regent) Mills. The roadway is level.

46 Regent Flour Mills, Bunhouse Rd, built 1887–90 for John Ure, miller and flour merchant, *A. Watt*, Aberdeen, architect (£16,000). The six storey, 3 by 19 bay building on the street was a warehouse, the five storey, 3 by 11 by 8 bay, L plan building by the river being the mill proper. The buildings are ashlar, with fireproof interiors, the warehouse having a rusticated ground floor. The brick chimney has a staircase round it and a water tank on top. The mills were bought by the SCWS in 1903, and their architect, *James Davidson*, added a four storey, attic and basement, 6 by 2 bay red brick wheat silo and a single storey, 5 bay block beside the railway. These mills were constructed on the site of the medieval Bunhouse Mill,

which was destroyed by fire in 1886.

47 Bishop Mills, 206 Old Dumbarton Rd, rebuilt 1839 and *c* 1853 for William Wilson, miller and grain merchant. A four storey, 2 by 10 bay coursed rubble building with wheatsheaves at the apices of the gables. There is a brick wheelhouse, now empty, on the south end. A four storey, 4 bay brick building was added later, and is linked to the older building by covered gangways. Originally powered by a waterwheel, a turbine was used until the early 1950s, with steam, gas and petrol auxiliary power at various times. The mill is now electrified.

48 Artizan Machine Tool Works, 214 Old Dumbarton Rd, built *c* 1882 for Campbell, Smart & Co., engineers, machine and toolmakers. A neat three storey, 4 by 5 bay red and white brick building on a triangular plan, with the windows in recesses. A single storey addition has been built on to the south end of the building, and there is a square brick chimney at the south-east corner.

49 Bridge, built *c* 1896 for the Lanarkshire & Dumbartonshire Railway. A two span plate girder bridge over the Kelvin, with the central pier on the weir of Bishop Mills.

Section M
Area outside Section Maps and key to sections

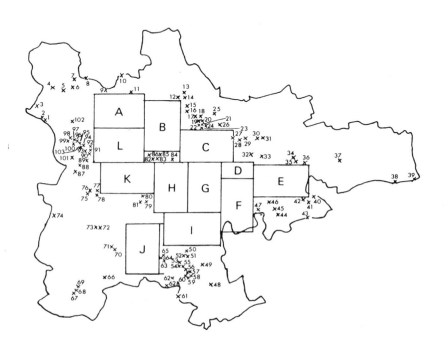

1 Bon Accord Works, Bulldale St, built
c 1908 for Drysdale & Co. Ltd, pump
manufacturers. A range of single storey,
north-light workshops, with a two storey,
25 bay office block. A more recent addition
is a tall single storey, 8 bay, steel-framed,
corrugated-iron clad block.

2 Metal Works, Bulldale St, built *c* 1901
for Bull's Metal & Marine Co., brass and
bronze founders. A large single-storey
engineering shop, with an arched doorway
flanked by pairs of round-headed windows.
There are roof ventilators at two levels.
Ancillary buildings include a two-storey
office block.

3 Halley Motor Works, 40–54 Hawick
St, built from *c* 1907 for Halley's Industrial
Motors Ltd, motor vehicle manufacturers.
A large block of single-storey, north-light
workshops, with a two storey, bay office
block facing Hawick St.

4 Garscadden Locks & Boghouse Bascule
Bridge, Garscadden Rd, built *c* 1790 for
the Forth & Clyde Canal. Four widely
spaced locks, with cut-down gates, and a
bascule bridge of the standard type. There
are two lock-keepers' cottages, one
original (1851) and the other modern, both
single storey. The bridge was replaced by
a modern structure *c* 1969.

5 Blairdardie Bascule Bridge, Bard
Avenue, built *c* 1790 for the Forth & Clyde
Canal. Of the standard F & C type, this
bridge, like most of the remaining ex-
amples, is now used by pedestrians only.
There is a small bridge-keeper's cottage.

6 Boulevard Swing Bridge, Great Western Rd, built 1928–30 for Glasgow
Corporation, *T. Somers* and *Sir William
Arrol & Co.*, engineers (£81,056). An
electrically operated rolling-lift bridge over
the Forth & Clyde Canal, with mass
concrete abutments faced with red sandstone. Demolished *c* 1968 and replaced by
an embankment.

7 Cloberhill Locks & Bascule Bridge,
Blairdardie Rd, built *c* 1790 for the Forth

& Clyde Canal. A pair of locks, with a
bascule bridge of standard pattern. There
were twin single storey canal cottages on
the south side of the canal. The locks and
bridge were demolished in 1965–6 and the
canal piped.

8 Knightswood Locks, Rotherwood
Avenue, built *c* 1790 for the Forth & Clyde
Canal. A flight of three locks, with balance
beams removed. There was a much altered
lock-keeper's cottage on the south bank.

9 Netherton Bridge, built *c* 1790 for the
Forth & Clyde Canal. A bridge of the
standard bascule type, with the ironwork
on the northern side altered, probably after
an accident.

10 Killermont Bridge, Maryhill Rd, built
1925–9 for Glasgow Corporation, *T.
Somers* and *Considére Constructions Ltd*,
engineers (£39,635). A two span reinforced-
concrete arch bridge, over the River
Kelvin, replacing Garscube Bridge, a
three span masonry structure which had
been extended in cast-iron to carry water
mains.

11 Bridge, Dalsholm Rd, probably built
c 1790. A low, masonry bridge over the
River Kelvin with four segmental arches.

12 Lambhill Iron Works, Strachur St,
built from 1881 for R. Laidlaw & Son,
gas and water engineers. A group of single
storey engineering shops, the most
interesting of which was a 13 bay red and
white brick block with round-headed
windows. The surviving shops are corrugated-iron clad, steel-framed. The works
had a wharf on the Forth & Clyde Canal.

13 Canal Stables, 21–5 Canal Bank,
Lambhill, built in the early 19th century
for the Forth & Clyde Canal. A neat, two
storey, masonry building, with 3 bays on
each side of a central pedimented bay.
Half was used as a dwelling house, the
remainder having stalls on the ground
floor and a hayloft on the first floor. SDD
category C.

14 Lambhill Bridge, Balmore Rd, built 1930 to replace a standard wooden bascule bridge, *T. Somers*, engineer. A single span rolling-lift bridge over the Forth & Clyde Canal, electrically operated, with concrete abutments.

15 Possil Station, 441 Balmore Rd, built *c* 1897 for the Lanarkshire & Dumbartonshire Railway. A three platform station in a shallow cutting, with an island platform and a single sided platform. The main offices were in a two storey and attic building spanning the through tracks, entered at first floor level from the street. This still survives, as does a 6 bay brick goods shed, and a small, 5 bay goods office. An elegant wooden platform shelter was demolished in 1967. This station was closed to passengers in 1908, reopened in 1934 and closed again in 1964.

16 Workshops, 343 Balmore Rd, built 1906–7 for the Glasgow Steel Roofing Co. (£9530) and extended in 1912–13 (£3390). A group of 3 bays of single storey corrugated-iron clad steel-framed buildings, with a single storey red brick office block.

17 Saracen Foundry, 73 Hawthorn St, built *c* 1869 for Walter Macfarlane & Co., architectural ironfounders, *J. Boucher*, architect. Between 1897 and 1902 £25,250 was spent on additions, *D. M. Tyre*, engineer and architect. A large rectangular block of single storey buildings behind a panelled ashlar outer wall. In the centre of the frontage was a large Gothic doorway flanked by smaller arched openings. Liberal use was made of ornamental ironwork. Demolished 1967.

18 Clydesdale Iron Works, 127 Hawthorn St, built from *c* 1876 for A. & J. Main & Co., iron fence and gate makers and wire merchants. The main office block was two storeys and attic high, 8 by 12 bay, while the main workshop bay, a steel-framed building on the corner of Ashfield St, was added in 1901 (£6000). The workshops housed a range of sheet-metal and girder

working tools by such makers as Craig & Donald and Loudoun Bros, of Johnstone. Closed in 1968 and demolished in 1969.

19 Possil Pottery, 85 Denmark St, built *c* 1881 for the Saracen Pottery Co. The only complete surviving building is a handsome three storey, 4 by 13 bay red and white brick structure, though there are fragmentary remains of another building. Additions were made in 1902 for Macdougall & Sons, china merchants, *Brand & Lithgow*, architects.

20 Possilpark Tram Depot, 240 Hawthorn St, built 1900 for Glasgow Corporation Tramways Department, *W. Clark*, engineer (£55,000). A single storey, 8 bay red brick building, with bays at right angles to Hawthorn St. There are two round-headed windows to each bay. The roof trusses are wooden, and are supported on cast-iron columns.

21 Oil Mills & Chemical Works, 123 Mansion St, built *c* 1889 for Mrs A. Kirkpatrick, oleine, alizarine oil and soap manufacturer. Two single storey, 7 bay buildings, with round-headed doorways.

22 Keppoch Iron Works, 130 Denmark St, built *c* 1885 for David King & Sons Ltd, makers of plain and ornamental cast-iron goods, and extended in 1898, *A. Myles*, architect (£4500). A group of one, two and three storey harled brick buildings on a rectangular site. There are one storey, 6 bay, two storey, 12 bay, three storey, 2 bay, two storey, 20 bay, and one storey blocks facing the street. The central three storey portion is surmounted by a cast-iron crown.

23 Possil Iron Works, 64 Denmark St, built *c* 1884 for Brownlie & Murray, iron roof and bridge builders and structural engineers, and extended in 1889 and 1896, *J. Lindsay*, architect, and in 1906 (£2000) and 1909 (£1190). A group of single storey engineering shops, with red and white brick end walls. There is a two storey, 5 bay red and white brick office block, and a corrugated-iron clad water tower with a cast-iron tank.

24 Possil Park Paint Works, 160 Bardowie St, built 1902 for A. H. Hamilton, oil and paint manufacturers, *Thomson & Sandilands*, architects (£1050). A one storey and attic, 3 bay red brick block, with gable end to the street. Badly damaged by fire in 1967.

25 Eastfield Engine Shed, completed in 1904 for the North British Railway. The single storey, 8 bay, red and white brick office, with its neat clock tower, dates from 1902. A disastrous fire occurred here in 1919, and the recently-existing structure, a single storey range of red brick sheds, probably dated largely from the ensuing rebuilding. The manual coaling stage was demolished in the early 1960s, and the old sheds were replaced by more modern structures (*c* 1970).

26 Workers' Houses, Elmvale Row, Ashvale Row, Colgrain Terrace, Ratho Terrace, Fernbank Place and Eastfield Terrace, built *c* 1863 for the Edinburgh & Glasgow Railway, *A. Heiton*, Perth, architect. Six rows of two storey houses, in Scottish Baronial style, on a sloping site. The bottom two rows were in two separate parts, and the upper rows were on a curve. This remarkable group of buildings was demolished in 1967.

27 City of Glasgow Brewery, 217 Petershill Rd, built 1866 for Peter Wordie, brewer, Edinburgh, and rebuilt in 1887 for Oswald, Paterson & Co., who renamed it Petershill Brewery. The principal surviving structure is a three storey, 7 bay rubble building, with two hoists, facing the railway, which probably dates from 1871 (£3250).

28 Eclipse Works, 459 Petershill Rd, built from *c* 1880 for Frederick Braby & Co., sheet metal workers and galvanisers. Between 1903 and 1914 £43,804 was spent on single storey workshops, steel-framed, corrugated-iron clad. Demolished 1968.

29 Germiston Iron Works, Petershill Rd, built from *c* 1883 for Arrol Bros. Additions in 1898 cost £9000, and reconstruction after a fire in 1901, £17,000. From 1908–14, £10,845 was spent on single storey steel-framed, corrugated-iron clad workshops for A. & J. Main & Co. Demolished 1968.

30 St Rollox Engine Shed, Broomfield Rd, built 1916 for the Caledonian Railway. A large single storey brick engine shed, with single storey offices, and a manual coaling stage. Closed 1967 and demolished 1969.

31 Anchor Chemical Works, 1005 Royston Rd, built 1901 for Alexander Hope Jun. & Co., *W. Tennant*, architect (£55,750) and extended in 1906–10, *W. Tennant* and *A. W. Macdonald*, architects. A group of single storey red brick buildings, dominated by a large circular-section, iron-bound chimney. There was a neat two storey office block. Closed 1968 and demolished 1969.

32 Provan Gas Works, Provan Rd, built 1900–4 for Glasgow Corporation Gas Department, *William Foulis*, engineer, and greatly extended after 1919. Dominated by two gas-holders each 280 feet in diameter, the main parts of the works are modern, though also a large two storey red brick stores, offices and workshops survive from earlier phases of development. There is a particularly neat gatehouse with a red sandstone pedimented front.

Monkland Canal (M33–M39) drained 1972.

33 Blackhill Locks and Incline, Craigendmuir St, built 1793 and rebuilt 1841. This flight of four locks was demolished in 1954 and the canal piped. From 1850 to 1887 the locks were supplemented by an inclined plane, on which ran a pair of caissons. The course of the incline can still be seen.

34 Canal Basin, Barlinnie (NS638663), probably built in 1773. The temporary terminus of the canal 1773–*c* 1781, recently visible as a widening in the canal, with level areas on both sides.

35 Jessie's Bridge, Gartcraig Rd, built 1772. A fixed wooden bridge with rubble abutments and iron rubbing strakes. The bridge had been widened at some time on the west side.

36 Milncroft Bridge, Croftcoighn Rd, built 1772. A fixed wooden bridge, similar to M35, but unaltered. About ten feet to the east was a modern reinforced concrete footbridge.

37 Queenslie Bridge, Garthamlock Rd, built 1772. A fixed wooden bridge, similar to M35, including widening. The wooden span was replaced c 1968 by concrete beams on the original abutments.

38 Netherhouse Bridge (NS691648), built c 1772. A fixed wooden bridge of the standard type, in original condition. The iron rubbing strakes are particularly well preserved.

39 Cuilhill Canal Bridge and Basin, built c 1843. The bridge, of the standard Monkland fixed type, was replaced in 1866. The basin has a central 'island' with masonry quay walls having curved recesses for turning barges. Cuilhill basin was linked with pits to the south by the Drumpeller Railway.

40 Glasgow Rope Works, 40 Annick St, built c 1877 for Archibald Thomson & Co. A long single storey covered ropewalk, with a small single storey, 2 by 4 bay office at the west end.

41 Wellshot Laundry, 35 Glenalmond St, built c 1904. A much altered range of single storey red brick buildings, originally with 1 wide and 3 narrow bays with gable ends to the street.

42 Stores, Creamery & Offices, 71 and 90 Pettigrew St, built c 1910 and 1912 for Shettleston Co-operative Society. The warehouse block (90), which is dated 1912, is a three storey, 5 by 7 bay red brick building with a Renaissance sandstone frontage. The offices and creamery are two storey red brick blocks, 7 and 3 bays respectively, the latter having a single storey extension at the rear.

43 Tollcross Tube Works, 1300 Tollcross Rd, built from 1913 for the Clydeside Tube Co. Ltd. The office block is a neat two storey and attic, 6 bay terra-cotta brick structure with short wings set back from the main frontage. The roof is steeply pitched, with dormer windows, *J. Miller*, architect. At the rear are extensive single storey workshops.

44 Govancroft Pottery, 1855 London Rd, founded 1914 by the Govancroft Pottery Co. Ltd, stoneware pottery manufacturers. The first three kilns were designed by *N. MacWhannell* (£1134). The present buildings are 4 bays of single storey workshops without windows to the street.

45 Steel Foundry, 67 Cuthelton St, built c 1906 for Rennie's Steel Casting Co. Two large single storey, steel-framed, corrugated-iron clad workshops, with a square-section brick chimney and brick gable ends. On Cuthelton St there was a neat two storey, 3 bay Renaissance office. Demolished c 1967.

46 Parkhead Tram Depot, 252 Tollcross Rd, built 1921 for Glasgow Corporation Tramways Department. An irregular group of single storey red brick buildings.

47 Wireworks, 636 Springfield Rd, built from c 1888 for W. Riddell & Co. and their successors. Between 1888 and 1914, £5560 was spent on additions, some designed by *McKissack & Son*, architects. A large complex of red brick buildings, much altered.

48 Horse Wheel House, Croftpark Avenue, probably built c 1806. A hexagonal structure, with a slate roof mounted on rectangular masonry pillars, adjacent to the stable block of Aitkenhead House. Demolished 1970.

49 King's Park Station, King's Park Avenue, built 1928 for the London, Midland & Scottish Railway. Situated partly on an embankment and partly in cutting, the station has a single island platform with access by subway at the west end and by stairway from a road overbridge at the east end. The platform building is of wood and steel construction, with a central booking office, and glazed end screens.

50 Mount Florida Station, built *c* 1886 for the Cathcart District Railway. An island platform station in a deep cutting, with access at both ends by footbridge. The wooden platform building is similar to that at Queen's Park (127).

51 Laundry, 340 Battlefield Rd, built 1906 for the Misses J. & J. Walker, R. *Duncan*, architect (£200). Single storey, 3 by 4 bay red brick building, with gable end to the street.

52 Langside Tram Depot, 260 Battlefield Rd, built 1900 for Glasgow Corporation Tramways Department, *W. Clark*, engineer (£20,000). A single storey, 14 bay red brick building, with two round-headed windows per bay. The two northernmost bays are cut off at an angle.

53 Tailoring Workshops, 42 Spean St, built 1913–22 for Wallace, Scott & Co., *J. J. Burnet*, architect (£19,156). A five storey, 8 by 12 bay flat-roofed brick building, originally decorated with poly-chrome bricks. A notable 'Modern Movement' building, SDD category B. The bridge linking Spean St to the factory was built in 1913, *Kyle, Dennison & Laing*, engineers (£4000).

54 Holm Foundry, 147 Newlands Rd, built from 1886 for G. & J. Weir, engineers. The western part of the main office block was built in 1912 and 10 bays in the same style added in the late 1940s. The 1912 block was an early example of reinforced-concrete building, four storeys, 6 by 8 bay. In 1913–14 a four storey, 8 bay reinforced-concrete building was added, in Inverlair Avenue. The main workshops are single storey, corrugated-iron clad steel and date in part from 1913 (£23,030).

The bridge over the White Cart at Spean St was also built in 1913.

55 Cart Bridge, Clarkston Rd, built 1901–2 when the tramway was extended to Netherlee. This flat segmental-arched masonry bridge over the River Cart, with granite balustrades, replaced a hump-backed bridge of *c* 1800.

56 Cathcart Station, built *c* 1894 for the Cathcart District Railway. An island platform on an embankment, with access by subways, one of which crosses the White Cart on a lattice girder bridge. The present wooden station building was cut down from a larger structure after a fire in 1957. Immediately to the south of the station the Lanarkshire & Ayrshire Railway joins the Cathcart District Railway, the L&A being carried over the Cart on a segmental masonry arch.

57 Bridge, Delvin Rd, built in the late 19th century. A two span, plate girder bridge over the River Cart, with cast-iron parapets.

58 Smithy, 137 Old Castle Rd, built in the 18th century, or earlier. A two storey, 1 by 2 bay corner block flanked by low single storey wings. There is an outside stair to the upper floor.

59 Cathcart Snuff & Cardboard Mill, Snuffmill Rd, built in the 18th century as Cathcart Meal Mill, and altered to a cardboard mill in 1812 for Solomon Lindsay of Penicuik: snuff milling was added in 1814. A block of low single storey buildings, now partly ruined.

60 Netherlee Road Bridge, built in the 18th century. A two span rubble bridge over the White Cart with the road on an incline. The southern arch is narrow and semicircular, the northern wide and segmental. A datestone '1624' was probably reinserted at a reconstruction of the bridge. SDD category B.

61 Bridge, Linn Park, built *c* 1835. A cast-iron arched structure, over the River

Cart, with four identical ribs, each apparently a one-piece casting, and simple wrought-iron railings. The oldest complete iron bridge in the city.

62 Cathcart Laundry, Gavinton St and Muirend Avenue, built *c* 1905 for the Cathcart Laundry Co. A single storey, 6 by 9 bay red brick building with gable ends to Gavinton St.

62a Muirend Station, Bogton Avenue and Muirend Rd, built *c* 1903 for the Lanarkshire & Ayrshire Railway. An island platform with a wooden building on a brick base. The signal box, of standard Caledonian Railway type, still survives, while the wooden goods shed was destroyed by fire in 1969. The platform is approached at the north end from a footbridge, and at the south by a long ramp from a road overbridge.

63 Langside Station, Tannahill Rd, built *c* 1894 for the Cathcart District Railway. An island platform with a wooden building. Access from both ends is by subway. The building was badly damaged by fire in *c* 1967 and cut down to 2 bays.

64 Millbrae Bridge, Langside Avenue, built 1898–9. A single segmental masonry arch over the River Cart, with granite balustrades.

65 Mill Cottage, Millbrae Rd, probably 18th century. A small single storey, 4 bay rubble cottage, long thought to be the only trace remaining of Langside Mill, which was destroyed by fire in 1848. In 1970, however, during road widening a 4 foot 6 inch diameter millstone 1 foot thick was discovered at the corner of Camphill Avenue and Millbrae Rd, apparently from the mill.

66 Kennishead Station, Kennishead Avenue, built *c* 1848 for the Glasgow, Barrhead & Neilston Direct Railway. A two platform station with a stone building containing a house on the up platform, and a wooden shelter on the down side.

The platforms are linked by a lattice girder footbridge.

67 Arden Lime Works, Corselet Rd, founded *c* 1874 by Allan Kirkwood. Two pairs of masonry kilns with a free-standing iron-bound brick kiln in between. To the east were the remains of open kilns, and to the north the roofless ruins of a two storey, rubble, processing building with an engine and boiler house. Limestone was supplied from Darnley quarries, about half a mile away, by rail until 1954. Demolished 1965.

68 Darnley Mill Farm, Corselet Rd, storey rubble buildings, with crow-stepped gables and a small turret. SDD category B.

69 Tramway Bridge, built *c* 1910 for the Paisley District Tramways Co. A small reinforced concrete bridge with a segmental arch, which carried double sleepered tramway tracks. The only 'tram only' bridge in Glasgow.

70 Sawmill, Pollok House, probably built in the mid-19th century. A single storey brick building, with 19th century saws and planes. The mill is driven by a Holyoake Turbine, built 1888, installed in place of a low-breast waterwheel. Adjacent is the disused single storey, 4 by 2 bay power station, with a Waverley turbine (Ritchie's Patent) built by Carrick & Ritchie of Edinburgh still in position. There was formerly an auxiliary oil engine. A mass dam provides sufficient head to operate the turbines.

71 Nether Pollok House Bridge, built *c* 1750, probably *John Adam*, architect. A single segmental arch spanning the White Cart Water, with well-proportioned balustrades. SDD category A.

72 Corkerhill Engine Shed, built 1896 for the Glasgow & South Western Railway. A 21 bay range of red brick sheds, subsequently re-roofed. A reinforced-concrete coaling tower was added by the LMS.

73 Corkerhill Village, built from 1896 by the Glasgow & South Western Railway. A group of rows of two storey red brick galleried tenements (demolished 1971), some of which were Scottish Baronial style, with crow-stepped gables. A combined institute and store is also red brick, two storeys high.

74 Crookston Station, Crookston Rd, opened 1 July 1885 by the Glasgow & South Western Railway. A two platform through station with single storey snecked rubble platform buildings having round-headed openings. The entrances to the offices are protected by an attractive glazed screen. The tracks are spanned by a lattice girder footbridge built by Arrol Bros, Germiston Ironworks.

75 Cardonald Station, Moss Rd, opened 1 October 1879 by the Glasgow & Paisley Joint Railway. A two platform through station, with access from a road over-bridge. The booking office and platform shelters are modern, but the covered wood and steel footbridge is original. To the north was an extensive goods yard, now disused.

76 Clydesdale Engineering Works, 81–7 Meiklewood Rd, built *c* 1900 for David Cockburn, valve maker, and added to in 1905, R. A. *Wightman*, architect, and 1912, *Whyte & Galloway*, architects. A large block of single storey workshops, with a main frontage 24 bays long, having a central crow-stepped gable and end two storey portions. A high single storey boiler shop in Moss Rd was added in 1902, R. A. *Wightman*, architect.

77 Drumoyne Sawmill, 426 Drumoyne Rd, built 1903 for W. Milne & Co., sawmillers and moulding manufacturers, *G. S. Hill*, architect. A group of single storey brick and timber buildings.

78 Clyde Engine Works, 428, 430 Drumoyne Rd, built *c* 1899 for J. Bennie & Son, machine tool makers. A block of single storey, steel framed, corrugated-iron clad workshops, with a two storey,

7 bay, red and white brick office building.

79 Clutha Works, 35 MacLellan St, built from 1872 for P. & W. MacLellan, engineers. An extensive complex of brick and corrugated-iron clad steel workshops, with a two storey and attic, 11 bay, terracotta brick and sandstone office block in clumsy Renaissance style.

80 Warehouse, 83 Brand St, built 1908 for Connal & Co., public storekeepers. A single storey steel-framed, corrugated-iron clad building.

81 Jam & Confectionery Works, 241 MacLellan St, built *c* 1911 for Thomas Neill. A range of one and two storey red brick buildings, with gable ends to the street.

82 Weir, Clayslaps Mills, Kelvingrove Park. A simple, low, masonry weir, with the site of a low breast wheel. All traces of the mill buildings have disappeared.

83 Bridge, Kelvin Way, built 1914. A single segmental masonry arch with solid parapets. There are impressive sculptured groups at the ends.

84 St George's Horse Bazaar, 110–26 St Georges Rd, built 1873 for Andrew Menzies. A neat three storey, 15 by 15 bay building with a central courtyard, roofed in 1911, *Burnet & Boston*, architects, £415. Access to the upper floors was by wooden ramps and galleries. The walls facing St Georges Rd and Buccleuch St were of sandstone and the others red brick. Demolished 1968.

85 Prince of Wales Bridge, Kelvingrove Park, built 1894–5. A single elliptical masonry arch with balustrades.

86 Weir and Sluices, Bunhouse Mills, Kelvingrove Park. A low masonry weir across the Kelvin, with six sluices controlling the flow of water to the lade and three controlling the overflow. Now derelict, though water still flows through the lade to Regent Mills (L46).

87 Shieldhall Veneer, Saw & Moulding Mills, 235 Bogmoor Rd, built from *c* 1899 for John Woyka & Co. A large group of single storey buildings, mostly wooden, with Belfast roofs.

88 Shieldhall Factory, Renfrew Rd and Bogmoor Rd, built from 1887 for the scws. A large complex of one, two, three, four and six storey buildings, mainly red and white brick. The front block, a six storey, 6 by 12 bay sandstone fronted brick building in French Renaissance style, is one half of a symmetrical composition never completed owing to the First World War. Immediately inside the main gate is the oldest building in the complex, a three storey, 7 by 7 bay building with a Flemish gable, dated 1888. The rest of the buildings are distinguished mainly by their number, making this one of the largest industrial sites in the city.

89 Shieldhall Sewage Works, Renfrew Rd, built 1898–1910 for Glasgow Corporation. A large area of settling tanks, with four wide bays of screening and pumping workshops. There is a wharf on the river for loading sludge for dumping down river. The works uses the chemical precipitation method of purification.

90 Clydeholm Shipyard, 359 South St, founded on this site in 1855 by Barclay, Curle & Co. The only pre-1914 part is the three storey, 17 bay office block, built 1883, the rest of the earlier buildings were demolished during modernisation in the 1950s.

91 Scotstoun (East) Station, built *c* 1896 for the Lanarkshire & Dumbartonshire Railway. An island platform station with access at the east end by subway. The platform building was steel framed, with awnings supported on lattice girders, and was clad in wood. Demolished 1968.

92 Cyclops Foundry, 42 Fore St, built 1898 for McEwan, Law & Lindsay, ironfounders, *R. Brown*, architect. A high single storey red and white brick building with a large arched doorway, round-headed windows, a roof ventilator and a circular-section chimney. A single storey dressing shed was added in 1914, *David Fulton*, engineer (£2600). There is a two storey, 5 bay red and white brick office block.

93 North British Diesel Engine Works, 739 South St, built 1913–14 for Barclay, Curle & Co., *J. Galt*, architect (£44,438). The main shop is a steel-framed structure, clad in brick and glass, with a 'flattened mansard' roof, having a strong resemblance to Peter Behrens's AEG factory. The office block is a three storey, 10 bay structure, faced with terra-cotta brick, with a flat roof.

94 Scotstoun Ironworks, 1037–57 South St, built from *c* 1900 for Mechan & Sons, engineers and contractors. A large, scattered, group of one, two and three storey brick buildings, with 8 bays of single storey steel-framed, corrugated-iron clad workshops. The buildings facing South St are a two storey, 11 bay; two storey, 18 bay; modern four storey block; one storey, 9 bay; two storey, 11 bay; one storey (mutilated); and modern two storey blocks.

95 Roxburgh Works, 24 Harland St, built *c* 1898 for Macfarlane Bros, enamellers. A two storey, 3 by 11 bay terra-cotta brick building, with a large arched opening in the centre having a glazed fanlight. At the rear is a range of low single storey workshops.

96 Clydeside Ironworks, 1120 South St, built *c* 1898 for the Clyde Structural Iron Co., iron roof and bridge builders. A range of high single storey steel-framed workshops, with brick and corrugated-iron cladding. There is a 3 by 20 bay flat-roofed office block.

97 Albion Motor Works, 1272 South St, built from 1903 for the Albion Motor Co. Ltd. A large block of buildings, of which the oldest is a 13 bay range of single storey north-light workshops. The office block is a two storey, 13 bay brick and sandstone structure in French Renaissance style, *A. N. Paterson*, architect (1912).

98 Balmoral Iron Yard, 51 Balmoral St, built 1914 for John Jackson & Co., metal merchants, *J. Lindsay*, architect (£1000). The office block is a two storey, 7 bay red brick structure with a Renaissance doorway. The rest of the yard has been built over.

99 Elderslie Drydocks, 1581 South St. The first of the three docks in this group was opened in 1904 by Shearer & Co., ship repairers, the second in 1933 by Barclay, Curle & Co., and the third by the same firm in 1965. Associated with the drydocks is a number of corrugated-iron clad workshops.

100 Shipbuilding Yard, 1465 South St, built from 1906 for Alfred Yarrow & Co. The yard has been extensively rebuilt and modernised, only fragments of the original surviving.

101 King George V Dock, Renfrew Rd, opened 1931 for the Clyde Navigation Trust. A large single basin, with unrestricted access from the river. The west side was undeveloped until the Second World War.

102 Scotstounhill Station, Kingsway, built 1887 for the Glasgow, Yoker & Clydebank Railway. A two platform through station with single storey brick buildings having awnings supported on short Tuscan columns with marked entasis. The up platform building was demolished in 1969.

103 Scotstoun Shipbuilding Yard, 903 South St, founded 1861 by Charles Connell. A much-rebuilt group of one and two storey brick and steel-framed, iron-clad buildings, with a two storey office block.

Bibliography

Manuscript sources. In the preparation of this book, relatively little use has been made of manuscript records, apart from plans. Those that have been used are the Boulton & Watt papers in Birmingham Reference Library, the Sun Insurance records in the Guildhall Library, London, the William Baird & Co. papers in the University of Strathclyde, the Clyde Navigation Trust records in the Glasgow City Archives, and Report Books (1859–85), Dean of Guild Inspector's Office, City Chambers, Glasgow. Of the plan collections, extensive use has been made of the Dean of Guild Plans for Glasgow and surrounding burghs, now in the Glasgow City Archives, and plans at the British Waterways Board headquarters in Applecross Street, Glasgow, in Register House, Edinburgh, at Carron Co.'s Falkirk Works, and in Glasgow City Archives have also been consulted. A manuscript tour of Scotland was kindly lent by J. Blakiston-Houston of Beltrim Castle, Gortin, Co Tyrone and is being edited for publication.

Photographs. Apart from my own photographs, the collections in the Glasgow City Archives, in the Mitchell Library, in the Scottish National Monuments Record, 52 Melville Street, Edinburgh, and those of Messrs Aerofilms Ltd, William Beardmore & Co. Ltd, Sir William Arrol & Co. Ltd, and Fullerton, Hodgart and Barclay Ltd, Paisley, have proved most useful.

Parliamentary Papers. Of the several parliamentary papers consulted the only one referred to is *Report of Select Committee on the State of the Children Employed in the Manufactories of the United Kingdom* (1816), vol 3, though the *Reports from the Committee on the Bill to regulate the Labour of Children in the Mills and Factories of the United Kingdom 1832–3* give a comprehensive account of working conditions (though not of premises) in Glasgow factories.

Scottish Development Department Provisional List of Buildings of Architectural and Historic Interest 1965 has been very helpful, and textual references are to this edition. See also A. McLaren Young and A. M. Doak, *Glasgow at a Glance* (Glasgow 1965), an architectural handbook.

Periodicals. The most important periodical consulted was the Post Office Directory, from 1787 to date, of which a full series exists in the Mitchell Library, Glasgow. The *Glasgow Herald, Evening Times, The Builder, The Building News, The Engineer, Engineering, The Railway Magazine, Scottish Wine, Spirit and Beer Trades Review, Transactions of the Institution of Engineers and Shipbuilders in Scotland*, and *Victualling Trades Review, Hotel and Restaurateurs' Journal* were used extensively. Individual articles in other periodicals are referred to in the notes.

Books. The general economic trends which have affected Glasgow since 1707 are discussed in R. H. Campbell, *Scotland since 1707* (Oxford 1965) and Henry Hamilton, *The Industrial Revolution in Scotland* (Oxford 1932, reprinted 1966); and *An Economic History of Scotland in the Eighteenth Century* (Oxford 1963). On the physical remains of Glasgow industry, see J. Butt, *The Industrial Archaeology of Scotland* (Newton Abbot 1968) and J. Butt, I. L. Donnachie and J. R. Hume, *Industrial History in Pictures: Scotland* (Newton Abbot 1968). Of the numerous general histories of Glasgow the most useful have been James Cleland, *Rise and Progress of the City of Glasgow* (Glasgow 1820), J. Gibson, *The History of Glasgow* (Glasgow 1777), J. F. S. Gordon (ed), *Glasghu Facies* (Glasgow 1866), J. McUre, *A View of the City of Glasgow* (Glasgow 1736) and more recently C. A. Oakley,

The Second City (London 2nd edn 1967). Other Glasgow books of value in this study include J. Cowan, *Glasgow's Treasure Chest* (Glasgow 1951), J. D. Marwick, *Glasgow: The Water Supply of the City* (Glasgow 1901), which is of more general interest than its title suggests, Senex (Robert Reid), *Old Glasgow* (London 1864) and *Glasgow Past and Present* (Glasgow 2nd edn 1884), W. Simpson, *Glasgow in the 'Forties'* (Glasgow 1899), *Stothers's Glasgow, Lanarkshire & Renfrewshire Christmas & New Year Annual 1911–12* (Hamilton 1911), A. Thomson, *Maryhill 1750–1894* (Glasgow 1898), and the most important *Industries of Glasgow* (London 1888), and *Stratten's Glasgow and its Environs* (London 1891). Sir J. Sinclair (ed), *The Statistical Account of Scotland* (Edinburgh 1795), vol 5, *New Statistical Account of Scotland* (Edinburgh 1845), vol 6, and J. Cunnison and J. B. S. Gilfillan (eds), *Third Statistical Account of Scotland: The City of Glasgow* (Glasgow 1958), are also important sources as are the three British Association Handbooks, *Some of the Leading Industries of Glasgow and the Clyde Valley* (Glasgow 1876), A. McLean (ed), *Local Industries of Glasgow and the West of Scotland* (Glasgow 1901), and R. Miller and J. Tivy (eds), *The Glasgow Region* (Glasgow 1958). The last-named contains some excellent aerial photographs of the city before redevelopment. J. MacLehose, *Memoirs and Portraits of 100 Glasgow Men* (Glasgow 1886), W. S. Murphy, *Captains of Industry* (Glasgow 1901), G. Stewart. *Curiosities of Citizenship in Old Glasgow* (Glasgow 1881) and *Glasgow Contemporaries at the Dawn of the 20th Century* (Glasgow 1904), though largely biographical, also contain information about industry.

Chapter 1   Food and Drink

There are no general books on food-processing in Glasgow, the best account being an article by J. B. S. Gilfillan in the *Third Statistical Account*, 264–73. Grocery chains based on Glasgow are discussed in P. Matthias, *Retailing Revolution* (London 1967), grain milling on the Kelvin in *The Incorporation of Bakers of Glasgow* (Glasgow 1931) and two bakery concerns in *Fifty Years of the Baking Trade* (Glasgow 1923) and W. Reid, *History of the United Cooperative Baking Society Ltd* (Glasgow 1920). City breweries and distilleries feature in A. Barnard, *Noted Breweries of Great Britain and Ireland* (London 1889) vol 2 and *The Whisky Distilleries of the United Kingdom* (London 1887, reprinted Newton Abbot 1969).

Chapter 2   Textiles

Published accounts of the textile industry in Glasgow are disappointing in that individual firms are seldom mentioned. The *New* and *Third Statistical Accounts* are probably the best. Case studies are also rare, but F. H. Young, *A Century of Carpet Making 1839–1939* (Glasgow 1943) is particularly good in relating building construction and acquisition to technical change and expansion of the firm (Templeton's).

Chapter 3   Chemicals

A. & N. L. Clow, *The Chemical Revolution* (London 1952) and L. F. Haber, *The Chemical Industry during the Nineteenth Century* (Oxford 1958) are particularly good, and the accounts in the 1876 and 1901 British Association Handbooks are also informative. J. MacTear, 'On the Growth of the Alkali and Bleaching Powder Manufacture in the Glasgow District', *Chemical News*, 35 (1877) and J. A. Fleming, *Scottish Pottery* (Glasgow 1923) have many references to Glasgow firms. Individual companies or groups are discussed in E. W. D. Tennant, *A Short History of the Tennant Companies* (London 1922), T. Chalmers, *100 Years of Guttapercha* (Glasgow 1946), I. C. and Ll. de S. Walker, 'McDougall's Clay Pipe Factory, Glasgow', *Industrial Archaeology*, 6 (1969), 132–6, 139–41, 145–6, and J. R.

Hume, 'The St Rollox Chemical Works, 1799–1964', ibid, 3 (1966), 185–92. There is much useful background material in S. G. Checkland, *The Mines of Tharsis* (London 1967).

Chapter 4   Engineering and Shipbuilding

There are general accounts of engineering and shipbuilding in the *Third Statistical Account* and of mechanical engineering by C. A. Oakley, in *Transactions of the Institution of Engineers and Shipbuilders in Scotland*, 89 (1945–6), 9–52, and by Robert Harvey in *Old Glasgow Club Transactions*, 4 (1919–23), 32–57 (to be treated with caution). Major branches of engineering are discussed in Robert Harvey, 'The History of the Sugar Machinery Industry in Glasgow', *The International Sugar Journal* (1916), in J. Thomas, *The Springburn Story* (Newton Abbot 1964), and in A. Craig Macdonald and A. S. E. Browning, 'History of the Motor Industry in Scotland', *Proceedings of the Institution of Mechanical Engineers, Automobile Division* (1961), 319–36. For studies of individual firms and entrepreneurs see *Note it in a Book: the Story of Begg, Cousland & Co. Ltd, 1854–1954* (Glasgow 1958), D. Bell (ed), *David Napier, Engineer, 1790–1869* (Glasgow 1912), J. Napier, *Life of Robert Napier* (London 1904), *The Building of the Ship* (London 1891) (Fairfields), *A Hundred Years of Howden Engineering* (Glasgow 1954), J. L. Carvel, *Stephen of Linthouse, 1750–1950* (Glasgow 1950), *A History of the North British Locomotive Co. Ltd* (Glasgow 1953), *Development of Shipbuilding on the Upper Reaches of the Clyde* (Glasgow 1911) (Barclay, Curle & Co.), *Half a Century of Shipbuilding* (London 1896) (J. & G. Thomson), *Fairfield 1860–1960* (Glasgow 1960), E. C. Barnes, *Alfred Yarrow: his Life and Work* (1924), A. Borthwick, *Yarrows: The First Hundred Years* (Glasgow 1965), *Bridges, Structural Steel Work and Mechanical Productions* (London 1909) (Sir William Arrol & Co.). Surveys of the engineering industries at a point in time are given in the 1876 and 1901 British Association Handbooks.

Chapter 5   Miscellaneous Industries and Warehouses

Some of the industries mentioned in this chapter are discussed in the *Third Statistical Account* but this is the only connected account. Firm histories include Agnes A. C. Blackie, *Blackie & Son 1809–1959* (London 1959) and J. L. Carvel, *One Hundred Years in Timber* (Glasgow 1949), while J. A. Flanagan, *Wholesale Cooperation in Scotland 1868–1918* (Glasgow 1920) is a history of the Scottish Cooperative Wholesale Society.

Chapter 6   Transport

There is a good brief account of the development of transport in Glasgow in the *Third Statistical Account*, and much may be gleaned from Marwick's *Water Supply*, especially on roads and bridges. Ferries are dealt with in C. L. D. Duckworth and G. E. Langmuir, *Clyde River and other Steamers* (Glasgow 3rd edn 1972). Trams are a popular subject, with the best summary probably C. A. Oakley, *The Last Tram* (Glasgow 1962) and a good descriptive account in *Glasgow Municipal Transport* (Glasgow 1934); I. L. Cormack's booklets *1894 and all that* (Glasgow 1968) and *Glasgow Trams beyond the Boundary* (Glasgow 1967) are also useful. J. Lindsay's *The Canals of Scotland* (Newton Abbot 1968) is the standard work but E. A. Pratt's *Scottish Canals and Waterways* (London 1922) is also of interest. On the Monkland Canal G. Thomson, 'James Watt, and the Monkland Canal', *The Scottish Historical Review*, 29 (1950), 121–33 is helpful. On Glasgow railways J. Thomas, *Regional History of the Railways of Great Britain: Scotland, The Lowlands and the Borders* (Newton Abbot 1971) is excellent, while the economic consequences of railway development are ably discussed in J. Kellett, *Railways and the Victorian City* (London 1969). Individual railways are the subjects of O. S. Nock, *The Caledonian Railway* (London 1961), C. Hamilton Ellis, *The North British Railway* (London 1955), C. Highet, *The Glasgow & South Western Railway* (Lingfield, Surrey 1965), while G. H. Robin's excellent series of articles on suburban lines in the *Railway Magazine* is referred to in the notes to chapter 6. The best account of the Subway is D. L. Thomson and D. E. Sinclair, *The Glasgow Subway* (Glasgow 1964). J. D. Marwick's *The River Clyde* (Glasgow 1909) is still the standard history of river improvement and dock construction.

Chapter 7   Public Utilities

Marwick's *Water Supply* is indispensible for the study of public services before 1900, and is complemented by *Municipal Glasgow, its Evolution and Enterprises* (Glasgow 1914), and by John Burnet's *History of the Water Supply to Glasgow* (Glasgow 1869). J. McL. Fraser, in his article 'Glasgow and the River Clyde in the Context of River Pollution', *Journal and Proceedings of the Institute of Sewage Purification* (1963), part 5, 402–18, admirably summarises developments in sewage disposal in the city. Glasgow Corporation Gas Department, *The Gas Supply of Glasgow* (Glasgow 1935) is a handy descriptive account, as are *Corporation of Glasgow Electricity Department, Description of Works for Lighting and Power* (Glasgow 1906), and *Electrical Handbook Part I, Glasgow and Edinburgh and Districts* (London 1906).

Plate 1
Tea Warehouse, 23 York Street (H57), built 1843 for William Connal. This building was
once flanked by similar multi-storey blocks, now cut down

Plate 2
Anderston Grain Mill, 27 Washington Street (H80). The building on the left was built
as a cotton store before 1845 and converted to a mill, while the store on the right was
added in 1865 for Harvie & McGavin, who still own the premises

Plate 3
City Grain Mills, 204–44 North Speirs Wharf (C45). Apart from the sugar refinery (on the extreme left) this fine range was constructed as a grain mill and stores between 1851 and 1870

Plate 4
The River Kelvin at Partick showing Regent Mills (L46, left), with the store on the left and the main mill building on the right, and Scotstoun Mills (L41, right), with the gable end of Bishop Mills (L47) beyond. The Lanarkshire & Dumbartonshire Railway bridge over the Kelvin (L49) is just visible

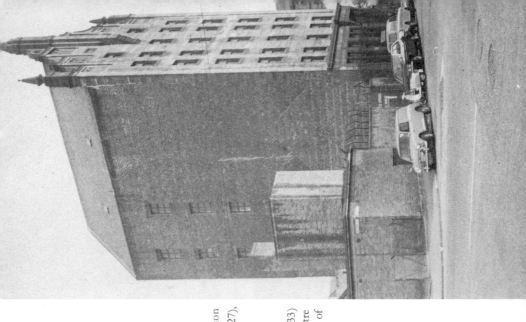

Plate 5

The Italianate splendour of Kingston Grain Mills, 21–3 West Street (H127), built 1875–6

Plate 6

Grain store, 104 Centre Street (H133) used in connection with the Centre Street Grain Mills (opposite side of street)

Plate 7

Port Dundas Sugar Refinery, 256 North Speirs Wharf (C44). This was the last sugar refinery built in Glasgow, the main block here being dated 1866

Plate 8

Confectionery Works, 71–3 Kingston Street (H132), with the water tower of Centre Street Mills showing over the roof ridge

Plate 9
Part of Vulcan Maltings (left, C67) with Scottish Grain Company factory (C66) damaged
by fire, Vintner Street

Plate 10
Victoria Bread and Biscuit Works, 30 Wesleyan Street (F41). Here we see the Forbes
Street frontage, with the main 1895 block on the left and the mansarded stable block in
the centre

Plate 11

Cold Store, 124–36 Cheapside Street and Anderston Quay (H93).
The main part, seen here, was built in 1911 for Eastmans Ltd. To the
left, part of Harland & Wolff's giant diesel engine works (H94) may
be seen

Plate 12

Ornamental gate and gateway, bonded warehouse, 38 Cadogan Street
(H48). The opulence of the entrance is indicative of the value of the

Plate 13
Bonded warehouses, 13–31 Inverkip Street (G152), built in connection with the Adelphi
Distillery (G151) which stood in the foreground

Plate 14
Interior of bonded warehouse, 105–69 Bell Street (G58), with blending vat. The large
diameter, cast-iron column and mass-concrete arches should be noted

Plate 15
The top floors of the Anderston Cotton Work, 93 Cheapside Street (H90). Note
particularly the cast-iron roof truss, in four sections. It seems likely that the centre column
is a replacement for two side columns, extended upwards from lower floors

Plate 16
Barrowfield Spinning Factory, 177 Reid Street, Bridgeton (F161). This is typical of the
smaller spinning mills built in the east end in the 1830s and 1840s, though the wood-
framed windows are unusual

Plate 17
The Glasgow Cotton Spinners Co. Ltd's mills in Dalmarnock (F165), seen from Swanston Street. In the background is the very large mill chimney, and in the foreground, part of Dalmarnock Factory (F166), a weaving mill

Plate 18
Part of Barrowfield Weaving Factory, 260 Broad Street, Bridgeton (left, F99), and the much-reconstructed Mile End Mills, 91–7 Fordneuk Street (F100)

Plate 19

Weaving Factory, 189–203 Rutherglen Road (G165), founded c 1822 by Alexander Brown & Co. Note the blocked-up central entrance

Plate 20

Weaving Factory, 11 Graham Square (F8), built c 1845. An unusually

Plate 21
Interior of a flat in weaving factory, 11 Graham Square (F8), showing the slender
columns and longitudinal beams. The ceiling is modern

Plate 22
Interior of typical east-end weaving shed. This one is in the Clyde Works, 1 Baltic Street
(F125), built in 1866

Plate 23
Clyde Works, 1 Baltic Street (F125), built as a jute factory in 1866. The corner block was cut down from a three-storey and attic structure

Plate 24
Main block of Grovepark Mills, 188 North Woodside Road (B54), built 1878 as a power-loom weaving factory. John Gordon, the architect, was also responsible for Clyde Works

Plate 25
Part of Craigpark Factory, 360 Townmill Road (D6), built 1860–5. The building with the
staircase was the engine house

Plate 26
Bloomvale Carpet Works, 10 Fordneuk Street (F84), built 1868–99 for J. & W. Lyle.
The red and white brick construction is typical of later east-end multi-storey mills

Plate 27
Great Western Steam Laundry, 459 Crow Road (L1), constructed in 1883. This, the first
large laundry in Glasgow, is also the most ornate

Plate 28
An interior view of Castlebank Laundry, 200 Anniesland Road (A23), taken in August
1930. There are washing machines on the right, a hydro-extractor in the foreground and
pressing machines on the left. The laundry was opened c 1896 by Alexander Kennedy

Plate 29
'New Office', St Rollox Chemical Works, 229 Castle Street (C83), just before demolition in 1964–5. The pipe in the foreground is a replacement for the 'Cut of Junction' between the Forth & Clyde and Monkland Canals

Plate 30
Part of Glasgow Rubber Works, 125–9 Shuna Street (B15), dated 1881. Note the canal wharf in the foreground

Plate 31
Possil Pottery, 85 Denmark Street (M19), built *c* 1881 for the Saracen Pottery Co.

Plate 32
W. White & Son's clay pipe factory, 26–42 Bain Street (G121). This appears to have been the largest of the Glasgow clay pipe factories. It was designed to be executed in stone

Plate 33
Milton Colour Works, 58–70 Dobbies Loan (G7), built 1873. To the right can be seen
the wood store and stables described in G9

Plate 34
Tradeston Paint Mills, 54 Cook Street and West Street (H186). In this view of the West
Street frontage the join between the original two-storey building of 1866 and the later
third storey is clearly visible

Plate 35
Oil store, 62 North Frederick Street (G39), built to replace a building destroyed by fire in 1866

Plate 36
The massive bulk of Scotia Leather Works, 108 Boden Street (F104). The frontage (left) dates from 1906, the water tower from 1904, and the main block from *c* 1873–93

Plate 37
Hide, Wool and Tallow Market, 33–43 Greendyke Street (G131). Behind and to the left may be seen a fragment of Mitchell's tobacco factory (G130)

Plate 38
Interior of single-storey part of Hide, Wool and Tallow Market, behind frontage seen in plate 37

Plate 39
Part of William Beardmore & Co.'s Parkhead Forge, Shettleston Road and Duke Street
(E11). The tallest building is the press shop. The slatted sides are for ventilation

Plate 40
Smithy, Old Castle Road (M58), probably dating in part to the eighteenth century

Plate 41

Two-column Rigby patent steam hammer out of use at Parkhead Forge (E11). Note the column crane for handling the work-piece.

Plate 42

Cupolas at Shettleston Ironworks, 619 Old Shettleston Road (E9). The owners, J. & T. Boyd, pioneered machine-moulding

Plate 43

Anderston Brass Foundry, 34 Elliot Street (H21), built 1870–83 and reconstructed as a paint and colour works in 1914. The large glazed fanlight and the blocked-up ventilator are notable features

Plate 44

Brass-finishers' workshop, Bridgeton Brass Foundry, 16 Muslin Street (F148). The entire workshop is line-shaft driven from a single electric motor

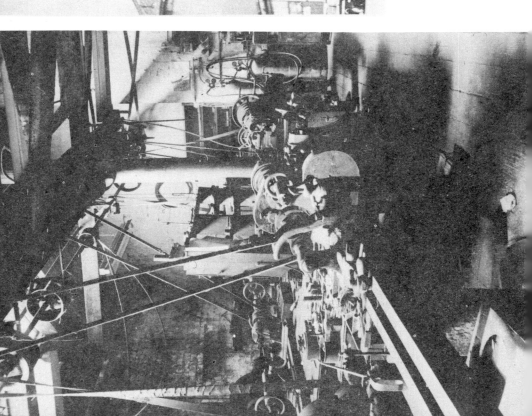

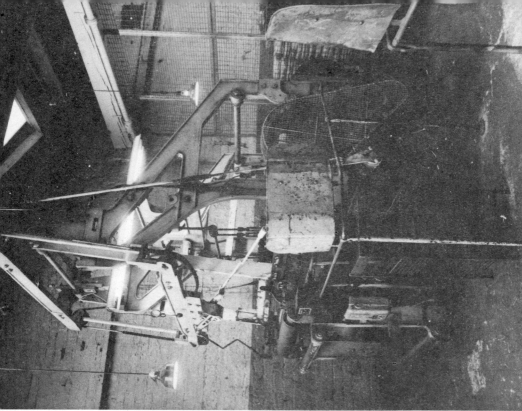

field Wireworks, 636 Springfield Road (M47) belonging to Begg, Cousland & Co. A loom of this type is now in store at Coplawhill for Glasgow Museum

Plate 46

Pattern shop and offices, Sentinel Works, Jessie Street (L22). This was the first reinforced-concrete building of any size in Glasgow

Plate 47

A bay in London Road Ironworks, 47 Summer Street (F104). On the
right is a large vertical boring and facing mill. The construction is
typical of large steel-framed engineering shops in the city, though this
bay is unusually narrow

Plate 48

Engineering Works, 8–18 Scotland Street (H191), built 1870–1 for
James Howden, engineer. After Howden vacated it the building was
occupied by Blair, Campbell & McLean, coppersmiths, for many
years

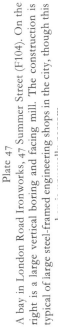

Plate 49
Eglinton Engine Works, 120 Tradeston Street (H188). In this view of the Cook Street
(left) and West Street frontages, the 1855 block is the three-storey painted building, while
the brick workshops on the right date from the 1870s

Plate 50
Bishop Street Engineering Works, 57 Bishop Street (H41), constructed in 1865 for
Walker, Brown & Co., and demolished in 1966. Very typical of engineering shop
architecture of the 1860s and 1870s

Plate 51
North British Diesel Engine Works, 739 South Street (M93), designed by J. Galt, with a tanker and a cargo vessel being engined. The Germanic appearance of the main bay of the works is referred to in the inventory. In the background, distinguished by its large arched doorway, is the Cyclops Foundry (M92)

Plate 52
The London & Glasgow Engineering & Iron Shipbuilding Co.'s boilerworks, 172 Lancefield Street (H112), dating from 1864–5. This view was taken just before demolition in 1970–1

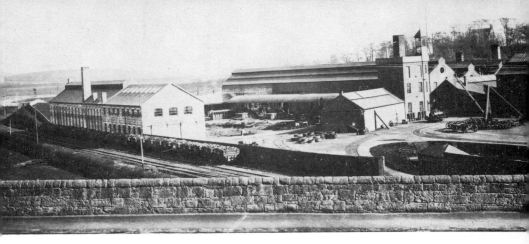

Plate 53
Hyde Park Locomotive Works, 170 Ayr Street (C9), photographed shortly after opening
in 1860. The iron and brass foundry and pattern store on the left lasted until the works
was demolished in 1969. In the left foreground is the site of the present Springburn
Station (C7)

Plate 54
Interior view of one bay of original three-bay erecting shop, Hyde Park Locomotive
Works, taken in 1965

Plate 55
The entrance to the main office, Fairfield Shipbuilding Yard, 1048 Govan Road (K1),
designed by John Keppie

Plate 56
An aerial view of part of Fairfield Shipbuilding Yard (K1) taken *c* 1932, with the massive
engine and boiler shop on the left and the fitting-out basin and covered building berth
in the background

Plate 57
Timber basin and gantry crane, City Sawmills, 119 Craighall Road (C19). The line of planks divides the basin from the Glasgow branch of the Forth & Clyde Canal

Plate 58
Power Station (left) and sawmill, Pollok House (M70). Both were turbine powered, though the power station is partly dismantled, and the sawmill is little used

Plate 59
Wright's workshop, 144 St Peter's Street (C39), typical of many of the smaller workshops in the city

Plate 60
Cathcart Snuff and Cardboard Mill, Snuffmill Road (M59), altered from a meal mill in 1812. The wing on the right contained the snuff mill

buildings. On the left is a stationery warehouse, 52–6 Darnley Street (19), built 1903, and on the right a splendidly *Art Nouveau* printing works, 50 Darnley Street (18)

Plate 61

Villafield Press, 15–17 Stanhope Street (G22). This view of the St James Road frontage shows the two oldest blocks (1838 and 1841) in the centre, with an addition of 1890 to the left. The upper storeys on the older buildings (above the cornice) are later additions

Plate 63
The exotic *Citizen* building of 1885-7, 24 St Vincent Place (G36)

Plate 64
Late-eighteenth-century warehouses, 19 Montrose Street (end five bays) and 7–13 Cochrane Street (G71). To the left is part of a large warehouse, 18 Montrose Street (G68) built in 1876

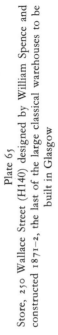

Plate 65

Store, 250 Wallace Street (H140) designed by William Spence and constructed 1871–2, the last of the large classical warehouses to be built in Glasgow

Plate 66

Store, 56–64 Kingston Street (H131) of 1878. There were hoists at the rear

Plate 67

Scottish Co-operative Wholesale Society warehouse, Wallace Street and Paterson Street (H142), typical of this large complex. The warehouse to the left is that shown in plate 47

Plate 68

More SCWS enterprise, this time at Shieldhall (M88). The front block on the right, with the base of the projected second half on

Plate 69
Nether Pollok House Bridge (M71). The weir of the sawmill (plate 58) may be seen
through the arch

Plate 70
Victoria Bridge (G139) from Carlton Place. The spire on the left is all that remains of the
Merchants' House

Plate 71
St Andrew's Suspension Bridge, McNeil Street (G135). The pylons are of cast iron. The building in the background is part of the United Co-operative Baking Society's establishment

Plate 72
Southern Terminal of the Harbour Tunnel, Plantation Place (H119). The opening on the left gave access for road vehicles to hydraulic lifts

Plate 73

Tollhouse, 1 Cross Street (J22), before integration into a roundabout. The multi-storey flats are part of the Pollokshaws redevelopment scheme

Plate 74

Interior of upper floor, Botanic Gardens Garage, 16–18 Vinicombe Street (B44). This view, taken in 1930, shows the unusual roof structure

Plate 75
Admiral Street Tram Depot, showing the Seaward Street frontage (H175). The first floor windows lit the stables, trams being accommodated on the ground floor. The bays on the right were adapted as part of the Kinning Park substation when the tramways were electrified

Plate 76
Pinkston Power Station, North Canal Bank Street (C71), built for the electrification of the Glasgow tramways. Originally the canal branch in the foreground supplied coal to the station; it now serves as a cooling pond

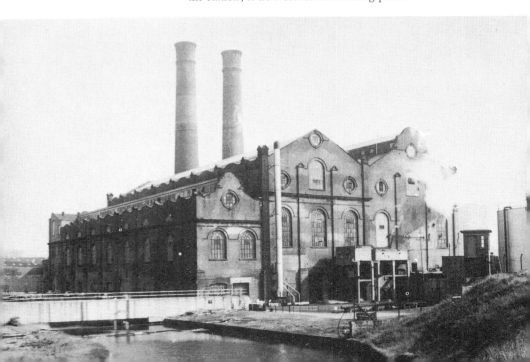

Plate 77
Kelvin Aqueduct (A12) carrying the Forth & Clyde Canal over the River Kelvin. In the foreground may be seen remains of Dalsholm Station on the Lanarkshire & Dumbartonshire Railway

Plate 78
Robert Whitworth, engineer of the Kelvin aqueduct, also designed the more modest Stockingfield Aqueduct, Lochburn Road (B3)

Plate 79
A standard Forth & Clyde Canal bascule bridge at Firhill Road (B21), demolished *c* 1969.
In the background are modern parts of Firhill Ironworks (B20)

Plate 80
A typical Monkland Canal fixed bridge, at Garthamlock Road (M37), built 1772 and
subsequently widened

Plate 81
Botanic Gardens Station, Great Western Road (B42), not long before destruction by fire
in 1970

Plate 82
Jordanhill Station, Crow Road (A33), showing the down platform building before
replacement in 1969

Plate 84

Stables and Garage, 181 Stanley Street and Vermont Street (H206).
One of the most flamboyant examples of polychrome brick design in
Glasgow

Plate 83

Overall roof, Central Station (G74), showing the junction between
the 1899–1905 extension and the older part of the station. Note the

Plate 85
Part of Custom House Quay, Clyde Street (G96), when still in use for sand and gravel traffic. To the right of the nearest crane can be seen part of the warehouse (G98), while on the extreme right is the RNVR ship *Carrick*, a former clipper

Plate 86
Travelling steam crane, Govan Graving Docks, Govan Road (K14)

Plate 87
Gauge basins, Mugdock Reservoir, Milngavie, part of the first stage of the Loch Katrine
scheme

Plate 88
Hydraulic Power Station, 295 High Street (G51). The chimney is long since demolished.
On the right are the two blocks of Cathedral Court, built 1894 by the Glasgow Workmen's
Dwellings Co. Ltd

Plate 89

Stables, muster hall and store, built as part of a refuse disposal works, 55 Kilbirnie Street (H222). Note the resemblance in style to the horse-tram depot in plate 75. Over the low building on the right can be seen part of Tradeston Gas Works (H224)

Plate 90

Shieldhall Sewage Treatment Works, Renfrew Road (M89), showing the large area of settling tanks. To the right can be seen part of Linthouse shipbuilding yard (L12) and across the river is Clydeholm Shipyard (M90). This view was taken c 1930

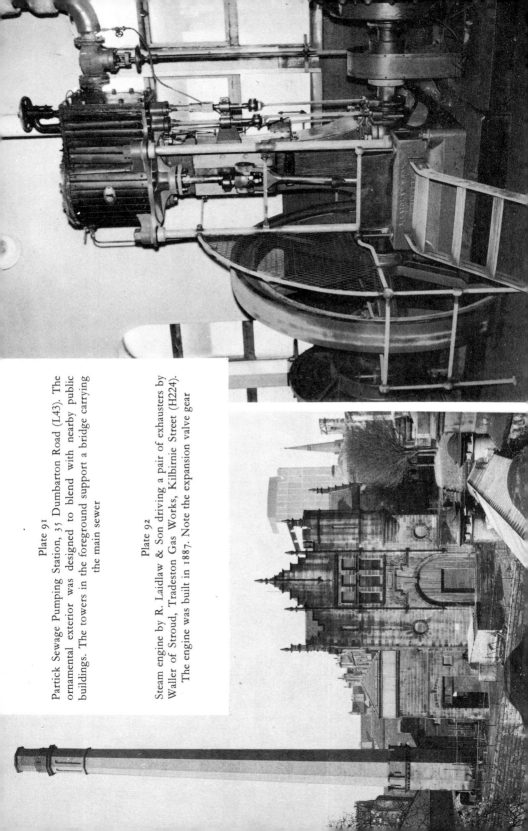

Plate 91

Partick Sewage Pumping Station, 35 Dumbarton Road (L43). The ornamental exterior was designed to blend with nearby public buildings. The towers in the foreground support a bridge carrying the main sewer

Plate 92

Steam engine by R. Laidlaw & Son driving a pair of exhausters by Waller of Stroud, Tradeston Gas Works, Kilbirnie Street (H224). The engine was built in 1887. Note the expansion valve gear

Plate 93
William Spence's Egyptian retort house, Dalmarnock Gas Works, 122 Old Dalmarnock
Road (F171)

Plate 94
Two gasholders built in 1872 at Dalmarnock Gas Works. The bricked-up footbridge was
for the use of pedestrians during shunting across Swanston Street

Plate 95
St Andrews Electricity Works, 245 Pollokshaws Road (G196), built as an electricity generating station in 1899–1900

Plate 96
Electricity Substation, 42 Haggs Road (J4), built to harmonise with existing residential development

General Index

Index of Sites

Streets and Places

Proper Names

Acme Machine Co., wringer makers F46
Acme Tea Chest Co., The 91, I21
Adam, A., architect F62, G100, G170
Adam, John, architect 106, M71
Adam, J. M. & Co., pneumatic engineers K31
Adam, William & Son, bleachers D9
Adams, J. Y., sacking manufacturer 40, F140
Aird & Coghill, printers and publishers 94, 95, H46
Aitken, James and Co., engineers, millwrights and founders 72, H22
Aitken, McNeil & Co., engineers 76, K57
Aitken, Wilson & Co., power-loom cloth manufacturers C37
Albion Motor Co. Ltd 81, M97
Alexander, Hugh, chair manufacturer F156
Alexander, J. H87
Alexander, J. Y., cartage contractor C18
Alexander, R. F. & J., thread manufacturers 34, 37, G53, fig. 8
Alexander, Fergusson & Co. 55, 58, 92, B10, B14, G97
Allan, James, ironfounder C32
Allan, John, boxmaker H33
Allan, John, horse dealer G9
Allan & Baxter, wrights H228
Allan & Bogle, brass founders & brewery engineers 68, F76
Allan & Orr, hat and cap manufacturers G93
Allan, Thomas & Sons, ironfounders B34
All British Car Co. 82, F114
Alley and McLellan, engineers 75, I22, I24
Allsopp, Sam, brewer, G17
Alsing, G. V., engineer 137
Alston, James C., storekeeper H59
Alston, William, engineer L19
Anderson, John, bricklayer 53
Anderson, J. W., power-loom cloth manufacturer F104
Anderson, D. & J., shirting manufacturers F127
Anderson, James, engineer and boilermaker K28

Anderson, James &˙ Co., calenderers G38
Anderson, James & Sons, engineers H89
Anderson, R. R., architect, Edinburgh G74
Anderson, William, spirit merchant G118
Anderson, W. J. (I), architect I11
Anderson & Lawson, carpet makers 40
Anderson & Lyall, engineers and boilermakers 78, K27
Anderson & Munro, engineers L2
Anderston Foundry Co., 72–3, 75, H92, plate 45
Annacker, William, sausage manufacturer 13, 14, H32
Apex Motor Engineering Co., B60
Argyll Motor Company 82, F123
Armstrong, J., grain and potato merchant K17
Armstrong, Sir Wm & Co., hydraulic engineers H120
Arnot, W., engineer K50
Arrol, William, structural engineer 73, F136
Arrol, Sir William & Co. Ltd, engineers 84, A3, A25, G142, H13, H94, H112–13, H197, I20, K15, M6
Arrol Brothers, engineers 85, M29, M74
Arrol Bridge Co., The, engineers F170
Arrol-Johnston Ltd, motor manufacturers 82
Arthur & Co., wholesale drapers H31
Arthur, George & Son, architects B53
Auld, David & Sons, ironfounders F32
Avery, W. & T., weighing machine makers L39
Baikie & Hogg, laundry props B9
Baillie, John, wine merchant G99
Baillie, William, architect D16, F48, G124, K63
Bain, William & Co., engineers, Coatbridge H40
Baird, Alexander & Son, stationers 96, B46
Baird, Hugh & Co., brewers and maltsters 16, C22
Baird, Hugh and Son, maltsters 16, C29, C67
Baird, H. & R., ironfounders 64
Baird, John II, architect H172
Baird, John, glass beveller and silverer C108
Baird, William, structural engineer A20

Glasgow Plate Glass Co. B23
Glasgow Railway Engineering Co. Ltd 80, K54
Glasgow & South Western Railway 21, 116, 119,
    120, 124, G56, G58–9, G88, G116, G138,
    G191, H214, M72–4
Glasgow Steel Roofing Co. 85, C8, M16
Glasgow Storage Co. Ltd 100, H140
Glasgow Tanwork Co. 58
Glasgow   Town   Council – see   Glasgow
    Corporation
Glasgow Tramway & Omnibus Co. 109, 111,
    A9, F68, H40, L42
Glasgow University 94, 119
Glasgow Waterworks Co. 133, F7, fig. 19
Glasgow & Yoker Turnpike Trust L44
Glasgow, Yoker & Clydebank Railway A33
Glass, John, aerated water manufacturer 22
Glen, A. & W., millers H91, fig. 1
Gleniffer Motors Ltd. A19
Glen & Ross, engineers 63, F111
Glover, John, brassfounder 68, F148
Goodall &, White, lace manufacturers 42, F104,
    F124
Gorbals Gravitation Water Company 133–4
Gorbals, Heritors of G140
Gordon, Cuthbert, Leith, cudbear manufacturer
    49
Gordon, John, architect B54, F65, F78, F123–5,
    G60, H181, H194, H199, H201, fig. 11, plates
    22–4
Gordon & Dobson, architects I8
Gordon, Son & Dobson, architects I9
Gossman & Smith, house factors D22
Gourlay, J. & Co., distillers 19, C65
Gourlie & Linn, upholstery manufacturers G194
Gourock Ropework Co., The 45
Govan Forge & Steel Co. K58
Govan Press 95, K22
Govan Rope & Sail Co. Ltd K49
Govan Tube Co. K46, K61
Govan Weaving Co., powerloom cloth manu-
    facturers K60
Govancroft Pottery Co. Ltd M44
Graham, G., engineer F182
Graham, J. Gillespie, architect, Edinburgh G33
Graham, William & Co., merchants G30–1
Graham & Roxburgh, sawmillers B22
Graham Telephone Co. 141
Grainger, James W., storekeeper H86
Grant, Alexander, cartwright, spring van &
    lorry builder G16
Grant, G. Jun., powerloom weaver 30, F8
Grant, George & Sons, powerloom weavers
    F89–90, F97
Gray, Andrew & Co., solder manufacturers
    G159
Gray, C. & D., distillers G151–2, G160

Gray, James & Co., calico printers' engravers
    G19
Gray, Thomas & Co., brewers F180
Gray, Dunn & Co., biscuit manufacturers 10, 11,
    12, H172, fig. 2
Great Clyde Street (Glasgow) Heritable Co. G98
Great Western Steam Laundry Co. L1
Greenlees & Sons, boot & shoe makers C3
Grosvenor, Frederick, earthenware manufac-
    turer F129
Gunn, William, powerloom shuttle manufac-
    turer 73, F128
Guthrie, David & Co., carpenters & joiners
    H161
Hagart & Co., timber measurers & cartage
    contractors K29
Hailstones, A., fish curer K30
Hall, C. Wishart & Co., oil refiners etc. K65
Hall, J. & W. D., architects C5
Hall, P. W., oil merchant C93
Hall-Brown, Buttery & Co., marine, electrical
    & general engineers K52
Halley's Industrial Motors Ltd M3
Hamilton, Andrew, miller C60
Hamilton, Arthur, architect G171, K38
Hamilton, A. H., oil & paint manufacturers M24
Hamilton, John, architect G17, G162, G171
Hamilton, John & Son, architects K38
Hamilton, J. & D., oil refiners etc. C111
Hamilton, J. & G., cartage contractors C74
Hamilton, R., carting contractor H3
Hamilton, T. & J., bobbin turners F63
Hamilton & Manson, grain millers H183
Hammermen, Incorporation of, in Glasgow 63
Handyside A. & Co., engineers, Derby G88
Hanna, Donald & Wilson, engineers, Paisley
    G137
Hannan & Buchanan, pressure gauge makers
    G78
Hannay, Gourlie & Hinshelwood, chemical
    manufacturers, drysalters & oil refiners 55, 56,
    F21
Harland & Wolff, marine engineers & ship-
    builders 66, 78, 82, 83, H104, K15, K20, K51,
    plate 11
Harper, A. & J., cabinetmakers F49
Hart, Alexander, cartage contractors E22
Harvey, G. & A., architects and engineers 74,
    F87, F163, K43 (own works)
Harvey, Robert, & Co., engineers 76
Harvie, Alexander, storekeeper H63
Harvie & McGavin, grain merchants & millers
    4–5, H64, H80, plate 2
Hawkshaw, Sir John, engineer 136
Hay Brothers, manufacturing confectioners 9,
    H207
Hayman, William M., contractor H131

McDiarmid & Co., aerated water manufacturers K55

Macdonald, A. B., architect G106

Macdonald, A. W., architect M31

Macdonald, D. & J., tobacco manufacturers F68

Macdonald, John & Co., mechanical engineers J11

McDonald, Robert, wireworker G153

McDougall, A., sawmiller L15

Macdougall, A. G., architect C18

McDougall, D. & Co., clay pipe manufacturers C81

McDougall, William, baker C50

Macdougall & Sons, china merchants M19

McDowall & Co. B56

McEwan, Law & Lindsay, ironfounders M92, fig. 13

McFadyen & Co., cartage contractors, G18

McFarlane, D. & Son, sawmillers B8

McFarlane, Daniel, distiller 19, C52

Macfarlane, Donald, launderer J23

Macfarlane Bros, enamellers M95

McFarlane & Co., cocoa fibre and mat manufacturers F94

McFarlane, John & Sons, bakers F41

McFarlane, J. & A. Ltd, wholesale ironmongers B34, H26

McFarlane, Peter, smith G40

Macfarlane, Walter & Co., architectural ironfounders 65, M17

Macfarlane, Lang & Co., bakers 10, 11

McGeoch, William & Co., wholesale ironmongers H49

McGhee & Burt, engineers 13

McGibbon, W. F., architect 7, F76, F99, G25, H183, H185, H187, L41, fig. 12

McGlashan, J. & Co., engineers & furnishers to the aerated water, wine, spirit and beer trades G45

McGregor, Duncan, nautical instrument maker H129

Macgregor, P. G., architect, Bishopbriggs C16

McHutcheon & Finlayson, galvanisers H110

McIlwraith, James, tarpaulin manufacturer K47

Macintosh, Charles, chemical manufacturer 48, 51

Macintosh, George, cudbear & shoe manufacturer 49, 58, 59

McIntosh, Peter & Sons, tanners G99

McIntyre, J, & J., dress goods & silk manufacturers G60

Mackay, John & Co., aerated water manufacturer 22, H210

Mackay, W. M., engineer H109

Mackell, Robert, engineer 114

McKelroy, James, trustee of, stablekeeper G133

McKenzie, George, stablekeeper C86

Mackenzie, J. R., architect, Aberdeen 45, L1

Mackie & Co., distillers C68

Mackinlay, R. & W., metal refiners H174

McKinnon, N. & Sons K35

Mackintosh, C. R., architect 95, G35, G72

McKissack, J., architect F145, F150

McKissack & Son, architects F121, F133, G104–5, G226, M47

McKissack & Rowan, architects F41

McLachlane, James, ironfounder 64

Maclaren, Robert & Co., ironfounders 65

McLaren, Wright & Co., wrought-iron tube makers H77

McLay & West, commission weavers F103

McLean, Donald, stable keeper B27

MacLehose, R. & Co., printers 94, A24

McLellan, A. & J., cartage contractors H150, H155, K59

McLellan, George & Co., rubber manufacturers 51, 52, B15

McLellan, Lewis & John, oil importers & refiners C113

MacLellan P. & W. & Co. Ltd, engineers 69, 70, 80, 84, 85, G33 (builders), G154, H205, M79 (own works)

McLintock, W. J., biscuit makers G162, G181

McMath & Pridie, powerloom cloth manufacturers F101

MacNair, Andrew D. & Co., curled hair manufacturers F185

McNair, C. J., architect C2

McNaught, D. & S., bakers I2

MacNaughtan, D., architect G1–2

Macnee, T. & Co., clothing manufacturers G107

McNeil, Charles Jun., blacksmith 63–4, H163

MacNeill, H. P., furrier G34

McOnie, P. & W., engineers 75, H190

McOnie, W. & A., engineers 75, 76, H190, H195

McOnie, Harvey & Co., engineers 76

Macowat, W. & R. B., rivet makers H193

McPhail, George, bag and mat merchant H30

McPhail, John, contractor H162

McPherson, D. & Co., ironfounders H42

McPhun, J. & D., wood turners F150

McQueen, John H68

MacTear, J., manager, St Rollox Chemical Works 48

MacWhannell, N., architect, F114, M44

MacWhannell & Rogerson, architects D22, F115, F169

Main, A. & J., iron fence & gate makers etc., 84, M18, M29

Mair & Dougall, bottlers 22, F10

Mann, Thomas, storekeeper H60, H62, fig. 14

Marquis Brothers, engineers F102

Marr, Hamilton & Co., wrights & builders K19

Marsdens of Heckmondwyke, steam engine builders H125

Marshall, Alexander, plane, saw & edge tool maker G123

Marshall, J., bread manufacturer K36

Marshall & Wylie, tube makers 69

Martin, George, engineer G140

Martin, J., sheep dip manufacturer H179

Martin & Millar, tanners 58, 59, 60, F18

Massey, Alexander & Sons, grocers 15, G168

Mathieson, Alexander & Son, edge tool makers G119

Mathieson, Donald, engineer G74

Mavor & Coulson Ltd, electrical engineers 140, F82–3

Measures, Harry B., engineer, London C71

Mechan & Sons, engineers & contractors M94

Meighan, James & Son, blindmakers 103, F74

Melville, George Ltd, sewing cotton manufacturer J13

Melville, William, engineer G88

Melvin Bros, boot & shoe manufacturers H208

Melvin, J. & Sons, engineers C50

Melvin, Thomas & Sons, hydraulic etc. engineers C80, K36 (as designer)

Menzies, Andrew, horse dealer and coach proprietor 114, M84

Menzies, C., architect L5

Menzies, J. & Co. C105

Menzies, Baillie William 19

Mercer, William, architect H178

Miller, A. L., architect H122

Miller, George, sawmiller H74

Miller, Hugh, grain merchant L22

Miller, James, architect 122, 123, B42, B63, C11, G74, G87, G178, M43

Miller, James, harness, muslin & lappet cutter F37

Miller, James, & Co., rivet, nut and bolt maker 70

Miller, R., architect F3, F21

Miller, R. B., sawmiller etc. H72–4

Miller, Thomas, dairyman C12

Miller, William, dyer F188

Miller & Black, architects D21, F3, F39, F99, H208, K48

Miller & Lang, stationers & art publishers 94, 95, H52, I8

Miller & Pyle, coppersmiths H51, H184

Mills, James, dyer H187

Milne, George & Co., rusk manufacturers H211

Milne, William, architect and engineer 105, 106

Milne, William, ice manufacturer G100

Milne, W. & Co., sawmillers etc. M77

Minto, David, coffee grinder G115

Mirrlees, J. B. & Tait, William, engineers 76, H196

Mitchell, A. Jun., & Sons, power-loom cloth manufacturers C21

Mitchell, Stephen & Co., tobacco manufacturers 103, G130, plate 37

Mitchell, William, boilermaker 79, H19

Mitchell, W. G., bleacher and finisher F159

Mitchell & Neilson, engineers and ironfounders 75, 79, 80, H102

Mitchell & Whytlaw, power-loom cloth manufacturers B54

Mo-car Syndicate, motor manufacturers 82

Moffat Bros, shoe accessory manufacturers F132

Money, J. & J. W., architects G34

Monkland Canal Co., 115, 116, 117, 118, D1–3, D8, D10, M33–39, plate 80

Monkland & Kirkintilloch Railway Co., 115

Monro & Son, architects C99, D14, D19, G144, G190

Monteith, Henry & Co., dyers 43

Monteith, John, power-loom cloth manufacturer 30

Montgomerie & Co., bakers K28

Montgomery, R., confectioner 9, H132

Moore, G. & C., aerated water manufacturers F137

Morier, William, wholesale & export brushmaker 103, K37

Morton, Alexander, lacemaker, Newmilns 42

Morton, J. G., architect L17

Mossman, J. & G., monumental sculptors 92–3, G23

Motherwell, Andrew, grain merchant G171, G195

Motherwell Bridge & Engineering Co., G74

Motherwell & Lapsley, nailmakers C117

Mouchel & Partners, licensees of Hennebique system F32

Muir, Robert, steam engine builder 26

Muir, William, grain miller G145

Muir, W. & G., bakers F39

Muir & Caldwell, engineers 77, H115

Muir & Mavor, electrical engineers 139

Muirhead, Andrew, tanner 59, F140

Munn, J. S., funeral undertaker & hirer F122

Munro, J. M., architect D14, F41, F129, G122, G185, H32

Murdoch & Aitken, engineers 79, 80

Murdoch & Cameron, engineers C80

Murdoch & Dodrell, sugar refiners C44

Murdoch, Warroch & Co., brewers 15

Murray, Richard, engineer G166

Murray, R. & Sons, grain millers H2

Myles, A., architect C8, C42, F82, F84, G76, G196, H94, I24, K7, K66, M22

Napier, David, 77, 78

Napier, John, ironfounder 64